THE STRATEGY OF CHEMOTHERAPY

THE STRATEGY OF CHEMOTHERAPY

EIGHTH SYMPOSIUM OF THE
SOCIETY FOR GENERAL MICROBIOLOGY
HELD AT THE
ROYAL INSTITUTION, LONDON
APRIL 1958

CAMBRIDGE

Published for the Society for General Microbiology

AT THE UNIVERSITY PRESS

1958

PUBLISHED BY
THE SYNDICS OF THE CAMBRIDGE UNIVERSITY PRESS
Bentley House, 200 Euston Road, London, N.W. 1
American Branch: 32 East 57th Street, New York 22, N.Y.

Printed in Great Britain at the University Press, Cambridge
(Brooke Crutchley, University Printer)

CONTRIBUTORS

AINSWORTH, G. C., Commonwealth Mycological Institute, Kew, Surrey.

ALBERT, A., Department of Medical Chemistry, The Australian National University, Canberra.

BYRDE, R. J. W., Long Ashton Research Station, University of Bristol.

GALE, E. F., Medical Research Council Unit for Chemical Microbiology, Department of Biochemistry, University of Cambridge.

GOODWIN, L. G., Wellcome Laboratories of Tropical Medicine, London.

KNOX, R., Department of Bacteriology, Guy's Hospital Medical School, London.

KREBS, Sir Hans, Medical Research Council Unit for Cell Metabolism, Department of Biochemistry, University of Oxford.

LACEY, B. W., The John Burford Carlill Pathological Laboratories, Westminster School of Medicine, London.

MCDANIEL, L. E., Merck Sharp and Dohme Research Laboratories, Rahway, New Jersey.

MARKHAM, R., Agricultural Research Council, Virus Research Unit, Molteno Institute, University of Cambridge.

MITCHELL, P., Department of Zoology, University of Edinburgh.

NEAL, R. A., Wellcome Laboratories of Tropical Medicine, London.

NEWTON, B. A., Medical Research Council Unit for Chemical Microbiology, University of Cambridge.

PARK, J. T., Walter Reed Army Institute of Research, Washington, D.C.

TAMM, I., Rockefeller Institute for Medical Research, New York.

TUCKER, R. G., Microbiology Unit, Department of Biochemistry, University of Oxford.

WOODRUFF, H. B., Merck Sharp and Dohme Research Laboratories, Rahway, New Jersey.

WOODS, D. D., Microbiology Unit, Department of Biochemistry, University of Oxford.

WOOLLEY, D. W., Rockefeller Institute for Medical Research, New York.

CONTENTS

EDITORS' PREFACE

Chemotherapy as a science dates from Ehrlich's pioneer work on the use of specific chemicals and compounds to attack micro-organisms in the tissues. Since then it has developed in two directions: the isolation of substances formed by other micro-organisms, and the synthesis of compounds related to essential metabolites. The first approach led to the discovery of penicillin and other important antibiotics, and methods for their isolation and testing are discussed in this Symposium. The chief representative of compounds of the second type is sulphonamide, which was discovered by trial and error before the rationale of its action was known.

The comparative failure of logical chemotherapy is due to gaps in our knowledge of metabolism of both host and invaders, and our neglect of the responses of the host. The organizer of the Symposium, Dr E. F. Gale, invited contributors to suggest fresh ways of attacking the micro-organisms without damaging the host. Each contributor wrote his article without detailed knowledge of what the others would say, and observed facts have been interpreted in different ways. Some of the contributions are largely speculative and the ideas put forward should keep many people busy at the bench for a long, long time.

Symposia of this type are of interest to workers belonging to different disciplines and, as Professor Knox says in his contribution, 'it is often difficult for workers in one branch to understand the thoughts or even the language of workers in other branches'. Unfortunately, in spite of all our efforts, the same word can mean quite different things in the hands of different contributors, but we have tried to ensure that the papers are expressed in simple, unspecialized language.

S. T. COWAN
ELIZABETH ROWATT

National Collection of Type Cultures and
Central Public Health Laboratory,
London, N.W. 9

THE RELATION OF STRATEGY TO TACTICS: SOME GENERAL BIOCHEMICAL PRINCIPLES

D. D. WOODS AND R. G. TUCKER

Microbiology Unit, Department of Biochemistry,
University of Oxford

Our Symposium is to range over a wide field of discovery and specula-tion; it should be the particular responsibility of the opener to try to help those who are not experts in the subject by providing some broad initial survey which links together the detailed contributions which follow. We shall be dealing in the main with chemotherapy in the sense for which Ehrlich coined the word—to describe the cure of infectious diseases by chemical agents without injury to the organism infected. The same approach, essentially that of selective toxicity, is applicable to any case where one organism affects adversely the well-being of another either directly or indirectly. The biochemical principles we discuss may also have application in pharmacology, though the problem is clearly differentiated from the present one in that it concerns only a single organism. Between these two extremes lies cancer, in which abnormal cells of the host itself multiply out of control; some tumours are of course transmissible but are not infectious in the usual sense of the word. General aspects of selective toxicity have been compre-hensively reviewed by Albert (1951).

From many points of view the virus-infected cell is best regarded as a single biological entity; although the virus particle can survive outside the host tissue it cannot multiply except in association with living host cells. There are other intracellular parasites which preserve their bio-logical identity and metabolism although completely dependent on the host cell for continued life. There are facultative saprophytes which infect and live in the host cell, but which can be cultivated in media of varying degrees of complexity. Finally, there are microbes which do not enter the host cells but which multiply in extracellular fluids. The chemo-therapist has therefore to deal with microbes showing an almost con-tinuous spectrum of increasing complexity of biological relation with the host. Although the same general methods may be applicable for attacking the invader, it is clear that the most appropriate means may be dictated by the type of relation with the host.

It has been sufficiently emphasized by almost everyone who has written or spoken on chemotherapy that there is no difficulty in finding chemical agents which will prevent the multiplication of the invading microbe, but that the essential problem is to find one that does not harm the host at the same time, or at any rate does so to a lesser degree. Two-thirds of the papers to be given in this Symposium concern possible methods by which microbes in general may be attacked and the explanation for, or prospects of, their selective action against the microbe. The remaining papers deal with particular problems set by certain groups of micro-organisms or, in one case, specifically with factors introduced by the host. It is clear that these detailed contributions are concerned mainly with tactics, the detailed appreciation of the use of various types of warfare. The grand strategy of the war against the harmful microbe can only emerge from the Symposium as a whole. Decisions must be taken as to which weapon or combination of weapons is most likely to be effective against particular enemies under a variety of circumstances. But strategy goes further than merely choosing from existing possibilities. Consideration of the problem as a whole may lead to the conclusion that progress will be impeded or impossible without further knowledge not necessarily directly concerned with the killing of microbes, and positive steps may have to be taken to obtain it. The Mulberry Harbour, not of itself an offensive or defensive weapon, was especially devised for the cross-channel invasion and was an essential factor for its success. Our Symposium will be all the more successful if it brings out and promotes discussion of knowledge we should like to have, and better still if it stimulates positive research to acquire it.

Since chemotherapy is based on the interaction of chemical substances with biological systems, the underlying principles must be biochemical ones; it is with these that the remainder of this introduction will be largely concerned. Any broad survey must of necessity be superficial, and to some extent dogmatic, since it must draw on current knowledge of the biochemistry not only of the various invading microbes but of all the hosts as well. Adequate discussion of all the work implicated would be impossible, and the list of references would occupy the rest of this volume. Since biochemistry is in a lively state of exponential growth some general statements will have to be made with which not all biochemists will agree; other statements will appear trite and obvious to the professional biochemist. References to the literature will therefore be as far as possible to reviews which cover a wide field. Later contributors will no doubt be giving the detailed biochemical background to their own topics and overlap is undesirable. We shall however take a number of detailed examples from the sulphonamides, partly because no-one else is dealing with them specifically, and partly because a good deal is known in biochemical detail about their action. Many of the views to be set out in this introduction have also been put forward in one context or another by other writers on chemotherapy or metabolite-analogues.

The Symposium is supposed to devote attention to the future rather than to the past. But when it comes to discussing basic principles it is impossible not to mention the contributions of Paul Ehrlich: probably the most we can do today is to expand his ideas and express them in more concrete and biochemical language. Thus in 1885, following his work on vital stains, he wrote (Ehrlich, 1885) 'We are obliged to adopt the view that the protoplasm is equipped with certain atomic groups (side-chains), whose function especially consists in fixing to themselves certain foodstuffs of importance to cell life...' and again 'The relationship of the corresponding groups i.e. those of the foodstuffs and those of the cell must be specific. They must be adapted to one another as e.g. male and female screw or as lock and key.' He suggested that toxic drugs were fixed to these side-chain receptors because of their chemical similarity to the foodstuffs in question. The value of such ideas for the design of drugs was clear to him (Ehrlich, 1913). 'I have explained above that parasites possess a whole series of chemo-receptors which are specifically different from one another. Now if we can succeed in discovering among them a grouping which has no analogue in the organs of the body, then we should have the possibility of constructing an ideal remedy.' An excellent brief account of Ehrlich's work from the present point of view has been given by Work (1954). Ehrlich and his colleagues were also the first to observe the development of resistance (in trypanosomes) to chemotherapeutic agents, and to suggest means (the simultaneous use of two different types of drugs) to surmount this obstacle (see Ehrlich, 1908). It is clear that the problem of development of resistance is still one of the most serious problems in a planned chemotherapy.

THE SEARCH FOR AGENTS ACTIVE AGAINST THE MICROBE

The first step in the search for a chemotherapeutic agent is to find a substance to kill or prevent further multiplication of the microbe. But the additional requirement for selective action (which introduces the idea of specificity) should be borne in mind from the start. To avoid substances which are general cell poisons it would clearly be profitable to seek substances which inhibit specific metabolic processes of the cell. The term essential metabolite is often used in discussions on chemotherapy: it defines (in the sense of Fildes, 1940) substances whose further metabolism is essential for the survival and multiplication of the microbe. It may be a raw material for growth or an intermediate in a metabolic pathway; a coenzyme must also be regarded as an intermediate since it undergoes cyclical chemical changes. If the organism is unable to synthesize the metabolite for itself then it is also an essential growth factor.

The agents with specific action which promote metabolism in the broadest sense may be divided into three types:

(1) *Enzymes*. Their importance from the present point of view is that their catalytic action depends upon an initial combination with the substrate (metabolite) and that they are protein in nature. They are of course common to host and microbe (or in the case of viruses, present in the infected cell).

(2) '*Templates*'. There is an increasing belief that the biosynthesis of complex substances of highly specific structure such as proteins and nucleic acids does not occur by a stepwise series of individual enzyme reactions leading to products of gradually increasing complexity. Instead, evidence is mounting for a one-step process in which the component units (e.g. amino acids in the case of protein) become attached in necessarily the right sequence to active groups borne by a 'template' molecule. Such attachment is followed by chemical combination of the units and the peeling off from the template of the new large molecule. The nature of the template is not yet fully determined but there is evidence that in bacteria the template for protein synthesis may be ribonucleic acid (or ribonucleoprotein), and that in turn the latter may be formed on a template of deoxyribonucleic acid (or nucleoprotein). Dr Gale will no doubt expand these views; work with micro-organisms, particularly with inducible enzymes, has played a notable part in their development (see Gale, 1956; Spiegelman, 1956). A simple general account of the template hypothesis of protein formation is given by Fowden (1957).

It will be noted that this mechanism also envisages combination of the metabolites with the agent and is highly specific. There is evidence that such mechanisms also occur in animal tissue.

(3) *Transport systems*. Recent work by Rickenberg, Cohen, Buttin & Monod (1956) on the induction of β-galactosidase in *Escherichia coli*, and the properties of certain mutants of that organism, led them to propose (convincingly) that there is a specific mechanism ('permease') for the transport of glycosides into the organism and their concentration within. In their own words (translated) 'We shall define a permease as

being a system of a protein nature bringing about the catalytic transfer of a substrate across a cellular osmotic barrier, possessing the properties of steric specificity and kinetic activity of an enzyme, but distinct and independent of enzymes bringing about the metabolism as such of the substrate.' Whether or not the process is enzymic in the usual sense is unsettled. The transport is active since the metabolite is concentrated and an associated energy-yielding reaction is necessary. There is strong evidence for a similar transport system for valine and other amino acids in *E. coli* (Cohen & Rickenberg, 1956; see also Britten, Roberts & French, 1955) and for citrate in *Aerobacter aerogenes* (Davis, 1956). If these mechanisms turn out (as seems likely) to be widespread both as regards microbe and metabolite, it is clear that another type of specific activity may be open to attack by chemotherapy. It is not yet known whether the same mechanisms exist for animal and plant cells: selective permeability of animal cells is of course known, and insulin has been suggested as playing a part in the penetration of glucose (see for example Wilbrandt, 1954; Stadie, 1954; Fisher & Lindsay, 1956). To summarize, specific combination of metabolite with an agent which is protein in nature is again envisaged. To complete the picture, passive transport systems in which specific combination of a metabolite and a protein occurs should be mentioned; haemoglobin (oxygen transport) is the obvious example. Systems of this type are so far unknown in micro-organisms and may be a consequence of the needs of a complex organism with separate specialized tissues. Dr Mitchell is to deal with selective penetration in detail.

The next point to consider is the general methods by which these metabolic agents could be prevented from working. Theoretically one could attempt to destroy them, though, because of their nature and possible or probable occurrence in the host cells as well, there seems little hope of doing so without equal damage to the host. The two other possibilities are to prevent their formation or to inhibit specifically their function. The latter will be considered first, with enzyme action as an example.

Inhibition of enzyme reactions by substances which are chemically similar to the substrate is well known. It is not proposed to go into details here, but an excellent account from the point of view of chemotherapy is given by Work & Work (1948). Such inhibition may be of two types, competitive and non-competitive. When there is competition (i.e. increase of substrate concentration overcomes the inhibition) it is supposed that the analogue combines with the same active centres of the enzyme as does the substrate itself. But combination does not result in activation and the analogue is not metabolized. The result is that the amount of enzyme available for the substrate is effectively reduced in proportion to the relative concentrations of substrate and analogue and their relative affinities for the enzyme. In non-competitive inhibition (which may be reversible by diluting the inhibitor) the analogue is thought to combine with different active groups on the enzyme protein; if the substrate combines with two or more active groups then one or more (but not all) of these may be the same ones at which the analogue combines. The molecule of the analogue masks the remaining group or groups with which the substrate would combine and thus denies the substrate access to the enzyme.

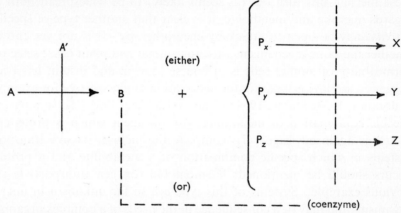

Fig. 1. Diagram showing types of substance likely to overcome inhibition by antimetabolites. A is a metabolite and A' an inhibitory analogue of it. B is the immediate product of the reaction. X, Y, and Z are secondary products and P_x, etc., their precursors.

From the point of view of chemotherapy it is important to realize that certain substances may overcome the inhibition and that these may be present in the host tissues. (It is assumed for the moment that these substances are permeable to the micro-organism.) In competitive inhibition the metabolite itself will overcome the inhibition, but the concentration required will rise in direct proportion to the concentration of the analogue applied. Neither competitive nor non-competitive inhibitor would affect the growth of the organism if the immediate product (B, see Fig. 1) of the enzyme reaction were available preformed in the environment; furthermore, the amount of B required is fixed by the need of the organism and would not increase with increasing concentrations of inhibitor. Now if B itself were either a coenzyme or a common reactant in further cellular syntheses leading to X, Y and Z it would also be expected that a mixture of these substances would overcome inhibition, again irrespective of the concentration of A'. An insufficient amount of B or X, Y and Z for the needs of the organism (or the provision of, say, X only) would at least reduce the amount of metabolite (A) required to overcome inhibition by a given concentration of analogue (A'). These matters have been considered in more detail by Woods (1953a).

With living cultures of micro-organisms the situation may be complex. The organism may be impermeable to the primary or secondary products of the utilization of the metabolite. Permeability may even change with the phase of growth; for instance the pneumococcus is permeable to deoxyribonucleic acid (transforming principle) for only a limited period during the existence of each organism (Hotchkiss, 1954). At first sight non-competitive inhibition appears to offer the best hope for chemo-therapy since the metabolite itself would not overcome the inhibition; however this would not apply to the products—a more serious problem in practice since the required concentration would not be affected by the concentration of analogue.

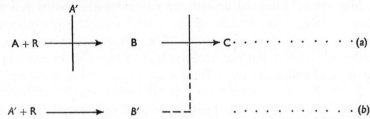

Fig. 2. Diagram illustrating lethal synthesis. C is the end product and R is another initial reactant; other symbols as in Fig. 1.

So far, only straightforward interference by metabolite analogues has been considered (Fig. 2 line (a)). The analogue may, however, so closely resemble the substrate that it is activated on combination with the enzyme and undergoes the same type of chemical change as the sub-strate itself. In this case the product (B') will be an analogue of the normal product (B) and may inhibit the further utilization of B either competitively or non-competitively (Fig. 2 line (b)), precisely as outlined above for the primary metabolite A. This is the principle of lethal synthesis and was first demonstrated by Peters and his colleagues (see Peters, 1952) in the case of poisoning by fluoroacetate of the respiration of bird tissues. Here the fluoroacetate (analogue of acetate) is converted to the fluoro-analogue of citrate and inhibits the utilization of the latter. It is possible also that the product B' may be inactive either as metabolite or inhibitor, but effectively stop metabolism by exhausting supplies of the other reactant (R) in the primary reaction (Fig. 2).

Dr Markham will be dealing in detail with the possible applications of lethal synthesis to chemotherapy; the only other general point which need be made is that the demonstration of the incorporation of an inhibitory analogue of an amino acid, purine or pyrimidine into cellular protein or nucleic acid is not of itself sufficient to prove that the growth inhibitory action is a consequence of this. In two cases there is evidence that incorporation of pyrimidine analogues into deoxyribonucleic acid is not related to their inhibitory action (Zamenhof, De Giovanni & Rich, 1956; Prusoff, 1957).

So far only the question of inhibition of enzyme reactions by analogues has been discussed. The mechanisms proposed for the action of both templates and permeases also require specific combination of metabolites with the agents. It is clear that, at any rate in theory, the conception of inhibition by metabolite-analogues applies with equal force to systems of the template or permease type, both as regards direct inhibition and, in the case of templates, of lethal synthesis also. Indeed, Cohen & Rickenberg (1956) have shown that the well-known competitive inhibition of bacterial growth by natural amino acids related in structure to other natural amino acids is very satisfactorily explained by competition for specific permeases. If, as a result, the analogue also enters the cell it may, but not necessarily, compete for the enzyme concerned in metabolism as well. The nature of the union between metabolite and enzyme may differ from that with permease (Rickenberg et al. 1956) since the metabolite is finally liberated unchanged in the latter case; an analogue effective with the enzyme may not therefore be effective with permease and vice versa.

A great deal of thought and work has been put into the question of what changes in the chemical structure of metabolites are most likely to produce effective antimetabolites. Dr Woolley has been a leader in this field and will no doubt review this among other aspects of the design of antimetabolites.

Another feature of enzyme action must be mentioned. Many enzymes are known to depend on the presence of metal ions of various kinds (activators). The metal may have an essential role in the chemical union of enzyme with substrate or coenzyme, and it may be considered perhaps either as part of the enzyme structure or as a coenzyme. Substances which chelate metals may compete with the enzyme for the metal and thus inactivate them; it has also been suggested that in some cases the chelating agent may inhibit indirectly by removing a metal which is protecting the enzyme from poisoning by another metal (Albert, Gibson & Rubbo, 1953). Professor Albert is to tell us about the possibilities of chelating agents in chemotherapy.

POSSIBILITIES OF SELECTIVE ACTION

In the preceding discussion of the general possibilities for killing or preventing the proliferation of the invader, the necessity for avoiding damage to the host has been taken into account only so far as to concentrate on agents with specific action on metabolic processes and thus unlikely to be general cell poisons. It must now be considered whether the antimetabolite approach offers any hope, from the biochemical standpoint, of selective action on the parasite. The growth of knowledge of comparative biochemistry has led to the realization that many basic cell reactions are common to all forms of life; this is perhaps particularly so with the energy-yielding mechanisms. The widespread requirement for B-group vitamins (many of them known to function ultimately as coenzymes in key cell reactions) exemplifies this point. This would tend to militate against the chances of finding agents with selective action, yet there is a real danger that too rigid a belief in the uniformity of biochemistry may stifle progress. Clearly there must be differences, especially in biosynthetic reactions, since we finish up with quite different organisms. It is the task of chemotherapy to find differences, albeit in detail, which are susceptible to the weapons at our disposal.

The question of selective action of antimetabolites may be considered broadly from qualitative and quantitative points of view.

Qualitative. In this case it is necessary to find a metabolite which is unique to the invader. A survey by Stanier (1954) produced remarkably few examples among low molecular weight substances and the situation has not changed materially since then. It is not proposed to give a list here; diaminopimelic acid (Work, 1955) and D-alanine (Snell, Radin & Ikawa, 1955) may be instanced. Both, as it happens, occur at least in part in the cell walls of certain micro-organisms (see also Cummins & Harris, 1956; Park & Strominger, 1957). Certain amino-sugars may also be unique to cell walls of bacteria, but Dr Park will be discussing these points in general and in relation to the action of penicillin. Differences in cell-wall structure may also make possible a selective action through disrupting them by surface-active substances, or enzymes (e.g. lysozyme), but here we impinge upon Dr Newton's subject.

Substances unique to the metabolism of the microbe (though not unique to the microbe) may be found amongst intermediates in the synthesis of compounds which the host cannot make for itself. Certain amino acids, for example, cannot be synthesized by animal tissues and are dietary essentials; some bacteria can synthesize them and the intermediates are in effect unique to the bacteria.

A novel pyrimidine (5-hydroxymethylcytosine) is present in the deoxyribonucleic acid of certain bacteriophages (Wyatt & Cohen, 1953); this would be a potential point of attack if we were interested in protecting *Escherichia coli* from the phages in question.

The number of substances likely to be unique to micro-organisms increases as the size of the molecule under consideration increases; even if the complex molecules of host and invader are built up from the same units the arrangement or sequence of the units will vary. Very different proteins, for example, are built up, even in one organism, from the same amino acids. But it is far less easy, though it may ultimately be possible, to apply antimetabolite theory to large molecules. There are two main difficulties: (*a*) it is necessary to ascertain the complete structure of the compound and then to synthesize a variety of analogues, (*b*) complex molecules are less likely to be able to enter the cell. It may become possible deliberately and specifically to modify the permeability of cell walls and membranes; perhaps Dr Newton will be discussing this.

Quantitative. The combination with the enzyme of metabolite and analogue depends not only on the chemical properties of these substances but on the nature and spatial distribution of the active groups of the enzyme itself. Slight differences in this respect may well affect the relative affinities of analogue and metabolite. Woolley (1952) has pointed out that even among micro-organisms one may differ markedly from another in sensitivity to a given antimetabolite. Although other explanations (e.g. differing permeability) are possible, such observations may point to species differences in the minute structure of enzymes. Similar or even greater differences may exist between the enzymes of host and parasite. These points cannot be established until the enzymes in question can be isolated and purified.

Similar arguments would also apply to direct competition in the case of template and permease mechanisms, and to lethal synthesis by enzymes and templates. Clearly it is not yet possible to predict whether an analogue of a metabolite of equal importance to host and invader may or may not have some degree of selective action.

Damage to host metabolism would be diminished if the host were less permeable than the microbe to the analogue. But this would only have chemotherapeutic value in systemic infections; when the parasite is inside the host cells it is equally necessary that the agent should penetrate the latter. Of course, if only certain types of host cells are infected, the ideal would be an agent that could enter only these cells and those of the parasite. Unfortunately the greatest gap in the biochemical background to chemotherapy is knowledge of the mechanisms by which organic substances enter cells. Until this is available it cannot even be said if specificity of the desired type is possible, and far less whether it can be combined in one molecule with the other required properties.

There is evidence that streptomycin interferes at a particular step of the tricarboxylic acid cycle of respiration, and that its comparative lack of toxicity to animal cells may be due to inability to penetrate permeability barriers of the host, both at the cell wall and at the surface of the mitochondria which contain this enzyme complex (Umbreit, 1952). Suter (1952) has found that the concentration of streptomycin required to inhibit growth of tubercle bacilli is about a hundred times greater when they are within phagocytes than when free in the medium.

From the biochemical point of view there is another quantitative difference between host and microbe which may be important in the chemotherapy of acute, though not chronic, infections. The metabolic rate of the micro-organism, under optimal conditions, is very much higher than the general metabolic rate of the host. This is reflected also in the rate of synthesis of new cell material and consequently the rate of reduplication of cells. It has frequently been argued or implied (see, e.g. Roblin, 1946) that a temporary interruption of host metabolism, especially anabolic reactions, might be unimportant to the host although permitting a control of the microbial multiplication sufficient at least to prevent it overwhelming the normal defence mechanisms of the host: if this position is accepted, then almost any metabolic reaction of the microbe might be attacked. Clearly those connected with synthesis offer the best hope since the host is likely to depend even for short-term survival on the main energy-yielding and energy-transfer reactions. Sir Hans Krebs is to examine in a broader way the chemotherapeutic possibilities of attack on energy metabolism. The main obstacle to predictions about what use could be made of differences in rate of metabolism (as opposed to nature of metabolism) is lack of real information concerning the metabolic rate of microbes growing in the host, and concerning the possible importance of particular syntheses to the well-being of the host over short periods. A particularly sensitive point might be the production of new blood cells since these have a comparatively short life.

It is difficult to draw any general conclusions about the possibilities of selective action in a chemotherapy based upon antimetabolites. From a theoretical standpoint it would seem that the principle of lethal synthesis offers the best hope since there are two chances of a difference in biochemical behaviour of host and invader. Firstly, the microbe may bring about the lethal synthesis reaction and the host not. Secondly, even if both do so, the host enzyme concerned in the next metabolic step may be less sensitive to the product than is its microbial counterpart. The biochemical study of the development of resistance to chemotherapeutic agents by the microbes themselves may serve as a model for the discovery of reasons for immunity of cells to agents expected to be toxic to them. Such studies have indeed pointed to a variety of mechanisms (Davis & Maas, 1952; Abraham, 1953); ones that appear to be relevant, for example, changes in affinity of enzymes or of permeability to toxic agent, have already been brought into the discussion.

CAN THE FORMATION OF ENZYMES AND OTHER METABOLIC AGENTS BE PREVENTED?

So far only the specific inhibition of the activity of enzymes, templates and transport agents has been considered. A second possibility for chemotherapy is to prevent their formation. Since the substances in question are all either proteins or nucleic acids this question is really one for Dr Gale. From the present point of view it seems likely, though not proven particularly in the case of permease, that similar mechanisms exist both in host and invader. On the other hand the active agents are all large molecules and there will certainly be differences in their structure especially in the case of templates. Specific inhibition of the synthesis of either ribo- or deoxyribonucleic acid might be achieved by analogues of metabolites since each contains a pyrimidine residue (uracil and thymine respectively) not present in the other. The fascinating results of Cohen & Barner (1954, 1955) with mutants of *Escherichia coli* requiring thymine for growth show that deprivation of this pyrimidine leads to unbalanced growth (increase in size in the absence of cell division) and death of the organism; deoxyribonucleic acid was not synthesized.

A notable feature of bacterial life is the ability of a number of organisms apparently to produce new enzymes in response to the presence of the substrate in the environment. This is due in many cases to a random mutation, but in others only phenotypic changes occur; the new enzyme is induced by the substrate. This subject was dealt with exhaustively in this Society's Symposium on *Adaptation in Micro-organisms* (1953). A case of an inducible permease has also been described (Rickenberg *et al.* 1956). Enzymic adaptation of this kind is rare in animal tissues although a few examples are known (see Knox, 1954). Whether or not this biochemical difference between host and microbe is a possible point of attack in chemotherapy must depend on answers to at least two questions:

(1) Is it possible to inhibit specifically the formation of induced

enzymes? Cohn & Monod (1953) have examined this point and list several types of inhibition. The one which seems to offer most immediate hope for chemotherapy is competition by an analogue of the substrate or inducer. An example of this type of action is the inhibition by thiophenyl-β-galactoside of the induction of the β-galactosidase of *Escherichia coli*. The action of this analogue may be to compete with the substrate for the permease which transports the latter into the cell (Rickenberg *et al.* 1956). This does not affect the argument since the result is that the enzyme is not induced. Other analogues, though not metabolized, may induce the enzyme.

(2) Is the induction of new enzymes important for the multiplication of pathogenic bacteria in the host? Clearly this must be investigated for each bacterium in the particular host environment. Enzymic adaptation in typical pathogenic micro-organisms has been very little studied, and the same is true even of their general metabolism within the host.

THE ACTION OF SULPHONAMIDES

It may be profitable at this point to illustrate some of the general principles discussed above by reference to one successful group of chemotherapeutic agents—the sulphonamides—whose mode of action and selective toxicity are reasonably well, though not completely, understood. The results of an early study of their biochemical mode of action (Woods, 1940) drew attention to analogues of metabolites as possible chemotherapeutic agents; they were also one of the cornerstones of Fildes' (1940) suggestion for a rational approach to research in chemotherapy. The preceding sections have been largely an expansion and restatement of this approach in the light of experience and of progress in biochemistry. It is not intended here to assess what contribution the antimetabolite principle has made to the actual design of successful drugs; this has been done excellently by Woolley (1952) and by Welch (1954).

It has been rightly said that sulphonamides led to the discovery of *p*-aminobenzoic acid (*p*-AB) and not vice versa. The discovery of *p*-AB has in turn assisted in biochemical developments which have made possible a more detailed explanation of the success of the sulphonamides. The present position will be set out briefly with emphasis on points which seem of possible wider application in chemotherapy; Fig. 3 illustrates the main points schematically.

It is now generally accepted that the sulphonamides owe their growth-inhibitory action to competition for an enzyme catalysing the metabolism of *p*-AB, which is an essential metabolite and to which they are structurally related: the case is a straightforward one of competitive inhibition by an analogue of a metabolite. The first known product of *p*-AB metabolism is folic acid, itself an essential metabolite and growth factor both for micro-organisms and higher creatures. The folic acid molecule contains residues of *p*-AB, glutamic acid and pteridine (or reduced pteridine); the detailed chemical steps in its biosynthesis from *p*-AB are not yet known and neither is the nature of the immediate product of *p*-AB utilization, which is presumably an intermediate in folic acid synthesis. The situation is complicated somewhat by the fact that folic acid, as extracted from natural sources, exists in a number of

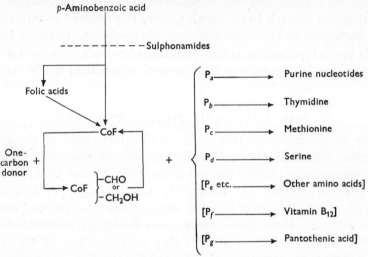

Fig. 3. Diagram summarizing the cellular functions of *p*-aminobenzoic acid and folic acid. CoF is the coenzyme form of folic acid; P_a etc. are precursors of ultimate products. [ ], reaction indicated in only one or a few organisms.

chemically distinct but closely related forms; the differences in structure lie in the state of reduction of the pteridine nucleus and the number of glutamic acid residues present. Individual forms may have differing biological activity with various test organisms.

The function of folic acid in cellular metabolism is that of coenzyme in reactions in which a one-carbon residue is transferred (Fig. 3). Such reactions occur at certain steps in the biosynthesis of a number of amino acids (methionine, serine and several others), purine ribotides, thymidine, and probably (at least with some organisms) vitamin B_{12} and pantothenic acid. The type of evidence which gave the initial information is summarized by Woods (1953*a*). The precise chemical nature of the ultimate coenzyme form of folic acid (CoF, Fig. 3) is not yet known but it is probably a derivative of tetrahydrofolic acid (see Greenberg &

Jaenicke, 1957). The mechanism of its catalytic action in one-carbon transfer is thought to be to accept a formyl (—CHO) or hydroxymethyl (—CH₂OH) from one activated substrate and then to donate it to an acceptor substrate.

On theoretical grounds it would be expected that growth inhibition by sulphonamides would be overcome (a) competitively by p-AB, and (b) irrespective of sulphonamide concentration, by (i) the direct product of the inhibited reaction, folic acid, or (ii) by secondary products, that is, a mixture of the substances in whose synthesis folic acid is concerned. In practice this is the case with (a) and (b) (ii): with (b) (i) there are complexities which need comment since the chemotherapeutic value of the sulphonamides depends on them. Known forms of folic acid over-come sulphonamide inhibition (and replace p-AB as a growth factor) with some micro-organisms but not with others; yet with all micro-organisms tested folic acid is synthesized from p-AB and such synthesis is competitively inhibited by sulphonamides. The reasons for this have not yet been determined in biochemical terms (see Woods, 1954). Possible explanations are (a) that the forms of folic acid tested are not themselves normal intermediates in the synthesis of CoF from p-AB, but are converted to such by some organisms but not by others; (b) that some organisms are impermeable to folic acid; and (c) that there is in some organisms a second function of p-AB in cellular metabolism, not exerted through folic acid, and also inhibited by sulphonamides. There are for instance brief reports (McCullough, 1957; Sloane, 1953) of a substance formed from p-AB acting catalytically in aromatic hydroxyl-ation reactions.

The reasons for the profound effect of sulphonamides on growth are clear. They can prevent, or slow down, the synthesis of a number of the raw materials of proteins, deoxyribonucleic acid and ribonucleic acid. In the case of purine synthesis there are two different steps at which CoF functions (see Buchanan, Flaks, Hartman, Levenberg, Lukens & Warren, 1957). Sulphonamides therefore attack the synthetic processes of the organism at many points simultaneously. It is conceivable that the microbe might have a second mechanism for synthesizing one of these end products, but much less likely that alternate pathways to all of them would exist. These are certainly points to be borne in mind when selecting a metabolite for attack.

Selective action against the microbe. Folic acid is also an essential metabolite for animals and has, as would be expected, the same bio-chemical function. From the work summarized above we have now to find an explanation for the selective toxicity of sulphonamides to the microbe. Of the synthetic pathways which folic acid catalyses, that to methionine may be peculiar to the microbe because this amino acid must be supplied preformed to animals (and indeed to some bacteria). On the other hand serine, thymine and the purines are not dietary essentials for the animal and are synthesized by them. The difference with methionine may aid selective action but clearly cannot be primarily responsible. Folic acid, however, is a vitamin for animals; its synthesis is therefore unique to the micro-organism. In other words the metabolic lesion induced by sulphonamides already exists in animals, which require a preformed source of the product of the missing reaction. (It may be noted in passing that certain enterococci, which also require preformed folic acid for growth, are clinically insensitive to sulphonamides (Spink, 1942).) It is probable that this is the key to the selective action of the sulphonamides, but is not of itself a sufficient explanation (Woolley, 1947; Woods & Nimmo-Smith, 1949). Since folic acid is essential for the host it must be present in host tissues. Why does it not overcome the inhibition of the growth of the microbe? The answer seems to be that the forms of folic acid present free in host tissues are not, possibly for reasons discussed above, available to the bacteria which are normally attacked by sulphonamide therapy. Again, the secondary products of the function of p-AB (amino acids, nucleic acid derivatives) are all metabolites potentially likely to be present in the host. In order to overcome inhibition they would all need to be present at effective concentrations. There is little direct evidence on this point, but, with mice, Bacon, Burrows & Yates (1951) have evidence that there is insufficient purine to support growth of a salmonella mutant; the mutant (of a virulent strain) was avirulent unless purine was also injected.

On the whole the selective toxicity of sulphonamides can be reasonably well explained. But the explanation provides no easy road to the choice of other antimetabolites with the same desirable property; a thorough knowledge of the metabolism and function of the metabolite in both host and microbe is a minimum requirement.

Other effects of individual sulphonamides. All sulphonamides of the general structure $H_2N.C_6H_4.SO_2NHR$ competitively inhibit the utilization of p-AB and to this their inhibition of growth is primarily due. Individual sulphonamides may also have effects on other metabolic processes which may add to their activity. Thus sulphanilamide interferes with some enzymes concerned in carbon dioxide metabolism and sulphapyridine with some aspects of nicotinic acid metabolism. Such effects are also given by derivatives of the sulphonamides which are without effect on bacterial growth. These matters (reviewed in greater detail by Woods, 1953*b*) are raised here for two reasons. First, it emphasizes to those seeking the biochemical mode of action of other antibacterial substances that a discovery of some metabolic event or even isolated enzyme which is inhibited by the drug does not prove that this is the important point of attack. Second, the sulphonamides have some degree of toxicity to animals also which must be explained. It might be due in part to second actions, or in part, especially where signs such as leucopenia and agranulocytosis suggest folic acid deficiency, to inhibition of the synthesis of folic acid by gut micro-organisms.

SOME OTHER FACTORS ASSOCIATED WITH THE HOST

Successful treatment with a chemical which acted solely by increasing the production or activity of the host defence mechanisms (antibodies, phagocytes) would be chemotherapy in the broadest sense, but is probably outside the scope of this Symposium. Adrenocorticotrophic hormone (ACTH) is said to stimulate the production of leucocytes by bone marrow, but the action may be indirect and the mechanism is obscure (see Macfarlane, 1954). Apart from this we can only quote that well-known physician Sir Ralph Bloomfield Bonington: 'Nature has provided, in the white corpuscles as you call them—in the phagocytes as we call them—a natural means of devouring and destroying all disease germs. There is at bottom only one genuinely scientific treatment for all diseases, and that is to stimulate the phagocytes. Stimulate the phagocytes.'*

It is not intended here to discuss matters such as the destruction and excretion of drugs. Clearly an otherwise promising antibacterial substance may be useless therapeutically because it is rapidly modified and excreted. A good deal is known of the biochemical methods by which unusual molecules are dealt with in animal tissues ('detoxication') and there might be hope of designing a molecule to avoid this fate. Unfortunately the chemical groups modified in the detoxication reaction may well be just those essential for the antibacterial activity. Sulphonamides, for example, are acetylated by animal tissues and the acetyl derivatives are without antibacterial action.

On the other hand metabolism by the host tissues of the chemical supplied may convert it to the true antimicrobial substance. The antimalarial drugs proguanil and pamaquin are both converted to more active compounds by the host. The very discovery of the sulphonamides

* Shaw, G. B. (1913). *The Doctor's Dilemma*, Act I. London: Constable & Co. The same gentleman went on: 'Drugs are a delusion.'

followed from the observation that Prontosil rubrum was active *in vivo* but not *in vitro*; sulphanilamide was formed by the action of the host. There is evidence that the most active forms of the arsenical drugs used against trypanosomes contain trivalent arsenic. Atoxyl (pentavalent arsenic) and the arsenobenzenes are reduced and oxidized respectively by the host to arsenoxides. Fuller discussion of these points and references are given by Albert (1951), and Welch (1954). It is possible that it may be an advantage in some cases to have the chemical preparation of the drug completed by the host. The rate of conversion might ensure a steadier supply of the active drug within the cell—a possible advantage particularly if a drug were being sought for prophylactic use. Again, in the case of intracellular parasites, the precursor might penetrate host cells more readily. Pentavalent arsenicals are said to gain access to the central nervous system and be effective in neurosyphilis. On the other hand the rate of conversion may limit the effectiveness of the drug; this is thought to be the case with proguanil, which is a better agent for prophylaxis than for treatment of active malaria.

A major problem, especially in the chemotherapy of cancer, is the toxicity of potentially useful drugs to normal host cells. As a pure speculation one wonders if it might be possible by treatment with the drug prior to the disease or infection to develop increased resistance of the host cells and thus to give a better chance for therapy should the disease arise. It is well known (at least to writers of detective fiction)* that resistance to arsenical poisoning can be built up in man by a series of small doses. Could this principle be applied more usefully?

The efforts of the host itself to contain the disease may make chemotherapy more difficult. In chronic tuberculosis the bacilli are walled in by a mass of epithelioid and giant cells and lymphocytes which eventually become fibrosed (the tubercle). Drugs effective against the tubercle bacilli (streptomycin, isoniazid), cannot reach them. One effect of administration of corticosteroids is to lead to the breaking down of fibrous tissue with consequent dissemination of the bacilli which can then be attacked (Houghton, 1954). There is no general agreement that this is a wise thing to do; the use of cortisone has many disadvantages, including preventing rise of temperature and other signs of active infection. The application of this principle, useful in theory, may have to await the discovery of more specific agents.

* See, e.g. *Strong Poison* by D. L. Sayers. London: Gollancz.

SOME OTHER FACTORS ASSOCIATED WITH THE INVADER

Bacteriostatic and bactericidal action. It is frequently stated or implied that a successful chemotherapy does not of necessity require that the invader be killed, and that all that is essential is that the proliferation of the invader be held in check while the defence mechanisms of the host operate. This may be true in some cases, but it is as well to remember that Ehrlich was led towards his research on what became chemotherapy partly because of the relative failure of immunological methods with protozoal and spirochaetal infections. Furthermore, the more rapid the removal of the parasite, the less chance there is for the selection of variants resistant to the drug.

It is not easy to state absolutely whether a given agent is bactericidal or bacteriostatic—the final result may depend on environmental factors. The penicillins and sulphonamides are both successful against bacteria; the former are predominantly bactericidal, the latter bacteriostatic. Penicillin is known to kill micro-organisms only when they are in a medium in which multiplication can occur (Hobby, Meyer & Chaffee, 1942; Chain & Duthie, 1945). With the detailed knowledge of bacterial nutrition now available it might be possible deliberately to create conditions (if they did not already exist, say, in some particular location) to promote cell division and thus to help to kill the microbe. It may be possible also to render sulphonamides bactericidal by making sure that certain substances are present in the environment. It will be recalled (see p. 15) that sulphonamide inhibition is overcome by a mixture of the ultimate products of the function of p-AB and folic acid (amino acids, purines, thymine, etc.). Cohen & Barner (1954) have found with *Escherichia coli* that if thymine is omitted the organisms die as a result of unbalanced growth (see p. 12), whereas if any of the other substances is left out there is no growth but the organisms survive. Whether or not this effect could be obtained *in vivo* would depend on how much thymine was present, and also how much p-AB; less of the latter factor would be required to overcome sulphonamide inhibition in the presence of a number of the products of its function.

Parasites with complex life-cycles. When distinct phases of the life-cycle occur in the host (as, e.g. with the malarial parasite) it should be remembered that the metabolism may differ in the various phases; consequently a drug effective at one phase may not be at another. It is fairly easy to control an acute attack of malaria, but difficult to eradicate the parasite (and prevent relapses) owing to the persistence in the host of exo-erythrocytic forms which are less susceptible to the drugs most effective

against the erythrocytic forms (see Davey, 1951). Attempts at a planned
chemotherapy of organisms of this type suffer from lack of precise knowledge of similarities and differences in metabolism during different phases.

Nutritional requirements of the invader. It is perhaps doubtful whether
treatment by withdrawing a chemical rather than administering one
should be called chemotherapy, but in certain instances the result could
be the same. If the parasite requires a growth factor which is unimportant to the host, then a diet (for the host) which is deficient in
the factor should (theoretically) reduce or prevent the proliferation of
the parasite without harming the host; it would be the same thing in
principle as giving an inhibitory analogue of the growth factor. One
example is known (Hawking, 1954): a milk diet was found to decrease
susceptibility of rats and monkeys to infection by malarial parasites.
There is good evidence that this is due to a deficiency in milk of *p*-AB,
which is a growth factor for these organisms but not for the host; the
result is the same as giving sulphonamides. It has been suggested that
there may be here an explanation of the relative natural immunity of
human infants in Africa to malaria (Hawking, 1955).

Harmful effects of the invader. We should not worry about the
microbes which live in or on our bodies if they did us no harm; indeed
many innocuous or even helpful microbes do so live with us. Here then
must be specific biochemical differences between host and microbe
which might be a point of attack in chemotherapy if there were sufficient
knowledge of the nature and mechanism of synthesis of the substances
which actually harm the host. The principles outlined in the first part
of this paper might then be applied in the hope of suppressing specifically the formation or activity of such substances. In 1955 our Society
held a Symposium on *Mechanisms of Microbial Pathogenicity* and it was
clear that from the biochemical point of view this approach is a possibility
for the future rather than the present.

Development of resistance. The main weapon of the microbe (or
cancer cell) against the chemotherapist is its ability to acquire resistance
to drugs. This is still one of the most important problems for the future
development of chemotherapy, though it was realized and attacked with
some success by Ehrlich himself (1908). The severity of the problem
varies from parasite to parasite and from one drug to another but
almost always exists. To quote but two examples, it is particularly
troublesome in treatment of tuberculosis with streptomycin and of
acute leukaemias with the purine and folic acid analogues which give
such hopeful initial results.

A detailed knowledge of the biochemical changes accompanying increase of resistance may eventually lead to the discovery of specific methods for prohibiting such changes. Known mechanisms (reviewed up to 1952 by Davis & Maas (1952) and Abraham (1953)) include: impermeability of the drug (Nichol, 1954), decomposition of the drug, increased synthesis of the metabolite antagonized, changes in the properties of an enzyme resulting in a different relative affinity of substrate and antagonist, and increased amount of an enzyme. Unfortunately resistance to the same drug may arise by different mechanisms with various organisms or even with the same organism.

The two methods at present used to control resistance accept the fact that it may develop and try to deal with the consequences. Both of them were stated and used by Ehrlich (1908). The first is to hit the microbe as hard as possible in the shortest time: the less the microbe multiplies and the shorter its survival time, the less chance there is for development of resistance. Ehrlich's second approach was combined therapy by two drugs which attack the microbe in different ways. He and his colleagues had found that trypanosomes could acquire resistance to each of three types of drug initially effective against them. Resistance was however specific, that is, an organism resistant to one type was not resistant to the others. It was presumed that lack of cross-resistance meant that the drugs had different modes of action and vice versa. Thus resistant variants either present in the original inoculum or appearing afterwards can be prevented from multiplying by the presence of a second drug of the right type. This principle has perhaps its main practical use today in the treatment of tuberculosis by a mixture of streptomycin (the most effective drug) and either isoniazid or p-aminosalicylic acid, though other factors probably contribute to the success obtained. There is some evidence that growth (*in vitro*) in the presence of p-aminosalicylic acid (or isoniazid) and streptomycin prevents the development of resistance to streptomycin (Graessle & Pietrowski, 1949) and that these two drugs have synergistic action (Vennesland, Ebert & Bloch, 1948). Isoniazid has the added advantage that it is effective against intracellular tubercle bacilli whereas streptomycin is less so (Mackaness & Smith, 1953). Further development of the general idea of the use of two drugs would seem to depend partly on whether the deliberate selection of points of attack (now becoming possible through increased knowledge of mode of action of drugs) might lead to a more effective combination. Perhaps one drug of the antimetabolite type with one acting through interference with cell-wall structure might be useful. Alternatively, a case could be made out for two drugs acting at different points in the same synthetic pathway.

A possibility, requiring the use of only one drug, comes from the work and ideas of Woolley (1952) concerning analogues of precursors of vitamin B_{12} and riboflavin. It may be possible to design a substance which is at the same time an antagonist of two different metabolites. Development of resistance might then require two simultaneous metabolic changes; this is less likely to occur. Resistance could of course still be achieved by other methods (e.g. decreased permeability to the drug).

Changes in metabolism resulting from acquired resistance to one drug may even result in increased susceptibility to another: an aminopterin-resistant strain of *Streptococcus faecalis* is more sensitive than the parent to azathymine (see Welch, 1954).

Finally, can anything be done to prevent the initial biological change leading to resistance? In most cases this is a random mutation to an organism with the necessary changed properties, or the potentiality to produce such properties if selective pressure is applied. Here one can only speculate that the most hopeful stage might be that during which the mutant is unstable—that is, before the new phenotype is fully expressed. When this mysterious process can be explained in biochemical terms there may be some hope of attacking it.

GENERAL CONSIDERATIONS RELATED TO THE HOST-PARASITE SYSTEM

Discussions of the metabolism of either the host or the invader have perforce been based on knowledge of the individual metabolism of these two biological entities in the absence of the other. In chemotherapy we are concerned in reality with the metabolism of the parasite within the special environment of the host, and with the metabolism of the infected host rather than the normal host. Information on both these subjects is woefully fragmentary. The capacity of micro-organisms to adapt themselves to their environment (either by the selection of mutants or as a result of the induction of enzymes) is well known. Furthermore, conditions of growth in the host often differ from those of the batch cultures mainly used in laboratory work in that the medium is continually renewed and end-products removed by the activities of the host; in other words the environment remains more constant in composition. A study of the metabolism of pathogenic organisms as it occurs within the host, although technically difficult, may well point the way to fresh points of attack in chemotherapy. Incidentally, knowledge even of the *in vitro* metabolism of pathogens lags far behind that of non-pathogens.

The situation with regard to cellular metabolism in the infected host is equally unsatisfactory. In 1954 the New York Academy of Medicine

(Section on Microbiology) planned to hold a symposium on this subject, but the organizers concluded that data were 'few, scattered and difficult to interpret' (Racker, 1954); the position has not yet altered appreciably.

Disturbances in the metabolism of the host often lead to increased liability to succumb to infection (the breakdown in carbohydrate metabolism in diabetes mellitus is an example). If we understood fully in biochemical terms the reasons for this we might be able to suggest means of decreasing susceptibility in normal hosts.

THE PARTICULAR PROBLEM OF THE VIRUS

There can be no doubt that a major outstanding problem for chemotherapy is the control of virus diseases both in animals and plants. From the point of view of the general principles we have outlined, the obstacle is clearly that the host cell infected with virus must be regarded as a single biological entity; there is no separate metabolism (in the usual sense) of the invader to attack. But the virus has substance (essentially nucleic acid and protein) which is reduplicated; the main hope of selective attack would appear therefore to be through lethal synthesis (in its widest sense) by template mechanisms, unless virus is found to contain unique components of simple structure. Dr Tamm will be examining the prospects for selective inhibition of virus multiplication, and much of the contributions of Drs Gale and Markham will certainly be relevant to this problem.

Virus multiplication occurs only within host cells. The only other possibility for chemotherapy would be either to prevent the virus entering the cell or to stop it leaving the cell after multiplication. With certain animal and bacterial viruses it is known that attachment to the cell (probably a necessary preliminary to penetration) depends on the presence of specific receptor substances at the cell surface. There are reports that an enzyme (of bacterial origin) which destroys receptor substance gives limited short-term protection in mice to strains of influenza virus. Receptor substance may also delay the release of the progeny; there is evidence in one case at least that the virus secures its release by enzymic attack on the receptor (for a fuller discussion see Burnet, 1955). Isolated receptor substance (or an analogous molecule) might also be used to compete with that at the cell surface for the virus. It is not clear whether the definite, though limited, success obtained with foreign polysaccharides in reducing multiplication of certain viruses results from a structural resemblance to receptor substance, or from other causes (see discussion by Woolley, 1952).

STRATEGY: CONCLUSIONS

It is impossible to reach any conclusions about a definite strategy without taking into account all the other contributions to this Symposium; the final assessment must be left to the reader.

A major difficulty in discussing general principles at the present state of knowledge has been to find illustrative examples. In almost every case these have been found not to be clear-cut and to introduce complexities which have sometimes had to be ignored in the interests of brevity and clarity. Such principles as have been set out are certainly to be regarded in the same light as working hypotheses. Perhaps the only conclusion we have reached ourselves is that using them as a basis it would be comparatively easy for a gathering of learned microbes to devise a rational chemotherapy of man!

A Commander-in-Chief of operation 'Chemotherapy' should certainly demand from his boffins an intensification of research on the metabolism of parasites within the host, and of the metabolism of infected host cells. He should also encourage to the utmost the development (and especially its extension to a variety of organisms and cells) of the promising work on the biochemical mechanisms by which substances enter cells. Recent advances in techniques for the growth of 'pure cultures' of animal cells of various types offer particular promise for the study of some of these problems and also for investigations of animal viruses.

Some antimetabolites have proved to be effective only against organisms requiring an external source of the metabolite; evidence is increasing that these act by preventing the metabolite entering the cell rather than by inhibiting its utilization. This of course limits their chemotherapeutic possibilities. In the light of increasing knowledge of selective transport through permeability barriers it may be that some, although blocking the entry of other substances, cannot themselves enter the cell. Yet certainly some do so, since they are incorporated into cellular protein or nucleic acid. Design of antimetabolites will in future have to try to take into account two specific factors—the necessity to be transported into the cell as well as to compete with the metabolite at the enzyme or template.

From the point of view of broad strategy it should be remembered that approaches which only partially fulfil promise of giving effective therapeutic agents may nevertheless be most helpful in increasing knowledge of specific aspects of cell metabolism essential for further research on chemotherapy. The antimetabolites, in the original sense, have been one of the valuable tools in the study of cellular synthesis of protein and nucleic acid, and of function of B-group vitamins.

There are still broader aspects of the strategy of chemotherapy which ought not to be neglected. The elimination of all microbial diseases of mankind, and the consequent further increase in world population, could well result in a serious addition to the already difficult problem of food supply. If we fail to take account of this we should be akin to an army commander who based his demand for rations, not on his total strength, but on the number of men he expected to survive. Fortunately, advances in knowledge of the principles of chemotherapy are applicable to diseases of crops and domestic animals. Broad strategy would require the maintenance of a proper balance between detailed research in these various fields.

It may be thought that, except for viruses, chemotherapy has few outstanding problems in human disease of microbial origin. In many cases, however, the drugs can only be used under close medical supervision, and certainly not indiscriminately because of the risk of resistant strains arising. This is a particular problem for those parts of the world which have, and are likely to have for a long time, inadequate medical services. There is still plenty of scope in chemotherapy for the control of resistance and for the development of safer drugs, particularly those which might be used for prophylaxis during epidemics.

It was suggested earlier that the individual contributions to this Symposium were inevitably more concerned with tactics than with strategy. May we finally introduce our colleagues in the words of the historian Walter Bagehot:

The soldier—that is, the great soldier—of today is not a romantic animal, dashing at forlorn hopes, animated by frantic sentiment, full of fancies as to a lady-love or a sovereign; but a quiet, grave man busied in charts, exact in sums, master of the art of tactics, occupied in trivial detail; thinking as the Duke of Wellington was said to do, *most* of the shoes of his soldiers; despising all manner of *éclat* and eloquence; perhaps, like Count Moltke 'silent in seven languages'.*

Perhaps not all this is appropriate!

* Bagehot, W. (1905). *The English Constitution*, ch. 7. Its supposed checks and balances, p. 248. Paternoster Library, Vol. **3**. London: Kegan Paul, Trench, Trübner & Co.

REFERENCES

ABRAHAM, E. P. (1953). The development of drug resistance in micro-organisms. In *Adaptation in Micro-organisms. Symp. Soc. gen. Microbiol.* **3**, 201.

ALBERT, A. (1951). *Selective Toxicity with Special Reference to Chemotherapy.* London: Methuen.

ALBERT, A., GIBSON, M. I. & RUBBO, S. D. (1953). The influence of chemical constitution on antibacterial activity. Part VI: The bactericidal action of 8-hydroxyquinoline (oxine). *Brit. J. exp. Path.* **34**, 119.

BACON, G. A., BURROWS, T. W. & YATES, M. (1951). The effects of biochemical mutation on the virulence of *Bacterium typhosum*: the loss of virulence of certain mutants. *Brit. J. exp. Path.* **32**, 85.

BRITTEN, R. J., ROBERTS, R. B. & FRENCH, E. F. (1955). Amino acid adsorption and protein synthesis in *Escherichia coli. Proc. nat. Acad. Sci., Wash.* **41**, 863.

BUCHANAN, J. M., FLAKS, J. G., HARTMAN, S. C., LEVENBERG, B., LUKENS, L. N. & WARREN, L. (1957). The enzymatic synthesis of inosinic acid *de novo*. In *The Chemistry and Biology of Purines*, p. 233. Edited by G. E. W. Wolstenholme & C. M. O'Connor. London: Churchill.

BURNET, F. M. (1955). *Principles of Animal Virology*, ch. 5. 1st ed. New York: Academic Press.

CHAIN, E. & DUTHIE, E. S. (1945). Bactericidal and bacteriolytic action of penicillin on the staphylococcus. *Lancet*, i, 652.

COHEN, G. N. & RICKENBERG, H. V. (1956). Concentration spécifique réversible des amino acides chez *Escherichia coli. Ann. Inst. Pasteur*, **91**, 693.

COHEN, S. S. & BARNER, H. (1955). Enzymatic adaptation in a thymine requiring strain of *Escherichia coli. J. Bact.* **69**, 59.

COHEN, S. S. & BARNER, H. D. (1954). Studies on unbalanced growth in *Escherichia coli. Proc. nat. Acad. Sci., Wash.* **40**, 885.

COHN, M. & MONOD, J. (1953). Specific inhibition and induction of enzyme bio-synthesis. In *Adaptation in Micro-organisms. Symp. Soc. gen. Microbiol.* **3**, 132.

CUMMINS, C. S. & HARRIS, H. (1956). The chemical composition of the cell wall in some Gram-positive bacteria and its possible value as a taxonomic character. *J. gen. Microbiol.* **14**, 583.

DAVEY, D. G. (1951). Chemotherapy of malaria. *Brit. med. Bull.* **8**, 37.

DAVIS, B. D. (1956). Relations between enzymes and permeability (membrane transport) in bacteria. In *Enzymes: Units of Biological Structure and Function. Henry Ford Hosp. Symp.* **4**, 509.

DAVIS, B. D. & MAAS, W. K. (1952). Analysis of the biochemical mechanism of drug resistance in certain bacterial mutants. *Proc. nat. Acad. Sci., Wash.* **38**, 775.

EHRLICH, P. (1885). *Das Sauerstoff-Bedürfniss des Organismus.* Berlin: Hirschwald. [Reprinted (1956) with a translation into English in *The collected papers of Paul Ehrlich*, vol. I, edited by P. Himmelweit. London: Pergamon Press.]

EHRLICH, P. (1908). *Experimental Researches on Specific Therapeutics.* (The Harben Lectures for 1907 of the Royal Institute of Public Health.) London: H. K. Lewis.

EHRLICH, P. (1913). Address in pathology on chemotherapeutics: scientific principles, methods and results. *Lancet*, ii, 445.

FILDES, P. (1940). A rational approach to research in chemotherapy. *Lancet*, i, 955.

FISHER, R. B. & LINDSAY, D. B. (1956). The action of insulin on the penetration of sugars into the perfused heart. *J. Physiol.* **131**, 526.

FOWDEN, L. (1957). A biochemical enigma: the mechanism of protein synthesis. *New Biology*, no. 23, p. 65. Harmondsworth, Middlesex: Penguin Books.

GALE, E. F. (1956). Nucleic acids and enzyme synthesis. In *Enzymes: Units of Biological Structure and Function. Henry Ford Hosp. Symp.* **4**, 49.

GRAESSLE, O. E. & PIETROWSKI, J. J. (1949). The *in vitro* effect of para-amino-salicylic acid (PAS) in preventing acquired resistance to streptomycin by *Mycobacterium tuberculosis. J. Bact.* **57**, 459.

GREENBERG, G. R. & JAENICKE, L. (1957). On the activation of the one-carbon unit for the biosynthesis of purine nucleotides. In *The Chemistry and Biology of Purines*, p. 204. Edited by G. E. W. Wolstenholme & C. M. O'Connor. London: Churchill.

HAWKING, F. (1954). Milk, *p*-aminobenzoate and malaria of rats and monkeys. *Brit. med. J.* i, 425.

HAWKING, F. (1955). The pathogenicity of protozoal and other parasites: general considerations. In *Mechanisms of Microbial Pathogenicity. Symp. Soc. gen. Microbiol.* **6**, 176.

HOBBY, G. L., MEYER, K. & CHAFFEE, E. (1942). Observations on the mechanism of action of penicillin. *Proc. Soc. exp. Biol., N.Y.* **50**, 281.

HOTCHKISS, R. D. (1954). Cyclical behaviour in pneumococcal growth and trans-formability occasioned by environmental changes. *Proc. nat. Acad. Sci., Wash.* **40**, 49.

HOUGHTON, L. E. (1954). Combined corticotrophin therapy and chemotherapy in pulmonary tuberculosis with special reference to hypersensitive reactions. *Lancet*, i, 595.

KNOX, W. E. (1954). Metabolic adaptation in animals. In *Cellular Metabolism and Infections*, p. 45. Edited by E. Racker. London: Academic Books.

MCCULLOUGH, W. G. (1957). A bacterial growth factor derived from *p*-amino-benzoic acid. *Bact. Proc. 57th gen. Meet. Soc. Amer. Bact.*, p. 124.

MACFARLANE, R. G. (1954). The reactions of the blood to injury: changes other than coagulation. *Lectures on General Pathology*, p. 212. Edited by H. W. Florey. London: Lloyd-Luke (Medical Books).

MACKANESS, G. B. & SMITH, N. (1953). The bactericidal action of isoniazid, strepto-mycin and terramycin on extracellular and intracellular tubercle bacilli. *Amer. Rev. Tuberc.* **67**, 322.

NICHOL, C. A. (1954). Studies of the mechanism of resistance to folic acid analogues in a strain of *Streptococcus faecalis. J. biol. Chem.* **207**, 725.

PARK, J. T. & STROMINGER, J. L. (1957). Mode of action of penicillin. Biochemical basis for the mechanism of action of penicillin and for its selective toxicity. *Science*, **125**, 99.

PETERS, R. A. (1952). Lethal synthesis. *Proc. roy. Soc.* B, **139**, 143.

PRUSOFF, W. H. (1957). Studies on the mechanism of action of azathymine. III. Relationship between incorporation into deoxypentosenucleic acid and inhibition. *J. biol. Chem.* **226**, 901.

RACKER, E. (1954). Preface. *Cellular Metabolism and Infections*, p. vii. Edited by E. Racker. London: Academic Books.

RICKENBERG, H. V., COHEN, G. N., BUTTIN, G. & MONOD, J. (1956). La galactoside-perméase d'*Escherichia coli. Ann. Inst. Pasteur*, **91**, 829.

ROBLIN, R. O. (1946). Metabolite antagonists. *Chem. Rev.* **38**, 255.

SLOANE, N. H. (1953). Biological activity of a metabolite of *p*-aminobenzoic acid (PABA) in a hydroxylating system. *J. Amer. chem. Soc.* **75**, 6352.

SNELL, E. E., RADIN, N. S. & IKAWA, M. (1955). The nature of D-alanine in lactic acid bacteria. *J. biol. Chem.* **217**, 803.

SPIEGELMAN, S. (1956). On the nature of the enzyme-forming system. In *Enzymes: Units of Biological Structure and Function. Henry Ford Hosp. Symp.* **4**, 67.

SPINK, W. W. (1942). *Sulphanilamide and Related Compounds in General Practice*, 2nd ed., p. 71. Chicago: The Year Book Publishers.

STADIE, W. C. (1954). Current concepts of the action of insulin. *Physiol. Rev.* **34**, 52.

STANIER, R. Y. (1954). Some singular features of bacteria as dynamic systems. In *Cellular Metabolism and Infections*, p. 3. Edited by E. Racker. London: Academic Books.

SUTER, E. (1952). Multiplication of tubercle bacilli within phagocytes cultivated *in vitro*, and effect of streptomycin and isonicotinic acid hydrazide. *Amer. Rev. Tuberc.* **65**, 775.

UMBREIT, W. W. (1952). The mode of action of streptomycin. *Symposium sur le mode d'action des antibiotiques*, p. 63. 2nd Int. Congr. Biochem. Paris.

VENNESLAND, K., EBERT, R. H. & BLOCH, R. G. (1948). *In vitro* effect of streptomycin and para-aminosalicylic acid (PAS) on the growth of tubercle bacilli. *Proc. Soc. exp. Biol., N.Y.* **68**, 250.

WELCH, A. D. (1954). Metabolic approaches to chemotherapy. In *Cellular Metabolism and Infections*, p. 61. Edited by E. Racker. London: Academic Books.

WILBRANDT, W. (1954). Secretion and transport of non-electrolytes. In *Active Transport and Secretion. Symp. Soc. exp. Biol.* **8**, 136.

WOODS, D. D. (1940). The relation of *p*-aminobenzoic acid to the mechanism of the action of sulphanilamide. *Brit. J. exp. Path.* **21**, 74.

WOODS, D. D. (1953*a*). The integration of research on the nutrition and metabolism of micro-organisms. *J. gen. Microbiol.* **9**, 151.

WOODS, D. D. (1953*b*). Significance of the metabolic interactions of growth factors and their analogues for the growth of micro-organisms. *Symposium on Nutrition and Growth Factors*, p. 3. 6th Congr. int. Microbiol. Rome.

WOODS, D. D. (1954). Metabolic relations between *p*-aminobenzoic acid and folic acid in micro-organisms. In *Chemistry and Biology of Pteridines*, p. 220. Edited by G. E. W. Wolstenholme & M. P. Cameron. London: Churchill.

WOODS, D. D. & NIMMO-SMITH, R. H. (1949). Aspects of the selective toxicity of sulphonamides and other antimetabolite inhibitors. In *Selective Toxicity and Antibiotics. Symp. Soc. exp. Biol.* **3**, 177.

WOOLLEY, D. W. (1947). Recent advances in the study of biological competition between structurally related compounds. *Physiol. Rev.* **27**, 308.

WOOLLEY, D. W. (1952). *A Study of Antimetabolites*. London: Chapman & Hall.

WORK, E. (1955). Some comparative aspects of lysine metabolism. In *A Symposium on Amino Acid Metabolism*, p. 462. Edited by W. D. & H. B. Glass. Baltimore: Johns Hopkins Press.

WORK, T. S. (1954). The work of Paul Ehrlich and his position in the history of medical research. *Int. Arch. Allergy*, **5**, 98.

WORK, T. S. & WORK, E. (1948). *The Basis of Chemotherapy*. Edinburgh: Oliver & Boyd.

WYATT, G. R. & COHEN, S. S. (1953). The bases of the nucleic acids of some bacterial and animal viruses: the occurrence of 5-hydroxymethylcytosine. *Biochem. J.* **55**, 774.

ZAMENHOF, S., DE GIOVANNI, R. & RICH, K. (1956). *Escherichia coli* containing unnatural pyrimidines in its deoxyribonucleic acid. *J. Bact.* **71**, 60.

THE ANTIBIOTIC APPROACH

H. B. WOODRUFF AND L. E. McDANIEL

Department of Microbiology, Merck Sharp & Dohme
Research Laboratories, Merck & Co., Inc.,
Rahway, New Jersey, U.S.A.

The antibiotic approach to chemotherapy often carries the stigma of randomness and of screening. Antibiotics have not been designed by a rational scientific process, therefore, many microbiologists, as the ostrich, willing to hide his head in the sand, refuse to undertake research on them. This is an illogical attitude. Many discussions have been held in the past on rational approaches to chemotherapy, and in this Symposium there are fifteen contributions concerning approaches for the future. However, it is the antibiotics, discovered by random methods, which today carry the burden of chemotherapy.

Table 1. *Antibiotics produced in the United States of America (1954)*
(From Beesch & Shull, 1956)

Antibiotic	Pounds produced	Dollar value (millions)
Penicillin	631,000	53·0
Tetracyclines	597,000	156·2
Streptomycin	144,000	5·4
Dihydrostreptomycin	446,000	19·4
Neomycin	15,000	4·5
Bacitracin	7,000	1·3

Measured by any terms, clinical effectiveness, cost of treatment, or commercial value, the antibiotics stand alone for the control of bacterial diseases. In monetary value, antibiotics are by far the major medicinal agent. In the United States of America alone, the value of antibiotics manufactured in 1956, as reported by the U.S. Tariff Commission, was 242 million dollars and totalled over 1·5 million pounds in weight. The value of all medicinals was less than twice as great, 465 million dollars. The synthetic therapeutic agents, whose discovery can be only partially credited to chemical logic, are far less costly per unit weight. The production value of the sulpha drugs in 1956, for example, was 19·6 million dollars, only a fraction of that of the antibiotics, and, in weight, the sulpha drugs totalled 2·8 million pounds, just above the antibiotics.

The importance which should be attributed to antibiotics in a consideration of the strategy of chemotherapy becomes clear from a listing of past
accomplishments, as summarized in Table 1.

Two series of questions should be posed, and the answers sought, in
this discussion concerning the antibiotic approach to the strategy of
chemotherapy. What future is there for the discovery of new, clinically
effective antibiotics? Has not the field been covered and have not the
obvious useful agents been discovered? Is it efficient to continue
searching by random methods for new antibiotics? Secondly, can the
scientists who have made the study of antibiotics their speciality contribute to the discovery of new chemotherapeutic agents by rational methods?

REQUIREMENTS FOR NEW ANTIBIOTICS

In spite of the past accomplishments as set forth in Table 1, there is a
need today for new chemotherapeutic agents and new antibiotics.
Penicillin, the tetracyclines, streptomycin and certain other antibiotics,
all have an established place in medicine and are effective on a wide
range of micro-organisms. However, there is a serious need to meet the
challenge of antibiotic-resistant pathogens, and to cover such areas as
systemic fungal infections, urinary tract infections with *Proteus* spp.,
and burns infected with *Pseudomonas* spp. All these respond poorly to
existing antibiotics. The incidence of allergic sensitivities and of secondary enterococcal or fungal infections following administration of antibiotics is sufficiently great to warrant the search for reserve antibiotics.
Antibiotics which are more effective as bactericidal agents, which can
penetrate to calcified lesions or the deepest recesses of the heart are
needed for chronic diseases such as tuberculosis and bacterial endocarditis. The wider fields of protozoan, parasitic and virus diseases
and cancer are being studied by antibiotic techniques and may also
yield to this form of therapy. Without question, there is a need for new,
clinically useful antibiotics, but will our present random screening
methods provide them?

To answer this question clearly, we must consider the present
techniques for discovering antibiotics. Practically every large pharma-
ceutical company and many university laboratories have antibiotic
screening programmes. Each differs in detail of technique, but basically
all are the same. One example serves to describe them all.

THE RANDOM SCREENING METHOD FOR
DISCOVERY OF ANTIBIOTICS

By definition, antibiotics are substances derived from micro-organisms which, in low concentrations, inhibit the growth of other micro-organisms. Thus, to operate a screening programme one must have a source of micro-organisms for study. These may be of any type, derived from any place. For the purpose of this example, members of the order Actinomycetales were selected from soil by conventional microbiological techniques. Appropriate dilutions were plated on glucose-asparagine agar and mannitol-asparagine agar and incubated at 28° for 5–7 days. All isolated colonies of Actinomycetales which were not obviously morphological duplicates were transferred to glucose-asparagine slants and incubated until good sporulation was obtained.

Detection of antibiotic activity

Spore suspensions prepared from the slants were spread on a variety of culture media contained in Petri dishes. After good growth had developed on the agar, a test for antibiotic activity was made by removing plugs of growth and agar from the Petri dishes with a No. 7 cork borer. These plugs were placed on an agar medium seeded with a test bacterium in other Petri dishes. After overnight incubation, zones of inhibited growth surrounding a transferred agar plug indicated the production of an antibiotic (Pl. 1, figs. 1, 2). On the average, 25 % of strains of *Streptomyces* isolated were found to produce an antibiotic. Obviously, antibiotic production occurs frequently among the streptomycetes.

The common occurrence of antibiotic activity does not indicate that discovery of a new, useful antibiotic is an easy accomplishment. Approximately 90 % of all antibiotic-producing cultures detected in this example were found to produce streptothricin or closely related antibiotics. At least half of the remainder produced streptomycin. Of the others, one-third proved to be tetracyclines and most of those remaining could be identified with one of the hundreds of antibiotics which have been described from *Streptomyces*. In a typical series of 10,000 Actinomycetales isolated, approximately 2500 produced antibiotic activity, all but 250 made streptothricin-like antibiotics, about 125 produced streptomycin, forty produced tetracyclines, fifty-five produced other previously described antibiotics and thirty produced new antibiotics.

The microbial resistance test

For efficiency, as many as possible of the producers of known antibiotics must be eliminated from consideration before purification of the
new antibiotics is undertaken. Elimination of producers of the streptothricin, streptomycin and tetracycline groups of antibiotics was accomplished by placing agar culture plugs on Petri dishes seeded with
bacteria specifically resistant to each of the three groups of antibiotics.
Lack of activity on antibiotic-resistant bacteria was considered to be
sufficient justification for rejection of cultures previously selected for
ability to inhibit growth of the normal, antibiotic-sensitive bacteria.

The paper chromatographic test

Many antibiotic-producing cultures were eliminated by the resistance
test. Many others formed zones of inhibition on all resistant bacteria,
but were later found to make mixtures of two or more known antibiotics. For further study, these cultures, as well as those which produced
new antibiotics, were grown on several nutrient media contained in
50 ml. quantities in 250 ml. Erlenmeyer flasks. The cultures were
agitated continuously during growth on a rotary shaking machine of
$2\frac{1}{2}$ in. amplitude at 220 r.p.m. Samples were removed for assay at
various time intervals and tested for antibiotic activity by the agar
diffusion method. Further identification of substances was made by
subjecting the culture filtrates to paper chromatography with various
solvent systems, followed by bioautography on various antibiotic-
resistant bacteria (Pl. 2). In some cases, partial purification was required
before a clear-cut decision could be made concerning the identity of
an antibiotic.

The toxicity test

The thirty cultures which produced new antibiotics in the above example
of 10,000 selections were found to contain duplications and, actually,
ten new antibiotics were produced in the series. Each of these was
isolated as a purified product from cultures grown in pilot-plant-scale
fermenters. Nine were very toxic and toxicity increased in direct proportion with antibiotic activity during isolation. Only one proved non-
toxic, effective in experimental infections of animals, active against
antibiotic-resistant cultures derived from infected individuals, and
clinically effective.

It is by methods similar to the one outlined above that recently introduced antibiotics, such as cycloserine and novobiocin, were discovered.

Table 2. *Newly named antibiotics in recent scientific literature*

Antibiot. Ann.	J. Antibiot. (*Japan*)	
1953–4	**1953**	
Hygromycin	Azomycin	Pyridomycin
Methylmycin	Flavicid	Sarcidin
Ruticin	Flaveolin	Sarkomycin
Streptocardin	Griseoflavin	Achromoviromycin
Streptogramin	Leucomycin	
Tetracycline	Pthiomycin	
1954–5	**1954**	
Actinomycin III	Actinoleukin	Fermicidin
Celesticetin	Albomycetin	Mediocidin
Etamycin	Angustmycin	Nocardorubin
P.A. 105 (Oleandomycin)	Aureothin	Seligocidin
Pleomycin	Brevolin	Zaomycin
Spiramycin	Eumycetin	Carzinophilin
1955–6	**1955**	
Amphotericin A and B	Amaromycin	Grasseriomycin
Cathomycin	Cerevioccidin	
Eulicin	Grisamine	
P.A. 114 (Synergistin)	Mesenterin	
Rubidin	Ractinomycin	
Streptolydigin	Tertiomycin	
Thiostrepton	Thiomycin	
Vancomycin	Violacetin	
1956–7	**1956**	
Alazopeptin	Carzinocidin	Mitomycin
Nucleocidin	Pluramycin	Phagomycin
P.A. 132	Gancidin	Phagocidin
Ristocetin A and B	Mikamycin	Phleomycin
		Toyocamycin

Each new name for an antibiotic is recorded for the year in which it first appeared in these two important publications devoted to antibiotics. In many instances, later studies showed the newly named antibiotics to be identical with antibiotics described nearly simultaneously in other publications or with older antibiotics.

Notwithstanding the frequency of occurrence of known antibiotics and the hundreds of previously described antibiotics, new ones are discovered with practically undiminished frequency (Table 2). Each year new antibiotics are found which are useful clinically and they are placed on the market. In part, they displace existing antibiotics as physicians study them as therapeutic agents. However, all have individual advantages. Each one saves lives. Each one becomes established to a degree dependent on its biological properties.

Future potentialities of random methods

As long as the random approach to new antibiotics continues to yield successes, as it is successful today, it will be continued. When a rational design for chemotherapy proves more successful, random screening will be dropped. Random screening is expensive in terms of money and of personnel. Successful screening programmes are not the work of technicians but of trained scientists.

Random programmes offer much opportunity for serendipity. Close watch of the operation and actual participation in the programme by biologists and chemists with a flair for detection of the unusual happening is essential for success. Obviously, there is a field for research in techniques and correlations in antibiotic screening programmes. Success comes to the most efficient and the most astute.

The random approach to chemotherapy is the popular way for discovery of new chemotherapeutic agents. The lessons of the past are not easily forgotten. The promise for the future, through the strategic approach, belongs to those few who are willing to accept its challenge—and its rare successes.

THE STRATEGIC APPROACH TO CHEMOTHERAPY THROUGH ANTIBIOTICS

The thesis has been presented that antibiotics, despite the randomness of their origin, are the favourite form of chemotherapy today, and are likely to continue as a successful conclusion of major screening programmes for some time in the future. However, does the antibiotic approach provide any opportunity to practise the 'Strategy of Chemotherapy'? Without detracting in any way from the importance of the foregoing conventional methods of antibiotic research, two strategic approaches to antibiotic chemotherapy are presented here as examples of new challenges which face the antibiotic specialist. These approaches are through synergism and biosynthesis.

SYNERGISM

By the application of recent discoveries, synergism provides an opportunity for a planned research approach to chemotherapy. As in new antibiotic screening, the first studies on synergism were descriptive. Strong synergistic responses were observed in the antibacterial action of mixtures of antibiotics. Also, antagonism, additive action or independence of action were described. The micro-organism, the culture medium, the physical conditions were all of importance in determining the response. Antibiotics could be classed into groups depending on the responses (Jawetz, Gunnison, Broff & Coleman, 1952). In spite of the disadvantages inherent in the variable nature of synergism, proposals have been advanced for the application of synergistic combinations in clinical practice (Welch, 1957).

In so far as synergism merely provides for the use of a lesser amount of two drugs to obtain an undiminished clinical effect, synergism is unimportant. However, when combinations show a potentiated antibacterial activity without concomitant increase in toxicity, synergism assumes great significance.

Streptomycin and dihydrostreptomycin together are merely additive in antibacterial action on *Mycobacterium tuberculosis*. Effective therapy results from a mixture of the two antibiotics. However, the limiting toxicities of streptomycin and dihydrostreptomycin differ. Patients sustain more auditory than vestibular damage from dihydrostreptomycin and more vestibular than auditory damage from streptomycin. Heck & Hinshaw (1953) have reported that

a mixture of 50 % streptomycin and 50 % dihydrostreptomycin has produced no neurotoxic manifestations when administered in a dose of 1·0 gram daily for 120 days in the small series of patients studied. Either drug alone administered in the same amount produces neurotoxic manifestations in about 15 % to 18 % of patients treated for the same period of time.

With practical results obtainable from combinations of antibiotics which have only additive effects, cannot even greater value be expected from synergistic action?

Detection of synergism

Techniques for rapid detection of synergistic combinations have been described. Subinhibitory levels of antibiotics placed in adjacent reservoirs on an agar plate will, through synergistic action, show a zone of growth inhibition (Pan & Foster, 1957). Combination of the gradient plate technique with diffusion from a paper strip will allow detection of synergistic action (Pl. 3). Synergistic pairs can be selected from collections of antibiotic broths obtained by random techniques, or fermentation broths can be screened for synergistic action with each of a series of known antibiotics. Because greater individual toxicity can be tolerated when a synergistic pair of antibiotics is employed for therapy, the opportunities of discovering new, useful agents are enhanced even though purely random methods of selection are employed. The advantages of this random experimental approach have been discussed (Pan & Foster, 1957).

Sequential blocking as an explanation of synergism

A planned approach to chemotherapy through synergism requires an explanation of its action. At least one explanation has been fully documented and provides the basis for a proposed logical approach to new chemotherapeutic agents (Potter, 1951). Metabolic blocks, whether mutational or nutritional in origin, are known to limit microbial growth. Even normal metabolites of one biochemical reaction series

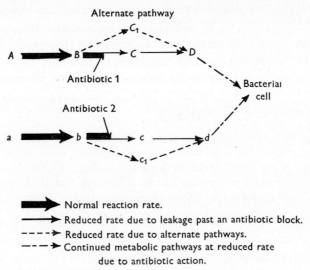

Fig. 1. Diagram of antibiotic effects resulting from non-sequential blocking.

can act as a restraining agent for another biochemical reaction series. 'Leakage' is characteristic of such blockage, however, and growth can occur as small amounts of each of the normal metabolites are produced. Combinations of antibiotics, or antimetabolites, which block different pathways may show improved antibacterial action, but inhibition of bacterial growth will not be complete if leakage occurs or alternate pathways can be developed (Fig. 1).

Because of a mass-action effect, substances which produce metabolic blocks occurring in sequence should behave synergistically. The trickle of leakage past the first block becomes entirely extinguished when faced with a second block. Development of an alternate pathway around the first antibiotic block usually requires the synthesis of alternative enzymes by the cell. These cannot form at all if new enzyme synthesis is prevented by the complete cessation of cellular activity due to the second of the two sequential blocks (Fig. 2).

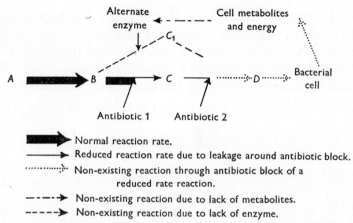

Fig. 2. Diagram of antibiotic effects resulting from sequential blocking.

Prediction of synergism through knowledge of mechanism of action of antibiotics

Once the mechanism of antibiotic action is known, or suspected, synergism can be predicted for substances which are both active on the same biochemical pathway. It may not be necessary that the initial site of antibiotic action be on the pathway. Synergism can result if any two of the multiple sites of activity of the two antibiotics are on the same pathway.

The synergistic action of streptomycin and p-aminosalicylic acid (p-AS) in the treatment of tuberculosis is well documented. Clinical emergence of streptomycin-resistant strains, often occurring in less than three months with streptomycin therapy alone, can be withheld for over a year with simultaneous administration of p-AS, in spite of the fact that p-AS is a relatively poor inhibitor of *Mycobacterium tuberculosis*. A suggestion for the action of these two agents as sequential metabolic blocks has been advanced as the explanation for the synergistic response (W. W. Umbreit, personal communication) (Fig. 3).

At this time, our knowledge of metabolic pathways is inadequate to allow the chemist to tailor-make antibiotics, although this Symposium may point the way to eventual successes. However, recent studies have disclosed a technique which should enable the antibiotic research scientist to practise sequential blocking in designing new chemo-therapeutic agents without prior knowledge of the metabolic pathways involved.

Antibiotics as metabolic blocks

The exact mode of action of most antibiotics has been exceedingly difficult to study. Clear-cut competitive reversal of action by normal metabolites over a wide range has been described for only a few anti-biotics without clinical utility (Woodruff & Foster, 1946; Ahmad, Schneider & Strong, 1950). The inhibition analysis studies of Shive

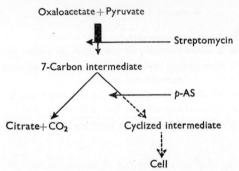

Fig. 3. Sequential blocking as an explanation for synergistic action of streptomycin and *p*-aminosalicylic acid.

have provided an approach to the discovery of critical pathways of biosynthesis which are inhibited by antibiotics (Williams, Eakin, Beer-stecher & Shive, 1950). Foster & Pittillo (1953*a*) found that studies can be made at the threshold concentration of an antibiotic if a chemi-cally defined agar medium is employed. In this manner, each bacterial cell is physically isolated and complications due to resistance develop-ment or to physiological factors caused by high cell concentration are eliminated. Each antibiotic tested could be reversed at the threshold level, and, over a range of two- to several-fold, by complex mixtures of nutrients. Furthermore, known metabolites could often be found which accomplished the reversal (Table 3). One may conclude that the known reversers must have a direct connexion with the metabolic sequence blocked by the antibiotic at the threshold level. A further observation supports the conclusion. Biosynthesis of the metabolite which acts as a specific antibiotic reverser is reduced at threshold levels of the antibiotic.

From the records of experiments of this type, it is possible to predict those antibiotics which will behave synergistically. Combinations of antibiotics reversed by the same metabolic agent should be synergistic. Predictions made in this manner have proved correct (Table 4).

Two of the combinants studied more thoroughly, cycloserine and chlortetracycline, proved synergistic not only at threshold levels in agar

Table 3. *Selective reversal, by individual metabolites, of* Aerobacter aerogenes *growth inhibition caused by streptomycin and by dihydro-streptomycin.* (From Pittillo & Foster, 1953)

Reversing agent, μg./ml. agar medium	No antibiotic	Streptomycin						Dihydrostreptomycin					
		0·5	1	2	4	8	16	0·5	1	2	4	8	16
None	+	+	−	−	−	−	−	+	−	−	−	−	−
Guanylic acid, 5	+	+	+	+	+	+	−	+	−	−	−	−	−
Cytosine, 5	+	+	+	+	+	+	−	+	−	−	−	−	−
Xanthosine, 5	+	+	+	+	+	+	−	+	−	−	−	−	−
Guanosine, 5	+	+	+	+	+·	+	−	+	−	−	−	−	−
Thymine, 5	+	+	+	+	+	−	−	+	−	−	−	−	−
L-Phenylalanine, 25	+	+	−	−	−	−	−	+	+	+	+	−	−
L-Phenylalanine, 50	+	+	−	−	−	−	−	+	+	+	+	+	−
Yeast autolysate, 1000	+	+	+	+	+	+	−	+	+	−	−	−	−

Plates incubated for 34 hr. at 37°.
+ =Growth of approximately 100 discrete colonies.
− =No colonies visible to the naked eye.

Table 4. *Synergistic antibacterial activity on* Aerobacter aerogenes *of pairs of antibiotics selected on the basis of common reversing agents.* (From Pittillo & Foster, 1954.)

Inhibitor pairs	Metabolic reverser			Reversal factor	Growth inhibiting conc. alone, μg./ml.	Growth inhibiting conc. combined, μg./ml.
	Agent	μg./ml.				
Dihydrostreptomycin	L-Phenylalanine	50		4–8	12	1·5
L-Tyrosine		*		*	720	90
Cycloserine	Glycine	100		32	30	1·0
Chlortetracycline		80		4	1·0	0·03
Isonicotinic hydrazide	Biotin	0·01		10–30	1000	30
Actathiazic acid		0·01		10	30	1·0

* Beerstecher & Shive (1947) reported that tyrosine is toxic for *Escherichia coli* because it inhibits synthesis of phenylalanine. *Aerobacter aerogenes* is not inhibited by the highest concentration of tyrosine tested, 720 μg./ml.

medium, but also were synergistic in bactericidal action in mass culture in broth. In the liquid culture, 60 μg. cycloserine/ml. was required to reduce the number of viable *Staphylococcus aureus* cells to one-half of the initial log count. The concentration of chlortetracycline required was 2.5μg./ml. In combination, one-fourth the normal concentration of cycloserine and one-fifth the normal concentration of chlortetracycline caused the same amount of bactericidal action (H. Wallick, personal communication).

Strategic design of chemotherapeutic agents through synergism

Thus a strategic pathway to chemotherapy is opened. For each useful antibiotic, a normal metabolite may be found which reverses it at the threshold level. Failing discovery of an effective known metabolic reversing agent, the effective agent in a complex nutrient which shows reversal can be isolated and identified. Inasmuch as the extent of antibiotic activity of an antibiotic is determined by the concentration of its metabolic reversing agent, either intracellular or extracellular, one may expect antibiotic potentiation to occur if the concentration of the specific metabolite is reduced. Certain chemical analogues of precursors of metabolites are known to block the biosynthesis of the metabolites. Although these analogues have proved successful in decreasing cellular accumulation of metabolites, they have proved disappointing as practical chemotherapeutic agents. With the antibiotic to carry the main chemotherapeutic load, however, metabolic antagonists may succeed as potentiators where previously they have failed as the primary chemotherapeutic agent.

Protected inhibition

According to this concept, antimetabolites are designed to protect the intrinsic inhibitory action of an antibiotic from reversal by normal cell metabolites. The term 'protected inhibition' has been coined for the phenomenon (Foster & Pittillo, 1953b). The practice of protected inhibition implies that one finds empirically, by a method such as that described above, a reversing metabolite for any antibiotic, then combines with that antibiotic a compound designed to inhibit synthesis of the metabolite.

Laboratory success has been attained by this strategic approach (Table 5, Fig. 4). Riboflavin shows marked reversal of chlortetracycline activity at the threshold antibiotic level. Chlortetracycline also specifically decreases riboflavin accumulation by bacteria. 1:2-Dichloro-4:5-diaminobenzene is structurally related to riboflavin. It is a logical compound to study as an antimetabolite for inhibition of riboflavin synthesis and, indeed, it is such an antimetabolite as was shown by

Woolley (1950). 1:2-Dichloro-4:5-diaminobenzene inhibits riboflavin biosynthesis by cells and can prevent cell growth. It behaves as a synergist with chlortetracycline.

Table 5. *Protected inhibition of chlortetracycline action by* 1:2-*dichloro-*4:5-*diaminobenzene* (From Foster & Pittillo, 1953*b*)

A. Reversal of chlortetracycline by riboflavin

Conc. of riboflavin (μg./ml.)	Ratio of inhibitory conc. of chlortetracycline in presence of metabolite to conc. in absence of metabolite
0·125	1
0·25	4
0·5	8
1·0	16

B. Inhibition of riboflavin synthesis

Aerobacter aerogenes		*Bacillus subtilis*	
Chlortetra-cycline (μg./ml.)	Riboflavin synthesized (μg./mg. dry-wt. of cells)	1:2-Dichloro-4:5-diamino-benzene (μg./ml.)	Riboflavin synthesized (μg./mg. dry-wt. of cells)
0	0·0041	0	0·0032
2	0·0039	200	0·0016
4	0·0030	400	0·0016

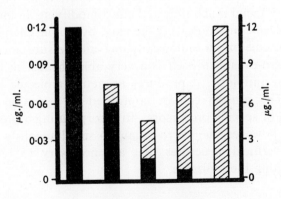

1: 2-Dichloro-4: 5-diaminobenzene

Chlortetracycline

Combination required
for growth inhibition

Fig. 4. Synergistic action of chlortetracycline and 1: 2-dichloro-4: 5-diaminobenzene on *Bacillus subtilis*. (From Foster & Pittillo, 1953*b*)

Stated concisely, protected inhibition provides a rationale for a strategic approach to synergism, and therefore to chemotherapy. Other related approaches can be conceived; for example, a chemical analogue which blocks utilization of an antibiotic-reversing metabolite should also behave as a synergist. In this case, sequential blocking would occur on either side of the metabolite in the metabolic sequence, whereas, in protected inhibition, sequential blocking occurs at two different stages prior to synthesis of the metabolite in the sequence.

CONTROLLED BIOSYNTHESIS

Controlled biosynthesis provides a second approach whereby the research specialist in antibiotics has the opportunity to practise strategic chemotherapy. Controlled biosynthesis may be defined as the technique of predetermining the structure of a new antibiotic by furnishing specific chemical precursors to the antibiotic-producing micro-organism. After the chemical structure of a new, useful antibiotic has been elucidated, the formation of modified forms of the antibiotic by controlled biosynthetic procedures is a promising method for developing antibiotics with new properties.

Much consideration has been given to the direct chemical modification of antibiotics. Through such modifications, it has been hoped that desirable changes in stability, absorption, activity or other properties might occur. There have been very few successes by such chemical modifications. Antibiotic molecules, in general, are rather labile and difficult to modify chemically. Furthermore, the chemist does not know what parts of the antibiotic structure are essential for biological activity and he may spend much time and effort modifying an unimportant part of the molecule or, conversely, he may, by simple changes, convert the whole molecule into a biologically unavailable substance.

The micro-organism itself is a very able chemist in this regard. In making an antibiotic, it produces an active molecule by a biological process. The process can be controlled to a certain extent by the furnishing of specific precursors. In incorporating a precursor into the molecule, however, the micro-organism simultaneously provides all of the other critical structures that are necessary to retain biological activity within the molecule.

Detection of controlled biosynthesis

To initiate a controlled biosynthetic process, one must first find portions of the molecule which can be incorporated by biosynthesis into the basic antibiotic. The simplest approach to this end is the determination of whether fragments of the antibiotic itself, when added to the fermentation medium, can be incorporated unchanged into the molecule. Providing the fragment added is a product of the rate-limiting biosynthetic reaction in the normal antibiotic synthesis, the addition of the fragment should give an increased yield of the antibiotic. An increased yield is an indication that the fragment may be incorporated as an intact unit. However, if biosynthesis of another portion of the molecule is the rate-limiting reaction, the addition of the fragment to the fermentation will not result in increased activity even though it may be incorporated as an intact unit into the antibiotic. One can then resort to labelling the precursor, for example, with deuterium or ^{14}C, in order to demonstrate incorporation.

Once specific fragments of the antibiotic molecule which can be incorporated as intact units have been selected, chemical modifications of these fragments may be tested for incorporation. One may hope, by such incorporations, that the resulting modified antibiotic will have changed biological properties, such as a modified antibacterial spectrum, increased bactericidal power, or less tendency towards induction of resistance. There is no way at present of predicting the kinds of chemical structures which control such biological properties and, therefore, the antibiotics which are biosynthesized may be improved or inferior on a random basis. In addition, alterations in chemical properties of antibiotics may be accomplished. A product which is more stable, a product which is more or less soluble, a product modified chemically to produce less allergenic properties, all may be a desirable result of controlled biosynthesis. In these instances, the chemist can frequently predict the kind of modification which is needed in the antibiotic structure to bring about the desired effect. Through the selection of the correct precursors, therefore, the chemist can practise a strategic approach to chemotherapy to obtain a molecule with desired chemical properties.

A new antibiotic made by controlled biosynthetic procedures may be detected in a fermentation by measuring one of the desired properties, for example, change in solubility, change in antibacterial spectrum or change in stability. However, a much easier approach is that of paper chromatography, employing a solvent system which gives good movement of the parent antibiotic and which can be expected to give a different R_F with an antibiotic of altered chemical structure. Altered substances which retain antibacterial activity can be located on the paper by the bioautograph procedure. The paper strips are placed on agar plates seeded with a sensitive test micro-organism and the position of zones of inhibited growth noted. Isolation and chemical characterization of the active substance may be required to give final proof of the direct incorporation of the specific precursor into a new antibiotic.

Penicillin derivatives as controlled biosynthetic products

For controlled biosynthesis, cyclic organic compounds, for example, phenylacetic acid derivatives, or relatively resistant aliphatic compounds, have proved most suitable as biosynthetic units. Indeed, the use of compounds related to phenylacetic acid to produce new penicillins is one of the best examples of the production of new antibiotics by biosynthetic means. The discovery that certain strains of *Penicillium notatum* produce predominantly benzylpenicillin in corn-steep liquor medium but largely 2-pentenylpenicillin in a synthetic medium resulted in the development of controlled biosynthesis. The addition of phenylacetic acid, or compounds easily degraded to phenylacetic acid, to a culture medium which normally allowed production of 2-pentenylpenicillin was found to increase benzylpenicillin production greatly. These studies led to extensive investigation of other possible benzylpenicillin precursors, as well as to precursors which would be expected to give modified penicillin molecules (Behrens, 1949).

In these early studies, the only method of measurement employed was that of increased antibacterial activity against a specific assay microorganism. Many modified penicillins, which may have been produced by the controlled biosynthesis procedure from added precursors, could have been overlooked if they did not produce increased antibacterial activity against the assay organisms employed.

An early example of a modified penicillin made by controlled biosynthesis which had altered biological properties is *p*-hydroxybenzylpenicillin, or penicillin X. This is produced when tyramine is added to the fermentation medium. *Penicillium notatum* will accept tyramine as a precursor and in its presence synthesizes *p*-hydroxybenzylpenicillin, whereas, in the absence of an added precursor, an aliphatic penicillin is the end product of the biosynthetic process. *p*-Hydroxybenzylpenicillin was found to be more active than 2-pentenylpenicillin or benzylpenicillin against pneumococci, streptococci, gonococci and meningococci.

The controlled biosynthesis approach led to discovery of hundreds of new penicillins of unpredictable biological properties. However, desirable changes in chemical properties of the penicillins can be induced by the introduction of precursors specifically designed to yield the changed property. For example, by the introduction of *p*-amino-phenylacetic acid, a non-solvent-soluble, water-soluble penicillin has been made which retained its antibacterial properties. The new anti-biotic is *p*-aminobenzylpenicillin (Brewer & Johnson, 1953).

Other examples of penicillins with desirable properties obtained by controlled biosynthesis are penicillins V and O. Through the intro-duction of phenoxyacetic acid, a phenoxymethylpenicillin is obtained which, on a physico-chemical basis, may be predicted to have increased stability. This compound, commonly called penicillin V, has been commercialized primarily on the basis of its increased acid stability, which results in higher blood levels after oral administration. The increasing incidence of allergic reactions to benzylpenicillin has led to the desirability of finding a penicillin with antibacterial properties retained, but lacking the phenyl grouping. This has been accomplished in clinical practice through penicillin O which is made through controlled biosynthesis from the addition of *N*-(2-hydroxyethyl)-allylmercaptyl-acetamide which is utilized by the mould to form allylmercaptyl-penicillin. This compound is well tolerated by many patients who are sensitive to the benzyl form of penicillin.

Other instances of controlled biosynthesis

Controlled biosynthesis has attained practical utility in determining the pathway of formation of the antibiotics chlortetracycline, tetracycline and bromtetracycline. Each molecule of chlortetracycline contains one chlorine atom, which obviously must be furnished to *Streptomyces aureofaciens* in the culture medium. From practical considerations, one would assume that an excess of added chloride ion would be desirable to allow optimum yield of antibiotic. However, antibiotic activity can be produced with a chloride-deficient medium. Fermentation with a chloride-deficient medium, or one in which chloride utilization is blocked by the presence of low levels of bromide, results in the pro-duction of a new antibiotic, tetracycline (Gourevitch, Misiek & Lein 1955). Tetracycline has unexpected biological advantages and has been accorded a large portion of the broad-spectrum antibiotic market. Controlled biosynthesis is a determining factor in the production of tetracycline or chlortetracycline, depending on the presence or absence of chloride in biologically available form as a precursor. A further direct result of the biosynthetic approach is bromtetracycline, which is produced through the addition of excess bromide to the fermenta-tion.

Many antibiotics are glycosides, often containing unusual sugars. The sugar residues appear to offer many positions for structural modifications, but work with such fragments has not been very successful. There are few suitable sugar compounds available for test. Frequently, such molecules are so quickly degraded by the micro-organism that little remains available to serve as a precursor in the fermentation broth. However, there is an indication of controlled biosynthesis with streptomycin involving the glycolic unit.

Streptomycin is a glycoside containing the monosaccharides streptose and N-methylglucosamine, whereas streptomycin B contains streptose, N-methylglucosamine and mannose. Both antibiotics are present in *Streptomyces griseus* fermentations. There has been much study of fermentation conditions which influence the proportion of the two antibiotics in a fermentation broth, as well as of the enzymic conversion of streptomycin B to streptomycin, which involves hydrolytic removal of the mannose unit.

Glucose fulfils one of the criteria mentioned for studies on controlled biosynthesis in the fact that it preferentially enters the streptomycin molecule. A three-fold increase of specific radioactivity has been observed in the streptomycin produced in a medium containing labelled glucose as compared with the specific radioactivity of the carbon in the nutrients supplied (Karow, Peck, Rosenblum & Woodbury, 1952). On the basis of this result, other sugars might be expected to enter the molecule. In fact, the supplementation of *Streptomyces griseus* fermentation with mannose has resulted in an increase in the proportion of streptomycin B as measured by the electrophoretic technique (C. J. Porter, personal communication). Mannose, therefore, fulfils a second criterion for controlled biosynthesis in the fact that it modifies the fermentation to result in formation of an antibiotic which contains mannose as an integral unit. That this is an authentic example of controlled biosynthesis has not been proved, however, inasmuch as mannose is known to inhibit action of the enzyme mannosidase, which converts streptomycin B to streptomycin (Hockenhull, Ashton, Fantes & Whitehead, 1954). Inhibition of the degradation of streptomycin B can be offered as an alternative potential explanation of the mannose effect.

Streptomycin B is undesirable because of its low biological activity. To the extent that its formation in a fermentation supplemented with mannose is the result of controlled biosynthesis, the micro-organism has been induced to synthesize a biologically undesirable compound rather than an active new antibiotic. The controlled biosynthesis technique may be employed strategically to design new molecules having desired chemical properties, but the biological properties of such new compounds remain unpredictable.

THE ANTIBIOTIC APPROACH TO STRATEGIC CHEMOTHERAPY

The antibiotic approach to chemotherapy provides much to challenge the research scientist. There is a wide background of practical successes attained, admittedly, through random methods. Random methods still offer opportunities for further successes and further discoveries. However, through techniques which are just becoming generally available, the antibiotic specialist has opportunity to apply rational methods to the design of new chemotherapeutic agents. There is much to challenge the ingenuity of the chemist, the biochemist, and the biologist in the field of antibiotics. The theoretical scientist may find much greater success in understanding and controlling biosynthetic pathways and designing new chemotherapeutic agents if he joins, rather than ignores, the field of antibiotic research.

REFERENCES

AHMAD, K., SCHNEIDER, H. A. & STRONG, F. M. (1950). Studies on the biological action of antimycin. *Arch. Biochem.* **28**, 281.

BEERSTECHER, E. & SHIVE, W. (1947). Prevention of phenylalanine synthesis by tyrosine. *J. biol. Chem.* **167**, 527.

BEESCH, S. C. & SHULL, G. M. (1956). Fermentation. *Ind. Eng. Chem.* **48**, 1586.

BEHRENS, O. K. (1949). Biosynthesis of the penicillins. In *The Chemistry of Penicillin*, p. 657. Princeton, New Jersey: Princeton University Press.

BREWER, G. A. & JOHNSON, M. J. (1953). Activity and properties of para-amino-benzyl penicillin. *Appl. Microbiol.* **1**, 163.

FOSTER, J. W. & PITTILLO, R. F. (1953a). Reversal by complex natural materials of growth inhibition caused by antibiotics. *J. Bact.* **65**, 361.

FOSTER, J. W. & PITTILLO, R. F. (1953b). Metabolite reversal of antibiotic inhibition, especially reversal of aureomycin inhibition by riboflavin. *J. Bact.* **66**, 478.

GOUREVITCH, A., MISEIK, M. & LEIN, J. (1955). Competitive inhibition by bromide of incorporation of chloride into the tetracycline molecule. *Antibiot. Chemother.* **5**, 448.

HARRIS, D. A. & RUGER, M. L. (1953). Microbiological aspects of new antibiotic screening. *Antibiot. Chemother.* **3**, 265.

HECK, W. & HINSHAW, H. C. (1953). Reduced neurotoxicity of a mixture of streptomycin and dihydrostreptomycin. *Trans. 12th Conf. Chemother. Tuberculosis.* Edited by the U.S. Veterans Administration, p. 294.

HOCKENHULL, D. J. D., ASHTON, G. C., FANTES, K. H. & WHITEHEAD, B. K. (1954). Actinomycete metabolism: α-phenylmannosidase. *Biochem. J.* **57**, 93.

JAWETZ, E., GUNNISON, J. B., BROFF, J. B. & COLEMAN, V. R. (1952). Studies on antibiotic synergism and antagonism. Synergism among seven antibiotics against various bacteria *in vitro*. *J. Bact.* **64**, 29.

48   H. B. WOODRUFF AND L. E. McDANIEL

KAROW, E. O., PECK, R. L., ROSENBLUM, C. & WOODBURY, D. T. (1952). Micro-
biological synthesis of C^{14}-labelled streptomycin. *J. Amer. chem. Soc.* **74**, 3056.
PAN, C. H. & FOSTER, J. W. (1957). A rationale for chemotherapy based on
screening filtrates of soil micro-organisms for synergistically active antibiotics.
J. Antibiot. (Japan), **10**, 1.
PITTILLO, R. F. & FOSTER, J. W. (1953). Differentiation of streptomycin and
dihydrostreptomycin inhibition, by means of reversing metabolites. *Proc.
Soc. exp. Biol., N.Y.* **84**, 568.
PITTILLO, R. F. & FOSTER, J. W. (1954). Potentiation of inhibitor action through
determination of reversing metabolites. *J. Bact.* **67**, 53.
POTTER, V. R. (1951). Sequential blocking of metabolic pathways *in vivo*. *Proc. Soc.
exp. Biol., N.Y.* **76**, 41.
STREITFIELD, M. M. (1957). The replica strip gradient plate technique for determi-
nation of synergism or antagonism of antibiotics paired in various concentration
ratios: a bacteriostatic and bactericidal assay. *Antibiotics Annual* 1956–1957,
p. 906. New York: Medical Encyclopedia, Inc.
WELCH, H. (1957). Opening remarks: *Antibiotics Annual* 1956–1957, p. 1. New
York: Medical Encyclopedia, Inc.
WILLIAMS, R. J., EAKIN, R. E., BEERSTECHER, E. & SHIVE, W. (1950). *The Bio-
chemistry of the B Vitamins*, p. 458. New York: Reinhold Publishing Co.
WOODRUFF, H. B. & FOSTER, J. W. (1946). Antibacillin, a naturally occurring
inhibitor of bacillin. *J. Bact.* **51**, 371.
WOOLLEY, D. W. (1950). Inhibition of synthesis of vitamin B_{12} and riboflavin by
1, 2-dichloro-4, 5-diaminobenzene in bacterial cultures. *Proc. Soc. exp. Biol.,
N.Y.* **75**, 745.

EXPLANATION OF PLATES

PLATE 1. Agar-plug method of detecting new antibiotics (Harris & Ruger, 1953)

Fig. 1. Petri dish containing *Streptomyces* sp. culture from which plugs have been removed
for a test of antibiotic production. For the screening test, plugs are usually removed from
the area of culture growth (1 and 2).

Fig. 2. Demonstration of antibiotic activity by *Streptomyces* spp. cultures on a normal
antibiotic-sensitive test bacterium. Zones of inhibited bacterial growth surround agar plugs
selected from six different strains of *Streptomyces*.

PLATE 2. Resolution of known antibiotics by paper
chromatography and bioautography

1, streptothricin; 2, cycloserine; 3, chloramphenicol; 4, streptothricin + cycloserine;
5, streptothricin + cycloserine + chloramphenicol.

Solvent system: *n*-butanol (8) + H_2O(2) + acetic acid (1). Antibiotic applied at opposite
end to numerals, developed by ascending technique. Visualized by bioautography with
Escherichia coli on nutrient agar containing 0·0033 % triphenyltetrazolium chloride.

PLATE 3. Method of detection of synergistic action of antibiotics
(Reproduced from Streitfeld, 1957)

Fig. 1. A synergistic bacteriostatic action is observed with penicillin, contained in a gradient
agar plate, and tetracycline, contained in a paper strip. The zone of inhibited growth of the
test bacterium, *Staphylococcus aureus*, flares out where the two antibiotics act together.

Fig. 2. A synergistic bactericidal action is observed on a replicate plate made from the
above. The replicate plate does not contain antibiotics.

Fig. 3. Synergistic action is not observed with *Pseudomonas aeruginosa* on a gradient plate
containing polymyxin B with a paper-strip containing chloramphenicol.

PLATE 1

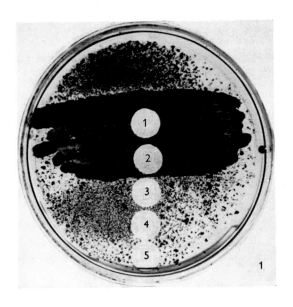

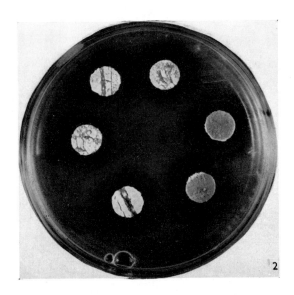

PLATE 2

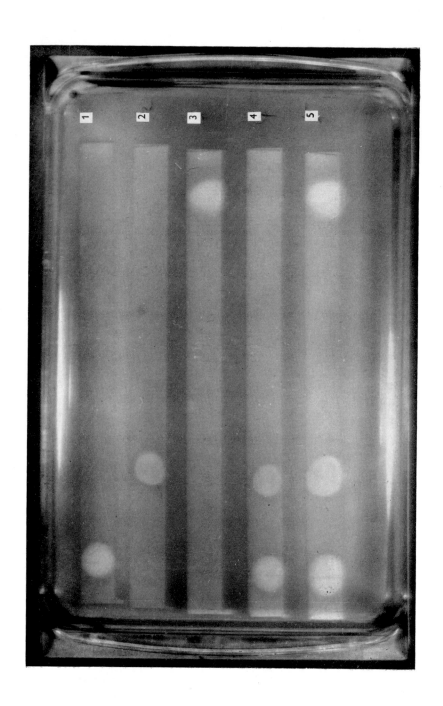

PLATE 3

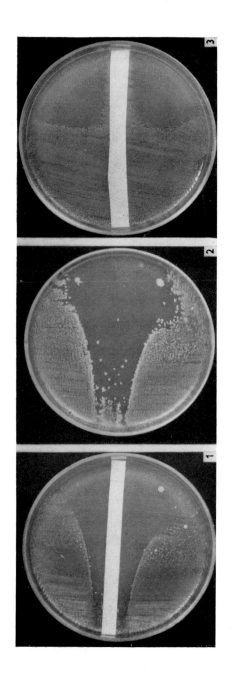

SELECTIVE INHIBITION OF BACTERIAL CELL-WALL SYNTHESIS: ITS POSSIBLE APPLICATIONS IN CHEMOTHERAPY

J. T. PARK

Walter Reed Army Institute of Research,
Washington, D.C.

Much knowledge of antimetabolite action has accumulated since the discovery by Woods (1940) that sulphanilamide was a competitive inhibitor of *p*-aminobenzoic acid. However, this knowledge of anti-metabolites has not resulted in the development of useful chemo-therapeutic agents as expected. On the other hand, in the time since Woods's discovery, many antibiotics have been found useful in the treatment of microbial diseases. There is some reason to hope that elucidation of the mechanism of action of these antibiotics will provide a basis for the successful application of our knowledge of antimetabolites to the design of effective chemotherapeutic agents.

Let us consider the unique characteristics of the antibiotics. They have three properties not usually possessed by synthetic antimetabolites, namely, selective toxicity, non-competitive action, and effectiveness at low concentration. Obviously, with those antibiotics used parenterally, as with the sulpha drugs, the key to their usefulness lies in selective toxicity. They are toxic to certain micro-organisms but relatively non-toxic to animals and man. The reason for the selective toxicity of anti-biotics has not been understood because their mode of action has remained obscure. Generally speaking, the useful antibiotics, because of their high activity, are thought to interfere with specific reactions essential to the sensitive organism.

The low toxicity of the antibiotic to animals may be accounted for if the hypothetical reaction blocked by the drug and vital to the organism (1) is not vital to the animal; (2) is vital to the animal, but is unaffected because of inability of the antibiotic to reach the site; (3) is vital to the animal, but is unaffected because the antibiotic is not firmly bound to the animal enzyme; (4) does not exist in the animal. So long as the nature of the reaction blocked by the antibiotic remains unknown, it is not possible to determine whether the hypothetical reaction is essential or even exists in the animal.

Antimetabolites to substances used by both bacteria and animals, if toxic to one are, in general, toxic to the other. However, there is considerable variation in the activity of antimetabolites between bacteria and animals or even between bacterial species. In fact, resistance to antibiotics often appears to develop by a reduction of the antibiotic-binding ability of the sensitive enzyme rather than by the development of alternate pathways. Saz, Martinez & Middleton (1957), for instance, have shown that specific reductases of aureomycin-resistant cells resist inhibition by aureomycin more than corresponding enzymes in the original sensitive cells, and in unpublished work I have observed that staphylococci made resistant to 5000 times the normal inhibitory level of penicillin will still respond biochemically (i.e. accumulate the uridine-muramic acid-complexes, see later) at a correspondingly higher level of penicillin. However, experience with analogues to metabolites such as vitamins, amino acids, purines and pyrimidines suggests that the essential nature of reactions involving these substances, and the sensitivity of these reactions to antimetabolites, are sufficiently similar in animals and in micro-organisms for the development of a selectively toxic agent to be extremely difficult and unpredictable on this basis. Examples in which the antimetabolite is much less toxic to one species than another have sometimes been explained by demonstrating destruction of the antimetabolite, counteraction by production of excess metabolite, or lack of permeability of the antimetabolite in the resistant species. These relations have been reviewed in detail in the excellent monograph by Woolley (1952).

Since the sulpha drugs compete with a precursor of folic acid and it has been observed that the sulpha drugs generally do not inhibit cells which require preformed folic acid, the synthesis of analogues to precursors used by bacteria and not by man has been suggested as a predictable method for producing selectively toxic agents. Indeed, Woolley (1951) has demonstrated that an analogue to a hypothetical metabolic precursor of riboflavin and vitamin B_{12} (1:2-dichloro-4:5-diaminobenzene) selectively inhibits organisms which synthesize both riboflavin and vitamin B_{12}. That is, it inhibits organisms which use the precursor but not organisms which require preformed riboflavin and vitamin B_{12} and therefore do not utilize the precursor. Riboflavin and vitamin B_{12} do not reverse the inhibition, as would be expected if the presence or absence of these vitamins were all that was involved. It would be valuable to understand why the inhibition by the precursor analogue was not reversed by the product but an explanation for this does not appear to have been sought as yet. It may be found that the known essential products (riboflavin and vitamin B_{12}) did not reverse the inhibition by the precursor analogue because (1) the self-sufficient (sensitive) organisms did not absorb the preformed products; (2) the sensitive organisms synthesized a non-competitive inhibitor from the precursor analogue; or (3) the synthesis of an unknown metabolite peculiar to the sensitive organism was inhibited.

Many of the problems that must be overcome in developing a selective agent when the metabolite in question is used by both bacteria and man would be obviated if the reaction sequence to be inhibited existed in bacteria and not in man. If essential reactions were to be found in bacteria, in which neither the metabolite involved nor the reaction products were used by animals, inhibitors of these reactions should be selective poisons. Reactions or metabolites essential and unique to bacteria were not known until recently. However, it now appears that several metabolites essential to a wide variety of bacteria are not utilized by animals. Stated more precisely and cautiously, several compounds have been identified in bacterial cell walls—notably diaminopimelic acid (Holdsworth, 1952), D-glutamic acid (Ikawa & Snell, 1956), D-alanine (Snell, Radin & Ikawa, 1955) and muramic acid (Cummins & Harris, 1954, 1956)—which have not yet been detected in mammalian tissues. Muramic acid is the name suggested by Strange for an acidic amino sugar tentatively characterized as 3-O-α-carboxyethylhexosamine (Strange, 1956) (for structure see Fig. 1). Antimetabolites to these substances might be expected to exhibit selective toxicity, whereas antimetabolites to other known building blocks usually do not.

It is the purpose of this paper (1) to consider the essential role of these unique metabolites in the synthesis of bacterial cell walls; (2) to cite examples of interference with synthesis and the consequences of this interference; and (3) to discuss the possibilities that antimetabolites can be devised which would be selectively toxic to bacteria because they interfere with the essential process of cell-wall synthesis. At present, cell-wall synthesis appears to be the only unique, vital metabolic pathway of general occurrence in bacteria. Unfortunately, our knowledge of these topics is quite limited, and to fulfil my assignment in this discussion it is necessary to make a free interpretation of the available data. It should be recognized that the purpose of these interpretations and speculations is to reveal areas where productive research is needed and investigation should prove fruitful.

THE BACTERIAL CELL WALL—ITS ESSENTIAL FUNCTIONS AND UNIQUE COMPONENTS

Several excellent reviews (Salton, 1956; Cummins, 1956; Work, 1957) have appeared which present current knowledge of the properties and composition of bacterial cell walls. Because of this, the background material for this discussion will be limited to a brief outline of the relevant facts.

The bacterial cell wall represents at least 20 % of the dry weight of bacteria, hence its synthesis is a major function of the cell. This wall surrounds the osmotically fragile part of the cell, termed by Weibull (1953) the protoplast, which has been shown to possess all the synthetic capabilities of the whole cell (see reviews by Weibull, 1956, and McQuillen, 1956). The protoplast has an outer membrane which is an osmotic barrier; since this membrane is fragile and since the internal osmotic pressure may be as high as 20 atmospheres in many Gram-positive organisms (Mitchell & Moyle, 1956), the protoplast must be protected from this pressure. The cell wall prevents the protoplast from bursting by resisting this hydrostatic pressure. Thus, under normal conditions, the cell wall is essential to bacteria in that it preserves the protoplast; in addition, the limited elasticity of the cell wall gives bacteria shape. It probably also facilitates constriction and division of the protoplast during growth.

The protoplast must continue to produce cell wall and to preserve the integrity of the wall during growth and division. In order for the wall to increase in mass and enlarge during growth, presumably linkages in the wall are continuously broken and new material is introduced. The protoplast synthesizes most of the unique building blocks and must have them available for polymerization to preserve the integrity of the wall. Thus a delicate balance exists during growth in that the absence of an essential building block could lead to lysis of the cell because splitting of linkages in the wall continues while incorporation of new material fails to repair the damage. As we shall see later, depletion of essential cell-wall building blocks or inhibition of utilization of these materials leads to changes in morphology, to exposure of the protoplast, and to lysis.

The essential building blocks of bacterial cell walls are many and varied. The Gram-negative bacteria have a complex wall composed of sugars, many amino acids, the amino sugars N-acetylglucosamine and N-acetylmuramic acid, and as much as 20 % lipid of unknown composition. The walls isolated from Gram-positive bacteria are less complex in composition; they contain a negligible amount of lipid, as many as four sugars, plus glucosamine, muramic acid, glutamic acid, alanine, and either lysine or diaminopimelic acid or both (Salton, 1956; Cummins & Harris, 1956). In addition, glycine is usually found in micrococci and aspartic acid in the lactobacilli.

The striking fact of interest here is that cell walls of all bacteria that have been analysed contain glucosamine, muramic acid, glutamic acid, alanine, and either lysine or diaminopimelic acid or both. Snell *et al.* (1955) have shown that D-alanine is present in high concentration in the cell walls of *Streptococcus faecalis* and *Lactobacillus casei*; Ikawa & Snell (1956) that a high percentage of the glutamic acid of the walls of these organisms is the D-form, and Park & Strominger (1957) that much

Table 1. *Muramic acid and D-glutamic acid content of bacterial cell walls*

Organism	Muramic acid % of cell wall dry weight	Molecular ratio $\dfrac{\text{Muramic acid}}{\text{D-Glutamic acid}}$
Staphylococcus aureus H	4·2	1·01
Staphylococcus aureus 209 P (res.)	9·2	0·96
Sarcina lutea	7·3	1·01
Micrococcus lysodeikticus	8·1	0·91
Bacillus megaterium KM	4·5	0·59
Bacillus megaterium (enzyme-treated)	7·3	0·80
Escherichia coli B	1·9	0·96

of the alanine and glutamic acid of staphylococcal cell walls is the D-isomer. From these few analyses it may be anticipated that D-alanine and D-glutamic acid are present in most if not all bacterial cell walls. Park & Wynngate (unpublished) have analysed the walls of several bacteria for muramic acid and D-glutamic acid. As can be seen from Table 1, the ratio of muramic acid to D-glutamic acid is close to 1 in all the bacteria examined with the exception of *Bacillus megaterium*, the cell-wall preparation of which may contain some of the D-glutamyl polypeptide from the capsule of this organism. Significantly, this ratio is found to be true in the Gram-negative organism, *Escherichia coli* strain B, though the absolute amount present is considerably less than in the Gram-positive organisms tested. Thus extrapolation of the available evidence, though quite limited, suggests that three unique entities—muramic acid, D-alanine, and D-glutamic acid—are present in most, if not all, bacterial cell walls; and that a fourth—diaminopimelic acid—is present in many species. None of these substances has been detected in animals, although a systematic examination of individual tissues has not been undertaken.

EXAMPLES OF INTERFERENCE WITH
BACTERIAL CELL-WALL SYNTHESIS

Since the cell wall determines the shape of bacteria, any change in the morphology of a micro-organism may be regarded as the result of detrimental effects on the cell wall—either interference with its synthesis or acceleration of its dissolution or both. The formation of filamentous forms, often considered as a defect in cell division, in most instances is probably the result of slight inhibition of cell-wall synthesis. Consequently, all agents which bring about changes in the shape of the cell may be viewed as interfering with the normal development of the cell wall. The importance of the cell wall and the ease with which its integrity is lost is illustrated by the observation of Pulvertaft (1952) that over half of the bacteria in a culture may lyse spontaneously at the beginning of logarithmic growth. A delicate balance thus arises during activation of cell-wall synthesis and continues to a lesser extent throughout the period of growth. Indeed, pleomorphic organisms (*Bacteroides*, *Corynebacterium* and *Streptobacillus* spp.) may be regarded as cells in which this balance is easily upset. Under certain adverse conditions, the formation of filamentous or thread-like growth by bacteria is common (Hughes, 1956, has listed thirty-five such conditions in a recent review). Many of the same factors induce the formation of bulbous forms, of large bodies, and of the transformation to the L-form of growth (see review by Dienes & Weinberger, 1951). Filamentous growth may occur under conditions such as depletion of nutrients, a temperature or pH change, or the presence of a low concentration of penicillin. These conditions are only slightly unfavourable for wall synthesis. Bulbous growth, large body formation, initiation of the L-form of growth, and lysis may result from a more severe shortage of an essential cell-wall building block caused by lack of nitrogen, antagonists such as glycine, DL-alanine, or certain antibiotics (discussed later), and by inhibitory levels of penicillin. These phenomena may be recognized as the inevitable result of the continuation of an autolytic process on the wall which results in greater elasticity and eventual rupture of the supporting wall and/or the protoplast. The recent success of Dienes & Sharp (1956) in producing L-forms of a number of Gram-positive bacteria in the presence of high concentrations of salt where previous attempts had usually failed, suggests that the L-forms do have a membrane and hence in this respect resemble protoplasts. Previously, most known L-forms had been produced from Gram-negative bacteria (which have a lower internal osmotic pressure and hence their protoplasts required a less protective medium). Thus, filaments, bulbs, large bodies, protoplasts, and L-forms probably represent varying degrees of loss of cell wall. The generality of the phenomenon, its occurrence to some degree in most cultures at some stage of normal growth, and the many substances which induce the phenomenon, indicate that cell-wall synthesis is particularly susceptible to adverse factors and hence is a natural point for attack by chemotherapeutic agents. We have yet to demonstrate (1) that most of the chemical inducers of abnormal forms, such as certain antibiotics and amino acids, act as inhibitors which cause deficiencies of specific cell-wall components; (2) that the induction of long forms by temperature and pH changes is caused by restricted synthesis of wall components; and (3) that antibodies and bacteriophage, which act directly on the wall, induce long forms or L-forms by making wall synthesis more difficult. Nevertheless, there is no doubt that a wide variety of agents or conditions brings about changes which are first recognizable as damage to the cell wall. Definite proof that a specific interference with cell-wall metabolism can cause such extensive changes is lacking, but the following two examples are strongly suggestive that this is the case. Meadow, Hoare & Work (1957) have recently observed that diaminopimelic acid-requiring mutants of *Escherichia coli* will grow in a limiting concentration of diaminopimelic acid until it is used up, when there is a change to the large body form followed by lysis. Since in vegetative bacterial cells, combined diaminopimelic acid has been found only in the cell walls, this would appear to demonstrate that lack of a single cell-wall constituent produces the general phenomenon associated with loss of integrity of the wall. *Lactobacillus bifidus* strain Penn., which requires *N*-acetylglucosamine in combined form as a growth factor, as pointed out by Rose & György (1956), behaves similarly. The amount of bound *N*-acetylglucosamine required in the medium is sufficient to provide the *N*-acetylglucosamine of the cell wall, and in the absence of the factor this organism produces large bodies (Park & György, unpublished).

EVIDENCE THAT PENICILLIN INHIBITS CELL-WALL FORMATION

By far the most general agent for the production of long forms and L-forms of bacteria is penicillin. At low concentrations of penicillin, bacilli will grow as filaments; at higher concentrations, the cells may become spherical and lyse, or under suitable conditions the L-forms, which are completely resistant to penicillin, will be produced. Since a single agent will induce the various phenomena, their formation may be construed as the result of different degrees of inhibition of a single process. The morphological changes were known as early as 1940; Gardner (1940) observed that a low concentration of penicillin allowed growth, but that division and separation did not occur. In 1946, Duguid stated that

The morphological changes...produced by the lower penicillin concentrations, in particular the failure of proper cell division and the ready occurrence of swelling and protoplasmic protrusion, suggest that penicillin in these concentrations interferes specifically with the formation of the outer supporting cell wall, while otherwise allowing growth to proceed until the organism finally bursts its defective envelope and so undergoes lysis.

This remarkable interpretation that the action was on synthesis of an outer supporting cell wall and that lysis occurred when the bubbles of protoplasm (protoplasts) burst has received more conclusive support recently from experiments designed in the light of present knowledge that bacteria possess a rigid cell wall which encloses and protects a protoplast and its fragile membrane. Liebermeister & Kellenberger (1956), Lederberg (1956, 1957), and Hahn & Ciak (1957) have shown that certain Gram-negative rods will balloon into large bodies or bacterial protoplasts under suitable conditions in the presence of penicillin. Lederberg (1957) and Hahn & Ciak (1957) recognized that this change in morphology must be caused by an effect of penicillin on the formation of cell wall. The excellent specific cell-wall reaction developed by Tomcsik (1954) has provided evidence that cell-wall material still covers the surface of *Bacillus anthracis* when it is converted to the spherical form by a low concentration of penicillin. It is probable that with higher concentrations of penicillin, the large bodies of *B. anthracis* would not contain demonstrable cell wall. Cell walls have also been reported on large bodies of *Proteus vulgaris* (Stempen, 1955). In the light of this, care should be taken in the description of bacterial protoplasts and a chemical test, perhaps of muramic acid or D-glutamic acid, should be employed to exclude the presence of cell wall.

The sequence of chemical reactions which results in cell-wall formation is unknown. A study of the events which follow addition of penicillin to a culture of *Staphylococcus aureus* strain H does suggest the portion of this sequence which penicillin interrupts. This study revealed that three uridine-5′-pyrophosphate compounds accumulated rapidly in the penicillin-inhibited cells. All three nucleotides contained an acidic N-acetylamino sugar (N-acetylmuramic acid) linked to the second phosphate through carbon 1. The principal compound (45 % of the total accumulated) contained a peptide composed of D-glutamic acid, L-lysine, and three residues of DL-alanine (Park, 1952) (see Fig. 1 for possible structure). Of the remaining two compounds one contained L-alanine and the other was without amino acids so that these may be precursors of the principal component. Analysis of staphylococcal cell walls revealed that muramic acid, D-glutamic acid, lysine, and DL-alanine were present in a ratio of about 1:1:1:3 just as in the accumulated nucleotide. This suggests that the uridine pyrophosphate N-acetyl-muramic acid peptide is a precursor of the staphylococcal cell wall

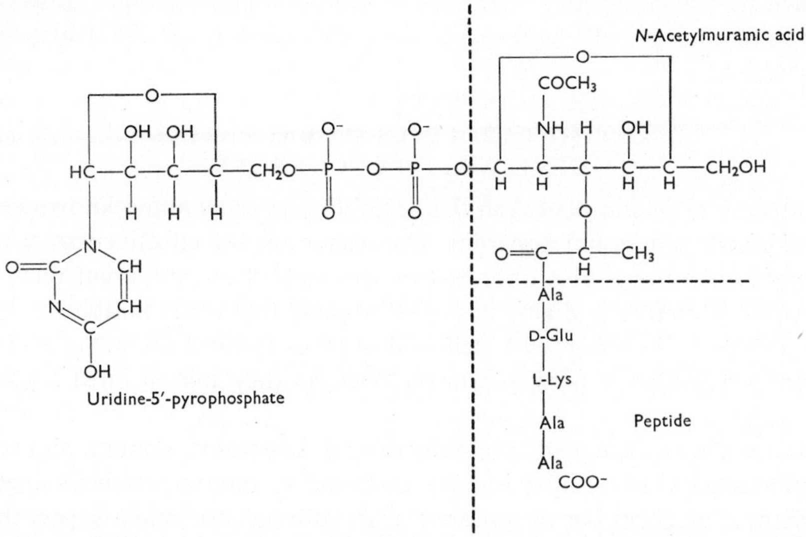

Fig. 1. A tentative structure of the principal nucleotide that accumulates in penicillin-treated *Staphylococcus aureus*. The sequence of amino acids is one of several possible arrangements (Strominger, 1955).

(Park & Strominger, 1957). Other considerations discussed by Park & Strominger lend support to this view, namely (1) many uridine pyro-phosphate glycosyl compounds are known which appear to participate in biosynthesis of polysaccharides (Leloir, 1955); (2) penicillin is specifically bound to a lipid-containing fraction from bacteria (Cooper, 1954, 1955) which is presumably protoplast membrane. This location for the site of action of penicillin is the logical one if the sensitive reaction is a transglycosidation of the N-acetylmuramic acid peptide from the uridine pyrophosphate compound formed inside the protoplast to a cell-wall site outside the membrane; (3) the rate of accumulation of the compounds in the presence of penicillin is comparable to the rate at which muramic acid-peptide components are normally incorporated into the cell wall; and (4) as indicated earlier, the N-acetylmuramic acid-peptide fragment appears to be a general component of bacterial cell walls and this correlates with the fact that nearly all bacteria lose the integrity of their cell wall when the growth phase is inhibited by penicillin.

From this circumstantial evidence, it seems probable that penicillin interferes with cell-wall synthesis by preventing the incorporation of the *N*-acetylmuramic acid peptide fragment into the wall. It is to be expected that any condition which seriously limits the availability of this fragment or of its unique component parts—*N*-acetylmuramic acid, D-glutamic acid, or D-alanine—would inhibit the growth of bacteria much as penicillin does. The similar morphological changes observed when diaminopimelic acid was limiting (Meadow *et al.* 1957) supports this thesis.

ANTIMETABOLITES OF BACTERIAL CELL-WALL PRECURSORS

A structural relation between the penicillin molecule and a known cell-wall constituent is not apparent. The reason for the effectiveness of the other antibiotics is also obscured by this lack of any apparent relation between structure and activity. It is possible that other antibiotics will be shown to interfere with cell-wall synthesis; certainly a number of them are similar to penicillin in the bacteria they inhibit most readily. A large number of antibiotics, such as erythromycin, carbomycin, pikromycin, spiramycin, novobiocin and streptolin, contain unusual amino sugars; some of these may be found to interfere with the metabolism of glucosamine or muramic acid, although one might expect that any substance that interfered with glucosamine utilization would be a general poison. Another antibiotic which may prove to be an inhibitor of cell-wall synthesis by interference with utilization of a wall component is oxamycin. Ciak & Hahn (to be published) have shown that this antibiotic causes lysis of *Escherichia coli* in the same way as does penicillin. Oxamycin, a derivative of D-serine, may be found to prevent normal incorporation of D-alanine into the wall. It should be possible to determine this since one might expect suitable oxamycin-inhibited organisms, such as *Staphylococcus aureus*, to accumulate uridine *N*-acetylmuramic acid derivatives lacking in D-alanine or peptide. Accumulation of uridine *N*-acetylamino sugar compounds which lack amino acids has already been shown to occur in crystal violet-inhibited *S. aureus* (Park, 1954). Snell & Guirard (1943) showed that glycine, DL-serine, DL-threonine and β-alanine inhibited growth of *Streptococcus faecalis* strain R. It was later shown that D-alanine was needed for growth of certain lactic acid bacteria but was usually synthesized in the presence of pyridoxal. Hence this also may be an example of inter-ference with cell-wall synthesis by competition with D-alanine. J. Snell (personal communication) recognized that the A ring of the tetracyclines, which he found to be labelled preferentially by DL-glutamic acid, re-sembles D-glutamic acid, and he has demonstrated that glutamic acid accumulates in oxytetracycline-inhibited *Escherichia coli*. Thus the tetracyclines may prove to be analogues of D-glutamic acid.

Hence, in the antibiotics cited, we may already have examples of antimetabolites of several cell-wall components; the amino sugars, D-alanine, and D-glutamic acid. Can analogues of D-alanine, D-glutamic acid, muramic acid, or larger wall fragments now be synthesized which will be effective chemotherapeutic agents? Certainly, competitive inhi-bitors can be devised, though these may not be sufficiently active since virtually all organisms make the unique wall components in abundance, thus nullifying competitive inhibitors. Some method of imitating the second virtue of antibiotics, non-competitive action, may be required. It has been noted in the past that antibiotics usually possess a reactive group which may be involved in the firm binding which causes the sensitive enzyme to be inhibited irreversibly. On the optimistic side is the fact that the inhibitors devised should prove relatively non-toxic to animals and that only partial inhibition of wall synthesis is necessary. Obviously much effort will be required to test these hypotheses.

CONCLUSIONS

Antibiotics may be considered to be non-competitive inhibitors which inactivate catalysts whose function is to make a structure which the cell itself must manufacture for survival. Consequently, the antibiotics should provide a means of detecting these unknown but uniquely vital reactions. Penicillin has revealed cell-wall synthesis as one of these vital reactions. The unusual constituents of the wall now offer the organic chemist an opportunity to design antimetabolites that interfere with this vital synthesis.

This paper is intended as a discussion and extrapolation of the few facts known about inhibition of bacterial cell-wall synthesis rather than as a review. It has been simplified and generalized in order to stress the viewpoint that abnormal bacterial forms are an expression of specific interference with wall synthesis and to present a new approach to the problem of selective toxicity.

REFERENCES

COOPER, P. D. (1954). The association of the penicillin-binding component of *Staphylococcus aureus* with a lipid fraction. *J. gen. Microbiol.* **10**, 236.

COOPER, P. D. (1955). The site of action of penicillin: some properties of the penicillin-binding component of *Staphylococcus aureus*. *J. gen. Microbiol.* **12**, 100.

CUMMINS, C. S. (1956). The chemical composition of the bacterial cell wall. *Int. Rev. Cytol.* **5**, 25.

CUMMINS, C. S. & HARRIS, H. (1954). Carbohydrate and amino acid constituents of the cell walls of *Corynebacterium diphtheriae*. *Biochem. J.* **57**, xxxii.

CUMMINS, C. S. & HARRIS, H. (1956). The chemical composition of the cell wall in some Gram-positive bacteria and its possible value as a taxonomic character. *J. gen. Microbiol.* **14**, 583.

DIENES, L. & SHARP, J. T. (1956). The role of high electrolyte concentration in the production and growth of L forms of bacteria. *J. Bact.* **71**, 208.

DIENES, L. & WEINBERGER, H. J. (1951). The L forms of bacteria. *Bact. Rev.* **15**, 245.

DUGUID, J. P. (1946). The sensitivity of bacteria to the action of penicillin. *Edinb. med. J.* **53**, 401.

GARDNER, A. D. (1940). Morphological effects of penicillin on bacteria. *Nature, Lond.* **146**, 837.

HAHN, F. E. & CIAK, J. (1957). Penicillin-induced lysis of *Escherichia coli*. *Science*, **125**, 119.

HOLDSWORTH, E. S. (1952). The nature of the cell-wall of *Corynebacterium diphtheriae*. *Biochim. biophys. Acta*, **8**, 110.

HUGHES, W. H. (1956). The structure and development of the induced long forms of bacteria. In *Bacterial Anatomy*. *Symp. Soc. gen. Microbiol.* **6**, 341.

IKAWA, M. & SNELL, E. E. (1956). D-Glutamic acid and amino sugars as cell wall constituents in lactic acid bacteria. *Biochim. biophys. Acta*, **19**, 576.

LEDERBERG, J. (1956). Bacterial protoplasts induced by penicillin. *Proc. nat. Acad. Sci., Wash.* **42**, 574.

LEDERBERG, J. (1957). Mechanism of action of penicillin. *J. Bact.* **73**, 144.

LELOIR, L. F. (1955). The uridine coenzymes. *3rd Int. Congr. Biochem., Brussels*, p. 154.

LIEBERMEISTER, K. & KELLENBERGER, E. (1956). Studien zur L-Form der Bakterien I. Die Umwandlung der bazillären in die globuläre Zellform bei *Proteus* unter Einfluss von Penicillin. *Z. Naturf.* **11**b, 200.

McQUILLEN, K. (1956). Capabilities of bacterial protoplasts. In *Bacterial Anatomy*. *Symp. Soc. gen. Microbiol.* **6**, 127.

MEADOW, P., HOARE, D. S. & WORK, E. (1957). Interrelationships between lysine and $\alpha\epsilon$-diaminopimelic acid and their derivatives and analogues in mutants of *Escherichia coli*. *Biochem. J.* **66**, 270.

MITCHELL, P. & MOYLE, J. (1956). Osmotic function and structure in bacteria. In *Bacterial Anatomy*. *Symp. Soc. gen. Microbiol.* **6**, 150.

PARK, J. T. (1952). Uridine-5′-pyrophosphate derivatives. I. Isolation from *Staphylococcus aureus*. II. A structure common to three derivatives. III. Amino-acid containing derivatives. *J. biol. Chem.* **194**, 877, 885, 897.

PARK, J. T. (1954). Uridine diphosphate derivatives in *Staphylococcus aureus* treated with crystal violet or various antibiotics. *Fed. Proc.* **13**, 271.

PARK, J. T. & STROMINGER, J. L. (1957). Mode of action of penicillin: biochemical basis for the mechanism of action of penicillin and for its selective toxicity. *Science*, **125**, 99.

PULVERTAFT, R. J. V. (1952). The effect of antibiotics on growing cultures of *Bacterium coli*. *J. Path. Bact.* **64**, 75.

ROSE, C. S. & GYÖRGY, P. (1956). Reaction of enzymes of *Lactobacillus bifidus* var. *pennsylvanicus* with bifidus factor: effect of monosaccharides. *Proc. Soc. exp. Biol., N.Y.* **93**, 58.

SALTON, M. R. J. (1956). Bacterial cell walls. In *Bacterial Anatomy. Symp. Soc. gen. Microbiol.* **6**, 81.

SAZ, A. K., MARTINEZ, L. M. & MIDDLETON, M. B. (1957). Inhibition of electron transport in *Escherichia coli* by aureomycin. *Fed. Proc.* **16**, 242.

SNELL, E. E., RADIN, N. S. & IKAWA, M. (1955). The nature of D-alanine in lactic acid bacteria. *J. biol. Chem.* **217**, 803.

SNELL, E. E. & GUIRARD, B. M. (1943). Some interrelationships of pyridoxine, alanine and glycine in their effect on certain lactic acid bacteria. *Proc. nat. Acad. Sci., Wash.* **29**, 66.

STEMPEN, H. (1955). Demonstration of a cell wall in the large bodies of *Proteus vulgaris*. *J. Bact.* **70**, 177.

STRANGE, R. E. (1956). The structure of an amino sugar present in certain spores and bacterial cell walls. *Biochem. J.* **64**, 23 P.

STROMINGER, J. L. (1955). Uridine nucleotides in animals and bacteria. 3rd *Int. Congr. Biochem., Brussels*, p. 165.

TOMCSIK, J. (1954). Über die Oberflächenstrukturen des *Bacillus anthracis*. *Schweiz. Z. allg. Path.* **17**, 457.

WEIBULL, C. (1953). The isolation of protoplasts from *Bacillus megaterium* by controlled treatment with lysozyme. *J. Bact.* **66**, 688.

WEIBULL, C. (1956). Bacterial protoplasts; their formation and characteristics. In *Bacterial Anatomy. Symp. Soc. gen. Microbiol.* **6**, 111.

WOODS, D. D. (1940). The relation of *p*-aminobenzoic acid to the mechanism of action of sulphanilamide. *Brit. J. exp. Path.* **21**, 74.

WOOLLEY, D. W. (1951). Selective toxicity of 1, 2-dichloro-4, 5-diaminobenzene: its relation to requirements for riboflavin and vitamin B_{12}. *J. exp. Med.* **93**, 13.

WOOLLEY, D. W. (1952). *A Study of Antimetabolites*. New York: John Wiley & Sons, Inc.

WORK, E. (1957). Biochemistry of the bacterial cell wall. *Nature, Lond.* **179**, 841.

SURFACE-ACTIVE BACTERICIDES

B. A. NEWTON

Medical Research Council Unit for Chemical Microbiology,
Department of Biochemistry, University of Cambridge

Surface-active compounds have played a major part in man's fight against disease, and their use as antiseptics can be traced from the beginning of medical history up to the present day. The cleansing and antiseptic properties of soaps have been known since the early days of the Roman Empire; a number of surface-active compounds which occur in plant and animal tissues, such as bile acids, lecithins, glucosides and unsaturated fatty acids have been used therapeutically for centuries, and in more recent times, the success of Lister's 'antiseptic system of surgery' was due to the surface-active and bactericidal properties of phenol. During the last forty years many synthetic surface-active substances have become available and, since the observations of Jacobs (1916) and Domagk (1935) aroused interest in this new group of disinfectants, reports too numerous to mention have revealed the bactericidal effects of these compounds. More recently still, the search for antibiotics has led to the discovery of a new group of surface-active bactericides— the polypeptide antibiotics. Many surface active compounds have been used as general purpose germicides and antiseptics on skin and mucous membranes, whilst others, for example the peptide antibiotic, polymyxin, have been used successfully for the treatment of intestinal infections (Kagan, Krevsky, Milzer & Locke, 1951) and meningitis (Swift & Bushby, 1951) but all so far tested have proved to be too toxic for parenteral use. Hope for the further development of surface-active compounds as chemotherapeutic agents has been raised by the recent work of Cornforth, Hart, Rees & Stock (1951) on the antituberculous activity of certain non-ionic compounds.

A rational approach to chemotherapy leading to the design of new chemotherapeutic agents is dependent upon knowledge gleaned from two main fields of research; first, the study of chemical, physical and biochemical properties of parasite and host cells and the relations existing between them; and secondly, studies of the action of existing chemotherapeutic agents and of the relation between their chemical structure and biological activity; at the present time knowledge in both fields is fragmentary. After summarizing the general properties of surface-active bactericides, it is the aim of this contribution to consider the nature of their bactericidal action and to discuss the factors which influence it.

CHEMICAL STRUCTURE AND GENERAL PROPERTIES

Surface-active compounds contain both fat soluble (hydrophobic) and water soluble (hydrophilic) groups in the same molecule; as a result of this structure these molecules tend to migrate to, and become orientated at, interfaces where they alter the energy relations. This definition, however, is of little practical value and we recognize surface-active agents as substances which, in dilute solution, act as wetting agents, emulsifying agents or detergents and which, when shaken, readily produce a stable foam. A detailed account of the chemical structures of the many types of synthetic surface-active bactericides would be out of place in this paper and only the general characteristics of the main classes will be mentioned. For further information see reviews by Price (1946) and Glassman (1948).

Surface-active compounds can be classified into three groups, anionic, cationic, and non-ionic compounds, depending upon the nature of the electrical charge on the hydrophilic portion of the molecule (Fig. 1).

Anionic compounds contain a hydrophobic residue which is usually a paraffinic chain or an alkyl-substituted benzene or naphthalene ring, balanced by a negatively charged hydrophilic group which may be a carboxyl, sulphate, sulphonate or phosphate group. The commercial detergent sodium tetradecyl sulphate (STS), fatty acids, soaps and phenols are representative of this group.

Cationic compounds contain the same type of hydrophobic groups as anionic compounds but have a positively charged hydrophilic group which may be a quaternary ammonium, sulphonium, arsonium, phosphonium or iodonium group; the most valuable bactericides in this class are the quaternary ammonium compounds (e.g. cetyltrimethyl-ammonium bromide, CTAB and cetylpyridinium chloride, CPC). The surface-active polypeptide antibiotics (e.g. tyrocidin, gramicidin S, subtilin, circulin, polypeptin and polymyxin) can also be included in this class since they are all basic peptides which are positively charged at neutral pH values. A cyclic structure has been postulated for a number of these peptides; the polymyxins and probably circulin and polypeptin have in addition a side chain containing a C_9 saturated fatty acid ((+)6-methyloctan-1-oic acid) (Fig. 1). The composition, structure and properties of these and other naturally occurring peptides has recently been reviewed by Bricas & Fromageot (1953).

Non-ionic compounds have their hydrophobic residue balanced by a non-ionized hydrophilic group such as a polymerized ethylene oxide or polyhydric alcohol. Tween 80, a polyoxyalkylene derivative of sorbitan mono-oleate, and the polyoxyethylene ethers (e.g. Triton WR 1339) are compounds of this type.

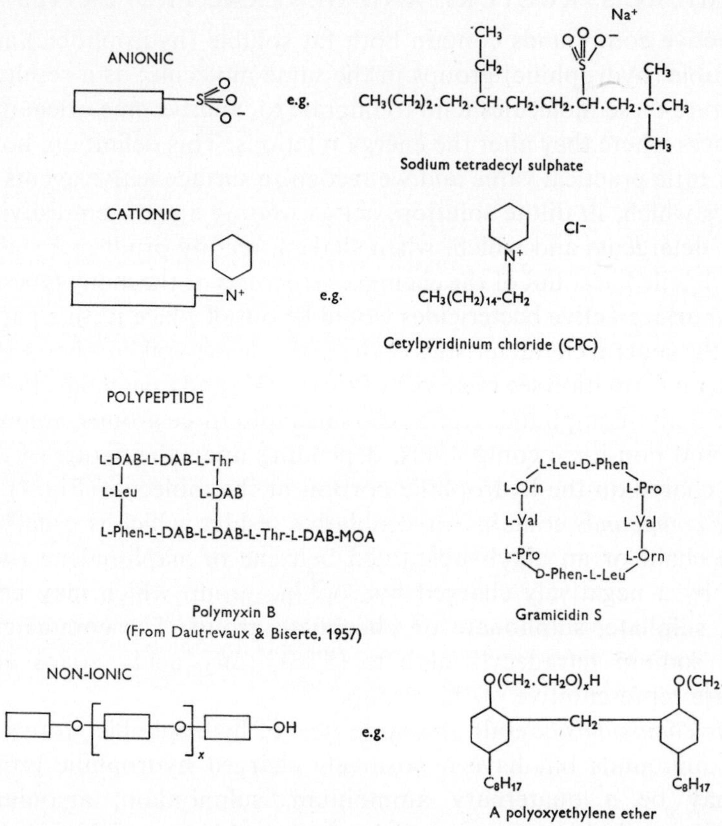

Fig. 1. General classes of surface-active bactericides: typical structures. ☐ represents a paraffinic chain or an alkyl-substituted benzene or naphthalene ring. L-DAB=L-αγ-diaminobutyric acid; L-Leu=L-leucine; MOA=6-methyloctan-1-oic acid; L-Orn=L-orni-thine; L-Phen=L-phenylalanine; L-Pro=L-proline; L-Thr=L-threonine and L-Val=L-valine.

Antibacterial activity

Certain conclusions may be drawn about the antibacterial action of anionic and cationic surface-active compounds. At neutral pH cationic compounds are more effective bactericides than anionic and are active against Gram-positive and Gram-negative bacteria, while anionic compounds are active only against Gram-positive organisms (Baker, Harrison & Miller, 1941). The efficacy of cationic surface-active agents increases as the pH rises and of anionic agents increases as the pH falls. Scales & Kemp (1941) showed that at pH 4 anionic compounds are active against both groups of bacteria and Putnam (1948) suggested that the change in activity at this pH is due to an alteration at the bacterial surface and not to a change in the degree of ionization of the detergent. The activity of cationic surface-active agents is decreased by the presence of anionic compounds and vice versa, and in this respect the poly-peptide antibiotics resemble cationic detergents. However, the polymyxin group of peptides differ from other cationic surface-active agents in being more active against Gram-negative than against Gram-positive bacteria.

Non-ionic surface-active compounds in general show little or no anti-bacterial activity although they are effective surface-tension depressants. Tween 80 has been widely used to promote submerged growth of tubercle bacilli (Dubos & Davis, 1946). Its action is probably due to its surface-active properties because oleic acid esters which are not surface active are ineffective. The optimal concentration of Tween 80 is *c.* 0·1 % and when a small inoculum is used in a medium without serum, growth may be inhibited, possibly by small amounts of unesterified oleic acid in the Tween 80 (Dubos, 1947). The inhibition can be reversed by serum albumin (Davis & Dubos, 1946; 1947). More recently Luzzati (1953) and Minami, Yamane & Yasui (1954) have shown that the tubercle bacillus can metabolize the Tween 80 molecule, using part as a carbon source and liberating oleic acid, which again may inhibit growth. The effect of fatty acids on the growth of bacteria has been discussed in detail by Kodicek (1949) and Pollock (1949) and will not be considered here.

Interest in another group of synthetic, non-ionic compounds has resulted from the report of Cornforth *et al.* (1951) that Triton WR 1339 and related compounds will suppress the development of experimental tuberculosis in the mouse. These agents will also produce appreciable regression and healing of established infections in the guinea-pig (Rees, 1953). None of these compounds shows any growth-inhibitory action against tubercle bacilli *in vitro*, suggesting that the various effects on tuberculous infections are dependent on the host.

Relation between chemical structure and antibacterial activity

Many investigations of the relations between the chemical structure of synthetic ionic detergents and their bactericidal activity were reviewed and discussed extensively by Work & Work (1948) and Sexton (1953); only the more general conclusions will be mentioned here.

Within a given homologous series, bactericidal activity is closely related to chain length; for most cases studied, activity is maximal in compounds containing chains of 12–16 carbon atoms. The chain length associated with optimal activity may vary for different organisms, the sulphonium iodides $(RS^+[CH_3]_2I)$ with $R = C_{16}$ being most active against *Escherichia coli* and that with $R = C_{12}$ against staphylococci (Kuhn & Dann, 1940). The optimal chain length is also related to the other alkyl groups in the molecule, to the nature of the hetero-atom, which may be nitrogen or sulphur (Valko & DuBois, 1944), and to the degree of unsaturation of the chain (Damodaran & Sivaraman, 1953); thus it is the structure of the molecule as a whole which determines the activity.

The properties of non-ionic surface-active agents were reviewed comprehensively by Goldsmith (1943) but little information was found which could relate structure to activity. More recently Cornforth, Hart, Nicholls, Rees & Stock (1955) found that the structural requirements for antituberculous activity of a series of non-ionic polyoxyethylene ethers (Fig. 1) in mice, depended upon the length of the polyoxyethylene chain. Compounds with an average chain length of 10–20 ethylene oxide units were most active; an increase of chain length to 25–30 abolished activity and a further increase to 45–90 enhanced infection. Thus decreasing the hydrophobic/hydrophilic ratio of these molecules results in a change of activity from antituberculous → inactive → protuberculous.

Little is known of the structural characteristics responsible for the biological activity of surface-active cyclic peptides. Gramicidin S, a cyclic decapeptide antibiotic produced by a strain of *Bacillus brevis* (Gause & Brazhnikova, 1944), has been studied in the greatest detail. The structure shown in Fig. 1 has been well substantiated by experimental results (Sanger, 1946; Consden, Gordon, Martin & Synge, 1947; Hodgkin, 1950; Battersby & Craig, 1951) and is unusual in that the peptide contains D-phenylalanine and L-ornithine. Harris & Work (1950) synthesized three pentapeptides having the same amino acid sequence as the antibiotic but found that these had little or negligible bactericidal activity; they concluded that activity was not directly related to the presence of D-phenylalanine or L-ornithine, but was probably intimately related to the cyclic structure of the decapeptide. Erlanger, Sachs & Brand (1954) synthesized two types of straight chain decapeptides, one having a structure and amino acid sequence identical to gramicidin S and the other having a similar structure but with the δ-amino group of each ornithine substituted with a *p*-toluenesulphonyl group; the former was bactericidal against *Staphylococcus aureus* and

Escherichia coli but the latter was inactive. The bactericidal concentration of the decapeptide against *E. coli* was 60 μg./ml. whereas gramicidin S tested under identical conditions was bactericidal at 5 μg./ml. These results suggest that the cyclic structure of gramicidin S may not be the essential factor in determining biological activity—unless it is assumed that the acyclic decapeptide and the cyclic form have entirely different modes of action despite the similarities in their structure. Erlanger & Goode (1954) have suggested that the greater activity of the cyclic peptide may be due to a lesser susceptibility to destruction by bacterial enzymes. From a study of molecular models of linear and cyclic decapeptides, Few (1957) concluded that the cyclic structure is important; the acyclic peptide is less rigid than the cyclic form and is thus liable to undergo kinetic flexing which possibly lowers biological activity by impeding absorption at an intracellular interface. The inactivity of the second acyclic peptide synthesized by Erlanger *et al.* (1954), in which the δ-amino groups of the ornithine residues were covered, suggests that free amino groups are involved in some way in the combination of the peptide with the bacterial cell. Similar results have been obtained for the polymyxin group of peptides and tyrocidin; acetylation of amino groups generally results in a complete loss of activity (Hotchkiss, 1944) although at least one of the four available free γ-amino groups of $\alpha\gamma$-diaminobutyric acid residues of polymyxin can be blocked without loss of activity (Newton, 1955). The importance of the C_9 saturated fatty acid in the polymyxin group of peptides has not been demonstrated since it has so far proved impossible to remove this without complete destruction of the peptide.

Nature of the antibacterial action

It is now generally agreed that ionic surface-active agents are bactericidal rather than bacteriostatic. A number of substances, known to form complexes with surface-active anions and cations (e.g. phospholipids, soaps, proteins and nucleic acids), will prevent this activity when they are added to a bacterial culture before, or at the same time as, the surface-active compound, but not after combination of the surface-active agent with the cell. Plate counts have shown that the proportion of a given population killed (up to 99 %) is related to the amount of surface-active compound added, maximum killing for a given concentration of surface-active agent probably occurring within the first few minutes (Gale & Taylor, 1947; Salton, 1951; Few & Schulman, 1953).

HYPOTHESES AND EXPERIMENTAL DATA

Many hypotheses have been advanced to explain the bactericidal activity of surface-active compounds including (1) inactivation of specific enzymes; (2) general denaturation of cell proteins; (3) disorganization of a cell permeability barrier. Before discussing the relative merits of these hypotheses an account will be given of the experimentally established facts. There have been few detailed studies of the mode of action of surface-active compounds so the data to be described will, of necessity, refer to only a small number of compounds. The experimental data available can be divided into three main sections; first, data relating to the combination of surface-active compounds with the bacterial cell; secondly, the disorganization of the cell resulting from this combination; and thirdly, the question of resistance and selective activity.

Combination of surface-active compounds
with the bacterial cell

Uptake by intact cells. Several workers have shown that the minimal concentration of a surface-active compound required to inhibit growth of bacteria is dependent upon the size of the inoculum used in the growth test, suggesting that there is a considerable absorption of the compound by the bacteria, see, for example, Bliss, Chandler & Schoenbach (1949). A more direct approach to the problem was made by Salton (1951) who showed that the uptake of CTAB by *Staphylococcus aureus*, expressed as a function of the CTAB concentration in the supernatant fluids, follows a typical absorption isotherm (Fig. 2). Agglutination of bacterial suspensions was observed in the region of maximal CTAB uptake. For the majority of organisms studied it was found that the uptake of CTAB at saturation level, was 300–400 μg./mg. dry weight of bacteria. Salton calculated that the amount of CTAB absorbed per cell at saturation levels was considerably more than the amount corresponding to a closely packed monolayer of detergent at the cell surface. With *S. aureus* the CTAB absorbed would occupy an area *c.* fifteen times the cell-surface area and could not exist as a monolayer unless it occupied additional sites within the cell. Alternatively, McQuillen (1950) has suggested that concentric shells of detergent build up around the bacterial cell but his electrophoretic data do not confirm this hypothesis.

Few & Schulman (1953) investigated the uptake of polymyxin by bacteria and found marked differences in the absorption isotherms obtained for polymyxin-sensitive and polymyxin-resistant organisms (Fig. 2); sensitive organisms absorbed about four times as much antibiotic as resistant organisms (Table 1). Calculations similar to those

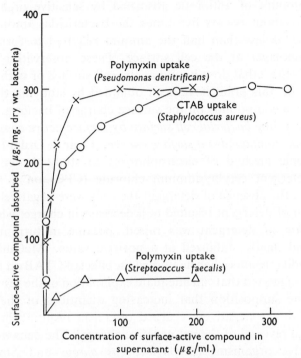

Fig. 2. Absorption of cetyltrimethylammonium bromide (CTAB) and polymyxin by bacteria. Uptake plotted as a function of the concentration of surface-active compound in the supernatant fluid. (Data from Salton, 1951; Few & Schulman, 1953.)

Table 1. *Absorption of polymyxin by bacteria and its relation to polymyxin sensitivity*

(Data from Few & Schulman, 1953; Newton, unpublished observations)

Organism	Polymyxin sensitivity	Gram reaction	Max. amount of polymyxin absorbed in 20 min. at 25° (μg./mg. dry wt. cells)
Pseudomonas aeruginosa	Sensitive	−	310
P. dentrificans	Sensitive	−	350
Escherichia coli	Sensitive	−	220
Bacillus subtilis	Sensitive	+	310
Micrococcus lysodeikticus	Sensitive	+	375
Streptococcus faecalis	Resistant	+	71
Staphylococcus aureus	Resistant	+	84
Proteus vulgaris	Resistant	−	82
Pseudomonas aeruginosa (strain McAlleese)	Resistant	−	70

made by Salton (1951) led Few & Schulman to conclude that at saturation levels polymyxin-sensitive organisms absorb an amount of antibiotic which would cover the cell surface area about twelve times. The maximal amount of antibiotic absorbed by sensitive organisms corresponds to about twenty-five times the bactericidal amount, i.e. the 'lethal dose' is less than half the amount required to form a closely packed monolayer at the cell surface. These observations raise the question: is the lethal dose bound at the cell surface or within the cell? Some data on this point have been obtained by studying the effect of surface-active compounds on the surface charge of bacteria.

Alteration of the bacterial cell surface by surface-active compounds and effect of ionic compounds on surface charge. Dyar & Ordal (1946) used a microscopic method of electrophoresis to study the effect of the cationic detergent cetylpyridinium chloride (CPC) on a number of bacteria. In the absence of detergent the cells were negatively charged; the addition of detergent resulted in a decrease in charge, which, as the concentration of detergent was raised, became in turn neutralized, reversed and finally stabilized at a positive value. McQuillen (1950) obtained similar results when he studied the effect of CTAB on *Escherichia coli* and he suggested that 'an adequate explanation of the results is to be found in the supposition that increasing quantities of the detergent combine with the negatively charged organism resulting in reduction and eventual reversal of the net negative charge'. The behaviour of two Gram-positive organisms (*Staphylococcus aureus* and *Streptococcus faecalis*) in the presence of CTAB was found by McQuillen to differ from that of *E. coli*. With increasing concentrations of CTAB, after a small initial fall in mobility, there was a sharp rise to a maximum negative mobility coincident with the saturation of the bacteria by CTAB (Fig. 3) followed by a decrease in mobility almost to zero. McQuillen suggested that this maximum could be due to a reabsorption of material, originally released from the bacterial cells in the presence of low concentrations of detergent, being reabsorbed on to the surface of the organisms, thus increasing their net negative charge. Such an explanation receives support from the work of Salton (1951) who found that CTAB caused the release from *S. aureus* and *S. faecalis* of material absorbing light at 260 mμ. (purines and pyrimidines). As the CTAB concentration was increased the amount of this material appearing in the cell suspension medium increased, fell to a minimum and then rose again; the minimum occurred at a CTAB/bacterial dry-weight ratio of about the same value as that for the peak in the electrophoresis curves obtained by McQuillen. These results do not provide sufficient data to decide where surface-active substances are absorbed in the bacterial cell but they provide evidence that some combination occurs at the cell surface.

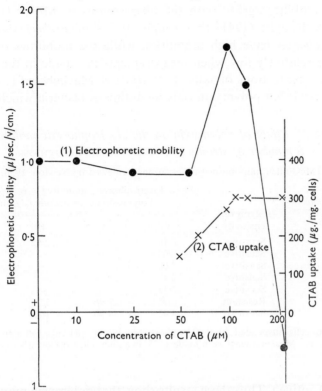

Fig. 3. Effect of CTAB concentration on (1) the electrophoretic mobility of *Staphylococcus aureus* and (2) the uptake of CTAB by *S. aureus*. (Data from McQuillen, 1950.)

Similar studies have been made of the effect of polymyxin on the electrophoretic mobility of a number of strains of *Pseudomonas aeruginosa* (McQuillen, unpublished observations, reviewed by Newton, 1956); it was found that in six of seven strains tested polymyxin did not cause a significant increase in electrophoretic mobility (Table 2). These results may be taken to indicate that polymyxin does not combine at the cell surface of these organisms although they absorb as much as 300 μg./mg. dry weight of cells. It is possible to calculate an approximate value for the minimum depth below the cell surface at which polymyxin could combine with components of the cell without affecting the surface charge (Mitchell, 1949); in a buffer of ionic strength [μ] 0·001, as used in these experiments, this would be c. 100 Å. In contrast to these results it was found that the electrophoretic mobility of one strain of

P. aeruginosa (strain 7 in Table 2) was markedly affected by polymyxin, and suspensions of the organism were agglutinated by the antibiotic. When plated, this organism was found to be 'rough' and its high electrophoretic mobility agreed with the observations of Moyer (1936) and Stearns & Roepke (1941) that rough strains of *Escherichia coli* and *Brucella abortus* have high mobilities, while the mobilities of smooth forms are relatively low when measurements are made in the presence of high concentrations of salts. Latterrade & Macheboeuf (1950) have also observed that polymyxin only agglutinates bacteria which lack the

Table 2. *Effect of polymyxin on the electrophoretic mobility of a number of strains of* Pseudomonas aeruginosa

(McQuillen, unpublished observations; reviewed by Newton, 1956)

Pseudomonas aeruginosa strain*	Polymyxin sensitivity	Electrophoretic mobility (μ/sec./v/cm.) Polymyxin concentration (μg./ml.)			
		0	1	10	100
1	Sensitive	2·10	2·13	2·12	2·06
2	Sensitive	2·03	—	—	1·92
3	Sensitive	2·00	—	—	1·86
4	Sensitive	2·18	—	—	1·97
5	Sensitive	2·18	—	—	1·98
6	Resistant	1·98	1·96	1·75	1·54
7	Sensitive	4·45	4·90	1·85	0·98

* Washed cells suspended in 0·003M-phosphate buffer, pH 7·0. Cell density=50 μg. dry wt. cells/ml. Measurements were made at 25° in a microelectrophoresis cell (McQuillen, 1950).

surface O antigen. Thus these results show that polymyxin may combine with sites at the bacterial cell surface when the right chemical groups are present, and that polymyxin molecules may penetrate to a depth of at least 100 Å below the cell surface.

Effect of non-ionic detergents on the bacterial cell surface. The dispersing action of low concentrations of Tween 80 (0·1 %) on tubercle bacilli growing in liquid media is almost certainly due to an alteration in the surface charge and/or structure of the organisms. A change in structure has not been demonstrated in the presence of these low concentrations but Bloch & Noll (1953) have shown that 2 % Tween 80 modifies the surface structures and reduces the virulence of tubercle bacilli. They demonstrated that under these conditions loss of virulence was associated with the removal of 'cord factor'—a lipid component of surface structures of virulent organisms—from the cells; 'cord factor' was detected in filtrates from cultures of virulent organisms grown in Tween 80 but not in its absence. Further evidence for the change in cell surface resulting from growth in Tween 80 has come from the work of Beguet (1952) who reported that the smooth form of *Serratia marcescens* is converted to a rough form when grown in peptone broth containing Tween 80.

Lovelock & Rees (1955) have shown that certain non-ionic poly-oxyethylene ethers may alter cell-surface structure although they are without effect on the growth of tubercle bacilli *in vitro*. Mackaness (1954) found partial or complete inhibition of growth of ingested bacilli in monocytes previously treated with Triton WR 1339, in contrast to the free intracellular multiplication in monocytes from untreated animals, which suggests that the non-ionic detergent can enter the monocyte *in vivo*. Lovelock & Rees (1955) elegantly demonstrated this penetration by the use of the dye Victoria Blue B 150, particles of which are readily soluble in polyoxyethylene ethers and can be phagocytosed by monocytes. Particles of dye ingested by monocytes from normal animals remained intact whereas those in monocytes from detergent-treated animals were readily dissolved, resulting in uniform coloration of the cell. These observations suggest that the monocyte plays an important part in the action of surface-active compounds in tuberculous infections but they do not explain the mechanism of growth inhibition of the tubercle bacillus within the monocyte. Hart & Rees (1955) consider that it is unlikely that these compounds are converted into antibacterial substances *in vivo* in view of their chemical stability and the fact that increasing the chain length produces a protuberculous effect; they suggest that the agents probably modify the surface of tubercle bacilli *in vivo* so that they become more sensitive to an intracellular environment. Indirect evidence in favour of this hypothesis has been obtained by Lovelock (1954) who found that treatment with polyoxyethylene ethers having chains of 10–20 ethylene oxide units decreased the sensitivity of red blood cells to thermal shock, those having 25–30 units had little or no effect, whilst those with 45–90 units/molecule markedly increased the sensitivity to haemolysis on cooling. Fig. 4 compares these effects with the antituberculous action of the compounds and shows a broad correlation between the two activities: agents which decrease the sensitivity of red cells to thermal shock are antituberculous, whilst those which increase it are protuberculous. The sensitivity of red cells to thermal shock is related to the ratio of cholesterol/phospholipid in the cell membrane; removal of lecithin increases haemolysis whilst removal of cholesterol decreases it (Lovelock, 1955). These findings led Hart & Rees (1955) to suggest that the polyoxyethylene ethers may act on tubercle bacilli in an analogous manner, as antituberculous agents displacing hydrophobic lipid components from the bacterial surface (an action which could conceivably render the cells more sensitive to digestion by monocyte enzymes) and as protuberculous agents displacing more hydrophilic lipids, thus rendering the bacteria more resistant and impermeable. In support of this view there is evidence that these non-ionic detergents modify the surface structures of tubercle bacilli growing *in vitro* although they do not have any antibacterial

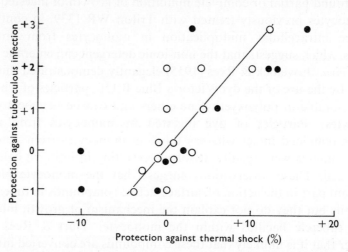

Fig. 4. Comparison of the effect of certain polyoxyethylene ethers upon the sensitivity of red blood cells to thermal shock *in vitro*, and upon a tuberculous infection in mice (●=linear polyoxyethylene ethers, and ○=macrocyclic compounds). Protection against thermal shock is measured by the percentage reduction in haemolysis from normal (+ =protection; 0=inactive; − =increased haemolysis). Protection against tuberculous infection is graded into +1, +2 or +3; 0=inactive; −1='protuberculous'. (Data from Lovelock & Rees, 1955.)

action; they promote dispersed growth in liquid media (Rees & Hart, 1952) and increase the rate at which organisms reduce methylene blue in the presence of glucose (Hart & Rees, 1955). Hart & Rees (1956) have also shown that repeated subculture of an avirulent strain of *Mycobacterium tuberculosis* in the presence of certain polyoxyethylene ethers results in a change from an amorphous growth form to a 'cord-forming' spreading type of colony the organisms of which are virulent.

Combination of surface-active compounds with isolated structures from bacterial cells. A second type of approach to the problem of locating the sites in bacterial cells which bind surface-active compounds has been to study the interaction of these compounds with isolated cell structures. This approach has only become possible since Dawson (1949) and Salton & Horne (1951) developed techniques for the isolation of bacterial cell walls in a highly purified state and since Tomcsik & Guex-Holzer (1952) and Weibull (1953) demonstrated that under suitably controlled osmotic conditions, it is possible to remove the cell wall of certain species of bacteria by lysozyme treatment and leave the rest of the cell as a spherical protoplast, an intact structural unit bounded by a lysozyme-resistant membrane. Salton (1957) tried to correlate the sensitivity of organisms to CTAB with the amount of this detergent bound by intact cells or isolated cell walls, and found none (Table 3).

Table 3. *A comparison of the maximum amounts of CTAB absorbed by bacterial cells and isolated cell walls*

(Data from Salton, 1951; 1957)

Organism	Sensitivity to CTAB (% killed in 5 min. by 45 μg. CTAB/ml.)	Absorption of CTAB (μg./mg. dry wt.)	
		Intact cells	Cell walls
Streptococcus faecalis	85	430	350
Staphylococcus aureus	50	320	150
Escherichia coli	31	420	385

In contrast to these results, marked differences have been found in the affinity for polymyxin of cell walls prepared from polymyxin-sensitive and polymyxin-resistant organisms. Few & Schulman (1953) and Newton (1954a) found that cell walls prepared from sensitive organisms absorb c. 5–6 times as much antibiotic as walls from resistant organisms (Fig. 5). Absorption of polymyxin by cell walls from sensitive organisms is accompanied by a marked increase in their electron density (Pl. 1); such a change was not observed when cell walls of polymyxin-resistant organisms were treated with the antibiotic. From a consideration of these results, Few & Schulman (1953) suggested that absorption of polymyxin takes place mainly at sites in the cell wall of bacteria with little penetration of the antibiotic into the cell. It must be emphasized, however, that the uptake of polymyxin by isolated bacterial cell walls may bear no relation to the amount absorbed by the cell walls when other cell components are present.

This question has been investigated by making use of a fluorescent derivative of polymyxin prepared by coupling 1-dimethylamino-naphthalene-5-sulphonyl chloride with the γ-amino groups of $\alpha\gamma$-di-aminobutyric acid residues in the polymyxin molecule (Newton, 1955). With limiting amounts of the sulphonyl compound the majority of the polymyxin molecules carried only one naphthalene group, and there was little loss in bactericidal activity. Fluorescence microscopy showed that this derivative of polymyxin was readily absorbed by polymyxin-sensitive bacteria in which it became associated with the boundary structures of the cells (Pl. 2). The distribution of fluorescent polymyxin in a number of organisms has been studied; cells were treated with a bactericidal concentration of the derivative and then disrupted by shaking and fractionated by differential centrifugation. More than 90 % of the fluorescent conjugate was associated with a small particle fraction

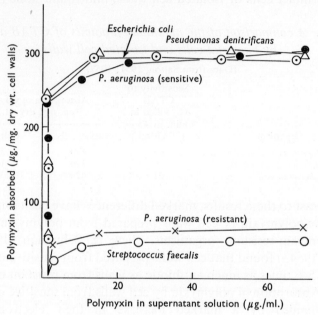

Fig. 5. Absorption of polymyxin by bacterial cell walls. Cell walls were incubated at 25° for 20 min. in 0·01 M-phosphate buffer (pH 6·3) containing polymyxin. (Data from Few & Schulman, 1953; Newton, 1954a.)

sedimented at 100,000 *g* and less than 10 % with the cell-wall fraction. When cell walls prepared from polymyxin-sensitive organisms were treated with fluorescent antibiotic they absorbed *c*. 300 μg./mg. dry-weight cell walls; this could not be removed by repeated washing with distilled water, but the addition of the small particle fraction prepared from untreated organisms resulted in more than 90 % being removed from the walls and taken up by the particles. Similar results were obtained when cells were fractionated after the walls had been removed by treatment with lysozyme. Fluorescence microscopy of antibiotic-treated cells before and after lysozyme treatment showed that the fluorescent compound was associated with the protoplast membrane; after mechanical or sonic disintegration of fluorescent protoplasts all the fluorescent compound was found to be associated with small particles which sedimented at 100,000 g. There is now considerable evidence to support the view that such small particles probably originate from a membrane which, in the intact cell, underlies the cell wall (Mitchell & Moyle, 1951; 1956a); if this is so it seems likely that polymyxin reacts specifically with some component of this membrane.

The chemical nature of detergent-binding sites in the bacterial cell. Data obtained from chemical studies of bacterial cell-wall preparations (reviewed by Cummins, 1956; Salton, 1956; Work, 1957) suggests that numerous acidic groups are present in the intact cell wall; these include the carboxyl groups of amino acids and amino sugars and the phosphate groups of phospholipid components. The net negative charge of bacterial cells demonstrated by microelectrophoresis techniques and the higher affinity of bacterial cells for cationic than anionic detergents support this view. Salton (1957) has suggested that the amount of a cationic surface-active agent absorbed by isolated bacterial cell walls is a reflexion of the number of negatively-charged groups and lipid molecules that can attract the positively-charged groups and hydrophobic portions of the surface-active molecules; the effect of pH on the absorption of CTAB by cell walls of staphylococci and *Escherichia coli* (Fig. 6) supports this view. In some cases it appears that the combination of a cationic detergent molecule with negatively charged groups of the cell is not a firm chemical combination; Salton (1957) has shown that CPC absorbed by cell walls of Gram-positive bacteria can be completely removed by repeated washing with distilled water. In contrast with these results, experiments with a fluorescent derivative of polymyxin (Newton, 1956, and above) suggest that this antibiotic is much more firmly bound to bacterial cell walls than is CPC.

It is now generally agreed that the cell wall and plasma membrane must be regarded as a unit in the intact cell; Mitchell & Moyle (1956b) have suggested that the cell wall of *Staphylococcus aureus* consists of a network of chains or fibres (with an effective pore diameter of $c.$ 1 mμ) with the plasma membrane, a close-packed lipoprotein sheet, immediately beneath, supported by the cell wall. If this is so, charged groups and lipid molecules of this membrane may play an important part in binding surface-active molecules to the cell. Some indication of the chemical nature of groups at the cell surface of *Pseudomonas aeruginosa* involved in binding polymyxin molecules was obtained from a study of the protection of organisms against the bactericidal action of this antibiotic by certain cations (Newton, 1953c; 1954b). This protective action of cations is not due to the formation of an inactive chelate between the ions and polymyxin but to a competition between them for sites on the bacterial cells, the cations preventing absorption of antibiotic by the cells. Certain cations are more effective than others, for example, the uranyl ion (UO_2^{++}) is effective at 1/5000th the concentration of other bivalent ions. It was found that a close relation existed between the

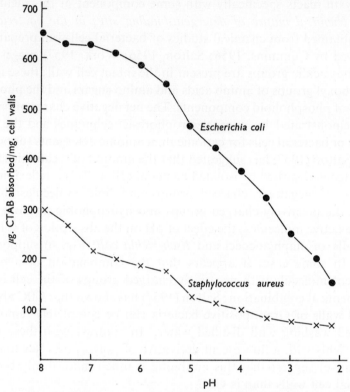

Fig. 6. The influence of pH value on the absorption of CTAB by cell walls of *Staphylococcus aureus* and *Escherichia coli*. Phosphate buffer (Na_2HPO_4-KH_2PO_4) was used over the pH range 8–5·8 and phosphate citrate buffer from pH 5·0–2·2. (Data from Salton, 1957.)

affinities of a number of cations for the polymyxin-combining sites of *P. aeruginosa* and the cation sequence worked out by De Jong (1949) for the reversal of charge on 'phosphate colloids'. These 'colloids' (e.g. soya bean phosphatides and egg lecithin) have ester phosphate as ionogenic groups, suggesting that the polymyxin-binding loci of the cell surface may be the phosphate groups of phospholipid. Further evidence of electrostatic bonding between polymyxin and ionized phosphate groups has been obtained by Few (1955) who found that cephalin and lipid extracted from *P. denitrificans* formed strong complexes with polymyxin; moderate complex formation also occurred with cardiolipin and lipid extracted from staphylococci, but lecithin did not react with the antibiotic. Discussing these results Few suggests that the positively-charged choline group of lecithin effectively shields the ionized phosphate group, thus preventing electrostatic bonding between the phosphate groups and amino groups of the polymyxin molecule. Analysis of the bacterial lipids showed that choline was not present in the nitrogenous constituents.

More recently Gilby & Few (1957) investigated the action of a number of detergents possessing a C_{12} n-alkyl chain on *Micrococcus lysodeikticus* and on protoplasts prepared from this organism. They found the same detergent reactivity sequence for bactericidal activity and for the lysis of protoplasts, suggesting a common site of action. This reactivity sequence, determined by the cationic group of the detergents, is as follows:

$$-NH_3^+ > -N(CH_3)_3^+ > -SO_4^- > -SO_3^-$$

and is the opposite of that reported for haemolysis by ionic detergents. Pethica & Schulman (1953) previously obtained evidence that cholesterol might be the site of attachment of ionic detergents to the red cell membrane; Gilby & Few argue that since a different reactivity sequence is obtained for protoplasts it is unlikely that membrane components of the sterol type, even if present, would constitute the site of attack in protoplasts. They detected the presence of phospholipids in the protoplast membrane of *M. lysodeikticus* by infrared spectroscopy and suggest that these would provide suitable ionic groups for electrostatic interaction with both anionic and cationic surface-active agents.

Disorganization of bacterial cells resulting from combination with surface-active agents

Effects on metabolism. Baker *et al.* (1941) found that cationic surface-active compounds inhibit the acid production and respiration of both Gram-positive and Gram-negative organisms; manometric studies showed that this action was rapid, inhibition usually being complete in less than 15 min. However, Sykes (1939), in an attempt to evaluate the relation between the effect of surface-active compounds on bacterial metabolism and on cell viability, concluded that, in general, viability is affected by concentrations lower than those which inhibit metabolism. Knox, Auerbach, Zarudnaya & Spirtes (1949) studied the action of several cationic compounds on *Escherichia coli* and found that loss of viability paralleled the inhibition of certain metabolic reactions of the cells, whilst other reactions persisted in the presence of lethal amounts of detergents. These effects of killing and inhibition were related to the detergent/bacterium ratio and not to the detergent concentration. Examination of the effect of cationic compounds on cell-free enzyme preparations led these workers to conclude that *E. coli* possesses certain detergent-sensitive enzymes, the inhibition of which would be sufficient to account for general metabolic inhibition and cell death. With polymyxin, Newton (1953*b*) found that a concentration three times the bactericidal concentration inhibited the endogenous respiration of washed cells of *Pseudomonas aeruginosa* and their ability to oxidize 2-ketogluconate, acetate, pyruvate, oxaloacetate and succinate. However, glucose was still oxidized with an oxygen uptake of two atoms/molecule of glucose, and 2-ketogluconate accumulated in the medium. Bactericidal concentrations of polymyxin doubled the rate of endogenous respiration of *P. aeruginosa* and did not inhibit the oxidation of glucose, acetate, pyruvate, oxaloacetate or succinate significantly. These findings are in agreement with the general observations of Sykes (1939) that viability is affected by concentrations of surface-active compounds lower than those which inhibit metabolism.

The stimulatory action of low concentrations of surface-active agents has been observed by a number of workers and explained in several ways. Surface-active compounds may inactivate an inhibitor already present, as in the acceleration of bacterial glutamic decarboxylase and glutaminase preparations by CTAB (Hughes, 1949). Alternatively, stimulation could be due to an alteration in cell permeability making substrates more readily available to enzymes, or to the death and lysis of a proportion of the bacterial population with a consequent increase in extracellular metabolites. Evidence to be described provides some support for the last two possibilities.

Effects on cell permeability. Schulman & Rideal (1937) showed the haemolysis of red blood cells by a number of synthetic surface-active compounds and in 1946 Hotchkiss suggested that these compounds might act in a similar manner against bacteria. To support this view he demonstrated the release into the suspending medium of nitrogenous and phosphorus-containing compounds from bacteria when they were treated with anionic or cationic surface-active compounds. This release of low molecular weight cell constituents by surface-active compounds has been confirmed by a number of investigators: Gale & Taylor (1947) showed that CTAB, Aerosol OT and tyrocidin all released amino acids from *Streptococcus faecalis* and Salton (1951) found that purines and pyrimidines, pentose and inorganic phosphate were released from Gram-positive and Gram-negative bacteria by CTAB. Newton (1953*a*) and

Few & Schulman (1953) demonstrated a leakage of materials absorbing at 260 mμ from polymyxin-sensitive bacteria treated with polymyxin, but not from polymyxin-resistant organisms. Postgate (1956) showed that treatment of *Desulphovibrio desulphuricans* with CTAB released cytochrome c_3, which has the highest molecular weight of any known to be released from detergent-treated bacteria. All these workers found that, below the concentration of detergent required for 99 % killing of a bacterial population, there is a quantitative relation between the amount of surface-active compound present, the proportion of cells killed and the quantity of soluble cell constituents released. This release of cell constituents is rapid and is equal in amount to the low molecular weight cell components which can be extracted from organisms by treatment with cold trichloroacetic acid (5 % w/v); thus autolytic breakdown of macromolecules would seem to contribute little to the initial leakage. Hotchkiss (1946) has suggested that autolytic breakdown of detergent-treated cells may occur as a secondary phenomenon and Salton (1951) found that the initial leakage process in *Staphylococcus aureus* treated with CTAB was followed by a slower release of cell constituents accompanied by a gradual change in the staining properties of the cells from Gram-positive to Gram-negative and a progressive decrease in the dry cell mass. A more rapid autolysis has been observed with strains of *Pseudomonas aeruginosa* treated with bactericidal concentrations of polymyxin (Newton, 1953a); the release of 260 mμ-absorbing materials is paralleled by a release of equimolecular amounts of pentose and phosphate, and has been correlated with the breakdown of cell ribonucleic acid. This breakdown does not occur at 2°, in the presence of concentrations of magnesium which inhibit ribonuclease (Lammanna & Malette, 1949) or in the presence of high concentrations of polymyxin (Fig. 7). High concentrations of polymyxin (Tai & van Heyningen, 1951) and of CTAB (Newton, 1953a) each inhibit autolytic mechanisms.

A more direct demonstration of the immediate change in cell permeability which occurs in the presence of polymyxin has been made possible by studying the penetration of a dye (*N*-tolyl-α-naphthylamine-8-sulphonic acid) into polymyxin-treated cells (Newton, 1954b). Aqueous solutions of this dye do not fluoresce when excited by ultraviolet light; in the presence of protein the dye combines with negatively-charged groups and the conjugate fluoresces strongly when excited by light of wavelength 436 mμ (Weber & Laurence, 1954). When washed cells of *Pseudomonas aeruginosa* were suspended in dilute solutions of this dye fluorescence was not seen, indicating that the dye could not combine

6

with any groups on the surface of the cells. The addition of polymyxin to such suspensions resulted in an immediate fluorescence because of an alteration in cell permeability that allowed the dye to penetrate to protein-containing portions of the cell.

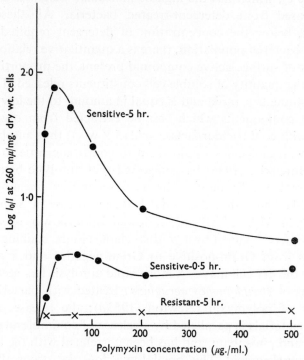

Fig. 7. Effect of polymyxin concentration on the release of 260 mμ-absorbing materials from a polymyxin-sensitive and a polymyxin-resistant strain of *Pseudomonas aeruginosa*. Cells were suspended in 1·0 % (w/v) saline + polymyxin at 30° and the absorption of the supernatant solution measured at 260 mμ after the times indicated. (Data from Newton, 1956.)

As already mentioned, there is some evidence that certain non-ionic surface-active compounds also alter the permeability of bacterial cells and increase the rate at which organisms reduce methylene blue in the presence of glucose (Hart & Rees, 1955).

Evidence for physical dissolution of cell structures by surface-active compounds. Henry & Stacey (1946) demonstrated that material believed to be involved in the Gram-staining reaction could be removed from Gram-positive bacteria by surface-active compounds such as bile salts and synthetic detergents. More recently Salton (1957) studied the action of surface-active compounds on purified preparations of bacterial cell walls and found that the mucocomplex of the cell walls of Gram-positive bacteria was stable to high concentrations of both anionic and cationic detergents. The cell walls of *Staphylococcus aureus*, *Strepto-coccus faecalis*, *Sarcina lutea* and *Bacillus megaterium* were all in-soluble in 2 % solutions of CTAB, CPC, Aerosol OT, sodium lauryl sulphate and sodium dodecyl sulphate at 37°. In contrast the cell walls of the Gram-negative organisms *Escherichia coli* and *Rhodospirillum*

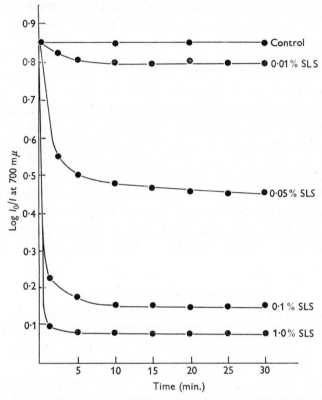

Fig. 8. Lysis of *Escherichia coli* cell walls by sodium lauryl sulphate (SLS) in phosphate buffer (ionic strength $\mu = 0.1$, pH 7·0) at 37°. (Data from Salton, 1957.)

rubrum were rapidly dissolved in the anionic compounds, sodium lauryl sulphate, sodium dodecyl sulphate and Teepol with a resulting decrease in turbidity. The shape of the curves obtained with different concentrations of sodium lauryl sulphate (Fig. 8) indicates clearly that this is due to the surface-active properties of the compound rather than the action of autolytic enzymes.

Morphological changes in bacterial cells following treatment with surface-active compounds. Electron microscope studies (Mitchell & Crowe, 1947; Salton, Horne & Coslett, 1951; Chaplin, 1952) have

6-2

shown that detergent-treated cells do not undergo complete lysis, but an alteration in the surface structures of cells has been detected. Similar effects have been observed for cells treated with polymyxin (Newton, 1953a). Minami (1957) observed the formation of 'electron-transparent areas' just inside the cell wall of tubercle bacilli which had been treated with oleate or linoleate; the concentration used (10^{-3}M) was, however, considerably higher than the bactericidal level and electron-transparent areas could not be detected in organisms treated with lower concentrations of the fatty acids.

A visual change in the properties of the bacterial protoplast membrane following treatment with surface-active compounds was demonstrated by Newton (1955) and Tomcsik (1955). When *Micrococcus lysodeikticus* was treated with a bactericidal concentration of a synthetic detergent or of polymyxin before treatment with lysozyme, both phase and electron microscopy showed that the normal transformation to spherical protoplasts did not occur; the protoplast membrane was fixed in a cubical or rod-shaped form (Pl. 3). Protoplasts from cells which had been pretreated with a surface-active compound differed from those obtained from untreated cells in that they were no longer sensitive to osmotic shock, suggesting that a marked change in the physico-chemical properties of the protoplast membrane had occurred.

Resistance and selective activity

Any theory for the mode of action of an antibacterial agent should provide an adequate explanation of the phenomena of developed resistance and the selective activity of the agent, but little is known of these phenomena in relation to surface-active agents.

Developed resistance. There have been few reports of organisms developing resistance against surface-active compounds. This is hardly surprising in view of the rapid disorganization of cell permeability barriers which these compounds appear to produce; a profound change in the cell surface seems to be an essential for the acquisition of such resistance. This view receives some support from the observations of Chaplin (1951, 1952) who found that *Serratia marcescens* can acquire some resistance to the action of alkyldimethylbenzylammonium chloride (ADAC). Growth of this organism was normally suppressed by 50 μg. ADAC/ml., but eight serial transfers in increasing concentrations of the drug resulted in a resistance to 10 mg./ml., a resistance which was rapidly lost on subculture in a drug-free medium. Chaplin found that the development of resistance was accompanied by a decrease in the electrophoretic mobility of organisms and an increase in their content of ether/alcohol-soluble material; resistant organisms treated with lipase immediately lost their resistance. Thus it appears that *S. marcescens* grown in sublethal amounts of ADAC can synthesize a protective surface layer of lipid or lipoprotein. Fischer & Larose (1952) confirmed the results of Chaplin (1951) and found, in addition, that the development of resistance was greatly influenced by pH value; maximum resistance was acquired in a medium of pH 6·8, whilst less resistance was developed at pH 7·7.

In the literature there are only two reports of bacteria developing resistance against surface-active polypeptide antibiotics. Szybalski & Bryson (1952), by the gradient plate technique, increased the resistance of *Escherichia coli* to polymyxin approximately 20-fold. Polymyxin and circulin produced an almost reciprocal resistance to each other and strains of *E. coli* resistant to both antibiotics exhibited a 2–6-fold increase in resistance to streptomycin and neomycin, but the reverse relation did not hold true. Haas & Sevag (1953) found that the sensitivity of strains of *Aerobacter aerogenes* and *Pseudomonas aeruginosa* to polymyxin is influenced by the amino acid and carbohydrate content of the growth medium; the development of resistance was much more rapid in a salts-glucose medium than in casein hydrolysate. Neither group of workers examined the lipid content of the resistant strains which, in view of Chaplin's (1951) results, would have been of interest.

Selective activity. The selective action of anionic detergents against Gram-positive bacteria and the effect of pH value on this selectivity have already been mentioned. A much greater selectivity of action is shown by the surface-active polypeptide antibiotics tyrocidin, gramicidin S and polymyxin. In general Gram-positive bacteria are more sensitive to tyrocidin but less sensitive to polymyxin than are Gram-negative organisms. Gramicidin S lies between the two, being rather more active against Gram-negative organisms than tyrocidin. Studies of the absorption of polymyxin by cell walls prepared from polymyxin-sensitive or polymyxin-resistant organisms suggest that this resistance may depend to some extent on the chemical composition and structure of the cell wall; the cell wall of resistant organisms has a low affinity for the antibiotic and as a consequence there may be little penetration of polymyxin to the underlying plasma membrane. From the results already described a difference in the phospholipid content of the cell walls of polymyxin-sensitive and polymyxin-resistant organisms might be expected, but at the present time little information is available on this point. Few (1955) and Newton (1956) compared the lipid content of cell walls prepared from four organisms, two polymyxin-sensitive and two polymyxin-resistant; lipid from the former had a P/N atomic ratio of $c.$ 1·75, a value typical of many phosphatides, whereas lipid from the latter contained phosphorus and nitrogen in approximately equimolecular amounts, suggesting that less than 50 % of these lipids were phosphatides. With these results in mind it is interesting that Mitchell & Moyle (1954) should find that Gram-negative organisms contain twice as much lipid phosphorus as Gram-positive organisms. The higher sensitivity of Gram-negative organisms to polymyxin may be related to their high lipid phosphorus content.

An alternative explanation for the selective activity of polymyxin has been proposed by Rhodes, Vila & Ferlauto (1953), who found that magnesium ribonucleate antagonized the action of polymyxin; they suggested that the magnesium ribonucleate content of Gram-positive organisms (Henry & Stacey, 1946) may contribute to the selective activity of the antibiotic, but there seems to be little experimental evidence in support of this view. Few (1957) has proposed that an additional factor contributing to the selective activity of polymyxin may be the number of basic groups attached to the cyclic peptide; polymyxin B contains four free amino groups whereas gramicidin contains two and tyrocidin only one. The high phospholipid content of Gram-negative organisms would perhaps favour reaction with the polybasic polymyxin, and the Gram-positive organisms, which have a low lipid-phosphorus content would react strongly with tyrocidin.

THEORIES AND SPECULATIONS

The experimental data summarized leave little doubt that the treatment of bacteria with certain anionic or cationic surface-active compounds results in a rapid disorganization of a membrane or structure which normally controls the osmotic equilibrium of the cells; this finding is in agreement with the original hypothesis of Baker et al. (1941) and provides an adequate explanation for the bactericidal activity of surface-active compounds. There is, however, at least one question which cannot be answered from the experimental results available: is the primary action of surface-active compounds a physical disorganization of the plasma membrane of bacteria or is the observed change in cell permeability a secondary phenomenon? Disorganization of the membrane could be the result of a decrease in interfacial tension produced by the surface-active agents combining with lipid components of the membrane, but other possibilities must be considered. It has long been known that surface-active compounds have the property of dissolving, dissociating and denaturing macromolecules: the prosthetic group of enzymes may be dissociated from the protein component (Kuhn & Dann, 1940), both plant and animal virus nucleoproteins can be split into nucleic acid and protein (Bawden & Pirie, 1938; Shedlovsky & Smadel, 1940) and proteins themselves are readily denatured by surface-active compounds (Putnam, 1948). Any one of these actions could account for the bactericidal activity of these agents.

In considering the possibility of denaturation of enzyme protein as the primary action of these compounds, Hotchkiss (1946) pointed out that the concentrations of detergent required to denature most soluble proteins are considerably higher than those necessary for killing bacteria. It can be argued, however, that certain enzymes may have a higher sensitivity to surface-active compounds than most other proteins of the bacterial cell; Knox et al. (1949) obtained some evidence in support of this view and suggested that the specific inhibition of a detergent-sensitive enzyme could account for cell death, with increased permeability as a secondary phenomenon. It has been argued that inhibition of intracellular enzymes is unlikely to be the primary action of ionic surface-active compounds as this would involve their penetration through the cell membrane, and, in the opinion of Hotchkiss (1946), the usual synthetic surface-active agents would not enter the cell while it was alive. This, however, does not rule out the possibility of enzyme inhibition as the primary action of surface-active agents, since it is now known that enzymes may be associated with the surface structures of micro-organisms. Rothstein & Meier (1948) and Demis, Rothstein & Meier (1954) have demonstrated that certain phosphatases and invertase are located on the surface of the yeast cell. Mitchell & Moyle (1956a) showed that some 90 % of the lactic, malic, formic and succinic dehydrogenases, acid phosphatase and the cytochrome system of Staphylococcus aureus was in or in close association with the protoplast membrane of this organism, and Monod (1956) presented evidence for a specific adaptive enzyme, responsible for the transport of lactose into cells of Escherichia coli, which might be closely associated with the cell membrane. Salton (1951), discussing the mechanism of action of CTAB, suggested that

it is not necessary to invoke the inhibition of a detergent-sensitive enzyme as being the primary cause of cell death. Indeed, if there were a chain of reactions initiated by a primary metabolic inhibition, a greater time lag before the observation of secondary effects, such as the release of cell constituents, might well be expected.

This argument would almost certainly hold true for the inhibition of most enzymes involved in cell metabolism, but it might not hold for the inhibition of enzymes involved in the maintenance of the protoplast membrane. There is little or nothing known about this aspect of bacterial metabolism, but recent studies with red blood cells have shown that the average life of a lipid molecule in the cell membrane is considerably less than the lifetime of the cell (Altman, 1953) and investigations on the haemolytic action of anionic detergents led Rideal & Taylor (1957) to conclude that 'the red cell membrane is not static but is maintained by a series of dynamic equilibria'. In my opinion it seems more than likely that the bacterial protoplast membrane is also a dynamic system, and the possibility that some surface-active bactericides may act by inhibiting enzymes involved in the maintenance of this membrane rather than disorganizing it by physical means cannot, at the present time, be eliminated.

Contributors to this Symposium were asked to speculate concerning the future development and exploitation of the material forming the subject of their particular section. Although the recent work on the polyoxyethylene ethers has raised hope for the future development of non-ionic surface-active agents, it seems unlikely, from what we know of the mode of action of ionic surface-active bactericides, that any highly selective cytotoxic compounds of this type will be developed. Although the majority of these compounds are valuable disinfectants, they are of little chemotherapeutic value. Since the major problem of chemotherapy is not the discovery of especially potent antibacterial agents, but rather the discovery of selective toxic compounds inhibitory to micro-organisms in the body at concentrations tolerated by the host, it may be wondered why surface-active bactericides warrant such detailed discussion in a symposium on the strategy of chemotherapy. However, since the majority of antibacterial agents depend for their activity upon their ability to penetrate into the bacterial cell, knowledge of the chemical nature of the bacterial surface and of the physico-chemical factors which control the permeability of bacterial cells is as important to a rational approach to chemotherapy as knowledge of bacterial nutrition and metabolism. Studies of the mode of action of surface-active bactericides have already yielded information about the bacterial surface and have led to more detailed studies of the structures controlling cell permeability; this information may be of value in the design of chemotherapeutic agents of a different type. The design of a new chemotherapeutic agent may possibly involve the introduction of special chemical groupings into the molecule to assist permeation, and knowledge gained from studies of the relations between chemical structure and antibacterial activity of surface-active compounds would thus be of value.

REFERENCES

ALTMAN, K. I. (1953). The *in vitro* incorporation of α-C^{14} acetate into the stroma of the erythrocyte. *Arch. Biochem. Biophys.* **42**, 478.

BAKER, Z., HARRISON, R. W. & MILLER, B. F. (1941). The bactericidal action of synthetic detergents. *J. exp. Med.* **74**, 611.

BATTERSBY, A. R. & CRAIG, L. C. (1951). The molecular weight determination of polypeptides. *J. Amer. chem. Soc.* **73**, 1887.

BAWDEN, F. C. & PIRIE, N. W. (1938). Liquid crystalline preparations of potato virus 'X'. *Brit. J. exp. Path.* **19**, 66.

BEGUET, M. (1952). Variations provoquées, transitoires ou durables de types microbiens. Etude faite sur *B. prodigiosus*. *C.R. Soc. Biol., Paris*, **146**, 820.

BLISS, E. A., CHANDLER, C. A. & SCHOENBACH, E. B. (1949). *In vitro* studies of polymyxin. *Ann. N.Y. Acad. Sci.* **51**, 944.

BLOCH, H. & NOLL, H. (1953). Studies on the virulence of tubercle bacilli. Variation in virulence effected by Tween 80 and thiosemicarbazone. *J. exp. Med.* **97**, 1.

BRICAS, E. & FROMAGEOT, C. (1953). Naturally occurring peptides. *Advanc. Protein Chem.* **8**, 1.

CHAPLIN, C. E. (1951). Observations on quaternary ammonium disinfectants. *Canad. J. Bot.* **29**, 373.

CHAPLIN, C. E. (1952). Cytological changes in *Bacillus* species in stasis and death by quaternary ammonium compounds. *J. Bact.* **64**, 805.

CONSDEN, R., GORDON, A. H., MARTIN, A. J. P. & SYNGE, R. L. M. (1947). Gramicidin S: the sequence of the amino-acid residues. *Biochem. J.* **41**, 596.

CORNFORTH, J. W., HART, P. D'A., NICHOLLS, G. A., REES, R. J. W. & STOCK, J. A. (1955). Antituberculous effects of certain surface-active polyoxyethylene ethers. *Brit. J. Pharmacol.* **10**, 73.

CORNFORTH, J. W., HART, P. D'A., REES, R. J. W. & STOCK, J. A. (1951). Antituberculous effect of certain surface-active polyoxyethylene ethers in mice. *Nature, Lond.* **168**, 150.

CUMMINS, C. S. (1956). The chemical composition of the bacterial cell wall. *Int. Rev. Cytol.* **5**, 25.

DAMODARAN, M. & SIVARAMAN, C. (1953). The germicidal activity of some pyridinium salts containing unsaturated hydrocarbon radicals. *J. Bact.* **65**, 89.

DAUTREVAUX, M. & BISERTE, G. (1957). Séquence peptidique de la polymyxine B. *Bull. Soc. Chim. biol., Paris*, **39**, 353.

DAVIS, B. D. & DUBOS, R. J. (1946). Interaction of serum albumin, free and esterified oleic acid and lipase in relation to cultivation of the tubercle bacillus. *Arch. Biochem.* **11**, 201.

DAVIS, B. D. & DUBOS, R. J. (1947). The binding of fatty acids by serum albumin, a protective growth factor in bacteriological media. *J. exp. Med.* **86**, 215.

DAWSON, I. M. (1949). Discussion in *The Nature of the Bacterial Surface*. *Symp. Soc. gen. Microbiol.* **1**, 119.

DE JONG, H. G. B. (1949). Reversal of charge phenomena, equivalent weight and specific properties of the ionized groups. In *Colloid Science*, **2**, 259. Edited by H. R. Kruyt. London: Elsevier.

DEMIS, D. J., ROTHSTEIN, A. & MEIER, R. (1954). The relationship of the cell surface to metabolism. 10. The location and function of invertase in the yeast cell. *Arch. Biochem. Biophys.* **48**, 55.

DOMAGK, G. (1935). Eine neue Klasse von Desinfektionsmitteln. *Dtsch. med. Wschr.* **61**, 829.

DUBOS, R. J. (1947). The effect of lipids and serum albumin on bacterial growth. *J. exp. Med.* **85**, 9.

DUBOS, R. J. & DAVIS, B. D. (1946). Factors affecting the growth of tubercle bacilli in liquid media. *J. exp. Med.* **83**, 409.

DYAR, M. T. & ORDAL, E. J. (1946). Electrokinetic studies on bacterial surfaces. I. The effects of surface-active agents on the electrophoretic mobilities of bacteria. *J. Bact.* **51**, 149.

ERLANGER, B. F. & GOODE, L. (1954). Gramicidin S: relationship of cyclic structure to antibiotic activity. *Nature, Lond.* **174**, 840.

ERLANGER, B. F., SACHS, H. & BRAND, E. (1954). The synthesis of peptides related to gramicidin S. *J. Amer. chem. Soc.* **76**, 1806.

FEW, A. V. (1955). The interaction of polymyxin E with bacterial and other lipids. *Biochim. biophys. Acta*, **16**, 137.

FEW, A. V. (1957). Structure in relation to surface and biological properties of cyclic decapeptide antibiotics. *Proc. 2nd Int. Congr. Surface Activity*, p. 168. London: Butterworth.

FEW, A. V. & SCHULMAN, J. H. (1953). The absorption of polymyxin E by bacteria and bacterial cell walls and its bactericidal action. *J. gen. Microbiol.* **9**, 454.

FISCHER, R. & LAROSE, P. (1952). Factors governing the adaptation of bacteria against quaternaries. *Nature, Lond.* **170**, 715.

GALE, E. F. & TAYLOR, E. S. (1947). The assimilation of amino-acids by bacteria. 2. The action of tyrocidin and some detergent substances in releasing amino-acids from the internal environment of *Streptococcus faecalis*. *J. gen. Microbiol.* **1**, 77.

GAUSE, G. F. & BRAZHNIKOVA, M. G. (1944). Gramicidin S. Origin and mode of action. *Lancet*, ii, 715.

GILBY, A. R. & FEW, A. V. (1957). Reactivity of ionic detergents with *Micrococcus lysodeikticus*. *Nature, Lond.* **179**, 422.

GLASSMAN, H. N. (1948). Surface-active agents and their application in bacteriology. *Bact. Rev.* **12**, 105.

GOLDSMITH, H. A. (1943). Polyhydric alcohol esters of fatty acids: their preparation, properties and uses. *Chem. Rev.* **33**, 257.

HAAS, G. J. & SEVAG, M. G. (1953). Critical role of amino acids on the sensitivity and development of resistance to polymyxin B. *Arch. Biochem. Biophys.* **43**, 11.

HARRIS, J. I. & WORK, T. S. (1950). The synthesis of peptides related to gramicidin S and the significance of optical configuration in antibiotic peptides. 2. Pentapeptides. *Biochem. J.* **46**, 582.

HART, P. D'A. & REES, R. J. W. (1955). Influence of certain surface-active agents on the host-parasite relationship in experimental tuberculosis. In *CIBA Foundation Symposium on Experimental Tuberculosis. Bacillus and host.* With an addendum on leprosy, p. 299. Edited by G. E. W. Wolstenholme, M. P. Cameron & C. M. O'Connor. London: Churchill.

HART, P. D'A. & REES, R. J. W. (1956). Induction of virulence in an avirulent strain of *Mycobacterium tuberculosis* by certain non-ionic surface-active agents. *Brit. J. exp. Path.* **37**, 372.

HENRY, H. & STACEY, M. (1946). Histochemistry of the Gram-staining reaction for micro-organisms. *Proc. roy. Soc.* B, **133**, 391.

HODGKIN, D. C. (1950). X-ray analysis and protein structure. *Cold Spr. Harb. Symp. quant. Biol.* **14**, 65.

HOTCHKISS, R. D. (1944). Gramicidin, tyrocidine and tyrothricin. *Advanc. Enzymol.* **4**, 153.

HOTCHKISS, R. D. (1946). The nature of the bactericidal action of surface active agents. *Ann. N.Y. Acad. Sci.* **46**, 479.

HUGHES, D. E. (1949). Acceleration of bacterial glutamic decarboxylase and glutaminase by cetyltrimethylammonium bromide. *Biochem. J.* **45**, 325.

JACOBS, W. A. (1916). The bactericidal properties of the quaternary salts of hexamethylenetetramine. The problem of the chemotherapy of experimental bacterial infections. *J. exp. Med.* **23**, 563.

KAGAN, B. M., KREVSKY, D., MILZER, A. & LOCKE, M. (1951). Polymyxin B and polymyxin E, clinical and laboratory studies. *J. Lab. clin. Med.* **37**, 402.

KNOX, W. E., AUERBACH, V. H., ZARUDNAYA, K. & SPIRTES, M. (1949). The action of cationic detergents on bacteria and bacterial enzymes. *J. Bact.* **58**, 443.

KODICEK, E. (1949). The effect of unsaturated fatty acids on Gram-positive bacteria. In *Selective Toxicity and Antibiotics. Symp. Soc. exp. Biol.* **3**, 217.

KUHN, R. & DANN, O. (1940). Über Invertseifen. II. Butyl-, Octyl-, Lauryl- und Cetyl-dimethyl-sulfoniumjodid. *Ber. Dtsch. chem. Ges.* **73**, 1092.

LAMMANNA, C. & MALETTE, M. F. (1949). Magnesium ion, an inhibitor of ribonuclease activity. *Arch. Biochem.* **24**, 451.

LATTERRADE, C. & MACHEBOEUF, M. (1950). Recherches biochimiques sur le mode d'action de la polymyxine. *Ann. Inst. Pasteur*, **78**, 753.

LOVELOCK, J. E. (1954). Physical instability and thermal shock in red cells. *Nature, Lond.* **173**, 659.

LOVELOCK, J. E. (1955). Haemolysis by thermal shock. *Brit. J. Haematol.* **1**, 117.

LOVELOCK, J. E. & REES, R. J. W. (1955). Possible site and mode of action of certain lipotropic macromolecules in tuberculosis. *Nature, Lond.* **175**, 161.

LUZZATI, D. (1953). Action des agents tensioactifs sur le bacille de Koch: le Tween 80. *Ann. Inst. Pasteur*, **85**, 277.

MACKANESS, G. B. (1954). Artificial cellular immunity against tubercle bacilli. An effect of polyoxyethylene ethers (Triton). *Amer. Rev. Tuberc.* **69**, 690.

MCQUILLEN, K. (1950). The bacterial surface. I. Effect of cetyltrimethyl-ammonium bromide on the electrophoretic mobility of certain Gram-positive bacteria. *Biochim. biophys. Acta*, **5**, 463.

MINAMI, K. (1957). Bactericidal action of oleic acid for tubercle bacilli. II. Morphological response. *J. Bact.* **73**, 345.

MINAMI, K., YAMANE, I. & YASUI, T. (1954). Tween 80 as a metabolite for tubercle bacilli. 1. On the metabolism of Tween 80 with the resting cells of tubercle bacilli. *Fukushima J. Med. Sci.* **1**, 95.

MITCHELL, P. (1949). The osmotic barrier in bacteria. In *The Nature of the Bacterial Surface. Symp. Soc. gen. Microbiol.* **1**, 55.

MITCHELL, P. & MOYLE, J. (1951). The glycerophospho-protein complex envelope of *Micrococcus pyogenes*. *J. gen. Microbiol.* **5**, 981.

MITCHELL, P. & MOYLE, J. (1954). The Gram reaction and cell composition: nucleic acids and other phosphate fractions. *J. gen. Microbiol.* **10**, 533.

MITCHELL, P. & MOYLE, J. (1956a). The cytochrome system in the plasma membrane of *Staphylococcus aureus*. *Biochem. J.* **64**, 19P.

MITCHELL, P. & MOYLE, J. (1956b). Osmotic function and structure in bacteria. In *Bacterial Anatomy. Symp. Soc. gen. Microbiol.* **6**, 150.

MITCHELL, P. D. & CROWE, G. R. (1947). A note on electron micrographs of normal and tyrocidin-lysed streptococci. *J. gen. Microbiol.* **1**, 85.

MONOD, J. (1956). Remarks on the mechanism of enzyme induction. In *Enzymes: Units of Biological Structure and Function. Henry Ford Hosp. Symp.* **4**, 7.

MOYER, L. S. (1936). Changes in the electrokinetic potential of bacteria at various phases of the culture cycle. *J. Bact.* **32**, 433.

NEWTON, B. A. (1953 a). The release of soluble constituents from washed cells of *Pseudomonas aeruginosa* by the action of polymyxin. *J. gen. Microbiol.* **9**, 54.

NEWTON, B. A. (1953 b). The action of polymyxin on *Pseudomonas pyocyanea*. *J. gen. Microbiol.* **8**, vi.

NEWTON, B. A. (1953 c). Reversal of the antibacterial activity of polymyxin by divalent cations. *Nature, Lond.* **172**, 160.

NEWTON, B. A. (1954 a). The absorption of polymyxin by cell-wall preparations from *Pseudomonas aeruginosa*. *J. gen. Microbiol.* **10**, iii.

NEWTON, B. A. (1954 b). Site of action of polymyxin on *Pseudomonas aeruginosa*: antagonism by cations. *J. gen. Microbiol.* **10**, 491.

NEWTON, B. A. (1955). A fluorescent derivative of polymyxin: its preparation and use in studying the site of action of the antibiotic. *J. gen. Microbiol.* **12**, 226.

NEWTON, B. A. (1956). The properties and mode of action of the polymyxins. *Bact. Rev.* **20**, 14.

PETHICA, B. A. & SCHULMAN, J. H. (1953). The physical chemistry of haemolysis by surface-active agents. *Biochem. J.* **53**, 177.

POLLOCK, M. R. (1949). The effects of long chain fatty acids on the growth of *Haemophilus pertussis* and other organisms. In *Selective Toxicity and Antibiotics. Symp. Soc. exp. Biol.* **3**, 193.

POSTGATE, J. R. (1956). Cytochrome c_3 and desulphoviridin; pigments of the anaerobe *Desulphovibrio desulphuricans*. *J. gen. Microbiol.* **14**, 545.

PRICE, D. (1946). Certain aspects of the chemistry of surface-active agents. *Ann. N.Y. Acad. Sci.* **46**, 407.

PUTNAM, F. W. (1948). The interactions of proteins and synthetic detergents. *Advanc. Protein Chem.* **4**, 79.

REES, R. J. W. (1953). Antituberculous activity of certain non-ionic detergents. *Proc. R. Soc. Med.* **46**, 581.

REES, R. J. W. & HART, P. D'A. (1952). The inhibition of growth of avirulent strains of *Mycobacterium tuberculosis* by a surface-active polyoxyethylene ether. *J. gen. Microbiol.* **7**, 372.

RHODES, R. E., VILA, O. A. & FERLAUTO, R. J. (1953). The nature of polymyxin activity against a Gram-positive organism. *Antibiot. Chemother.*, **3**, 509.

RIDEAL, E. & TAYLOR, F. H. (1957). On haemolysis by anionic detergents. *Proc. roy. Soc.* B, **146**, 225.

ROTHSTEIN, A. & MEIER, R. (1948). The relationship of the cell surface to metabolism. I. Phosphatases in the cell surface of living yeast cells. *J. cell. comp. Physiol.* **32**, 77.

SALTON, M. R. J. (1951). The absorption of cetyltrimethylammonium bromide by bacteria, its action in releasing cellular constituents and its bactericidal effects. *J. gen. Microbiol.* **5**, 391.

SALTON, M. R. J. (1956). Bacterial cell walls. In *Bacterial Anatomy. Symp. Soc. gen. Microbiol.* **6**, 81.

SALTON, M. R. J. (1957). The action of lytic agents on the surface structures of the bacterial cell. *Proc. 2nd Int. Congr. Surface Activity*, p. 274. London: Butterworth.

SALTON, M. R. J. & HORNE, R. W. (1951). Studies of the bacterial cell wall. 2. Methods of preparation and some properties of cell walls. *Biochim. biophys. Acta*, **7**, 177.

SALTON, M. R. J., HORNE, R. W. & COSLETT, V. E. (1951). Electron microscopy of bacteria treated with cetyltrimethylammonium bromide. *J. gen. Microbiol.* **5**, 405.

SANGER, F. (1946). The free amino group of gramicidin S. *Biochem. J.* **40**, 261.

SCALES, F. M. & KEMP, M. (1941). A new group of sterilizing agents for the food industries and a treatment for chronic mastitis. *Bull. int. Ass. Milk Deal.* **33**, 491.

PLATE 1

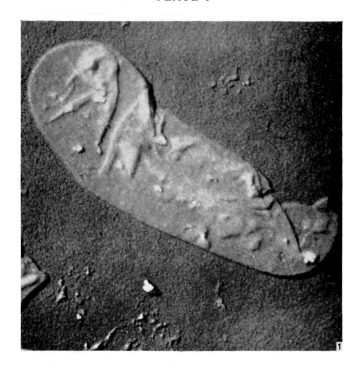

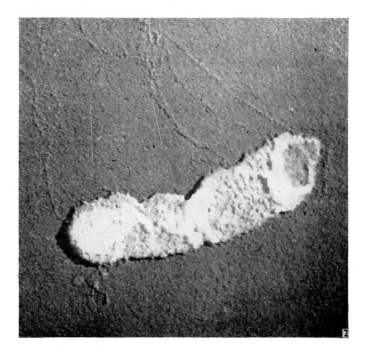

PLATE 2

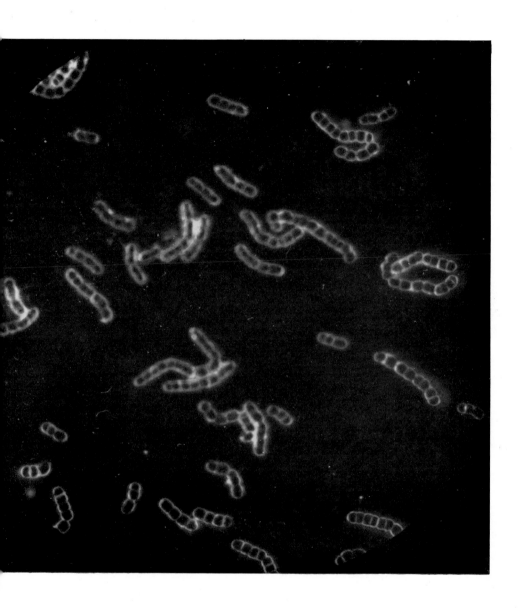

PLATE 3

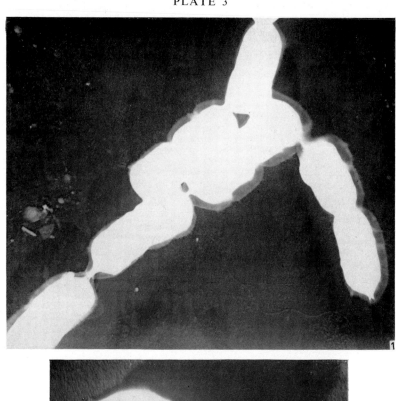

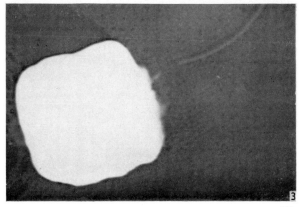

(*Facing p.* 93)

SCHULMAN, J. H. & RIDEAL, E. K. (1937). Molecular interaction in monolayers. 1. Complexes between large molecules. *Proc. roy. Soc.* B, **122**, 29.

SEXTON, W. A. (1953). *Chemical Constitution and Biological Activity*, 2nd ed. London: Spon.

SHEDLOVSKY, T. & SMADEL, J. E. (1940). Electrophoretic studies on elementary bodies of vaccinia. *J. exp. Med.* **72**, 511.

STEARNS, T. W. & ROEPKE, M. H. (1941). The effect of dissociation on the electro-phoretic mobility of brucella. *J. Bact.* **42**, 745.

SWIFT, P. N. & BUSHBY, S. R. M. (1951). *Haemophilus influenzae* meningitis treated with polymyxin. *Lancet*, ii, 183.

SYKES, G. (1939). The influence of germicides on the dehydrogenases of *Bact. coli.* Part I. The succinic acid dehydrogenase of *Bact. coli. J. Hyg., Camb.* **39**, 463.

SZYBALSKI, W. & BRYSON, V. (1952). Genetic studies on microbial cross resistance to toxic agents. I. Cross resistance of *Escherichia coli* to fifteen antibiotics. *J. Bact.* **64**, 489.

TAI, T. Y. & VAN HEYNINGEN, W. E. (1951). Bacteriolysis by a species of *Streptomyces. J. gen. Microbiol.* **5**, 110.

TOMCSIK, J. (1955). Effect of disinfectants and of surface-active agents on bacterial protoplasts. *Proc. Soc. exp. Biol., N.Y.* **89**, 459.

TOMCSIK, J. & GUEX-HOLZER, S. (1952). Änderung der Struktur der Bakterienzelle im verlauf der Lysozym-einwirkung. *Schweiz. Z. allg. Path.* **15**, 517.

VALKO, E. I. & DuBOIS, A. S. (1944). The antibacterial action of surface-active cations. *J. Bact.* **47**, 15.

WEBER, G. & LAURENCE, D. J. R. (1954). Fluorescent indicators of adsorption in aqueous solution and on the solid phase. *Biochem. J.* **56**, xxxi.

WEIBULL, C. (1953). The isolation of protoplasts from *Bacillus megaterium* by controlled treatment with lysozyme. *J. Bact.* **66**, 688.

WORK, E. (1957). Biochemistry of the bacterial cell wall. *Nature, Lond.* **179**, 841.

WORK, T. S. & WORK, E. (1948). *The Basis of Chemotherapy*. London: Oliver & Boyd.

EXPLANATION OF PLATE

PLATE 1

Effect of polymyxin on cell walls prepared from *Pseudomonas aeruginosa*. Fig. 1, untreated walls. Fig. 2, cell walls after treatment with 200 μg. polymyxin/mg. dry wt. cell walls. × 53,000.

PLATE 2

Fluorescence photomicrograph of *Bacillus megaterium* treated with 25 μg. 1-dimethyl-aminonaphthalene-5-sulphonamido-polymyxin/mg. dry wt. cells. × 1500.

PLATE 3

Fig. 1. Washed cells of *Bacillus megaterium*. × 18,000.
Fig. 2. Protoplast prepared from *Bacillus megaterium* by controlled lysozyme treatment; preparation fixed with mercuric chloride and formalin. × 38,500.
Fig. 3. Subcellular unit obtained by lysozyme treatment of *Bacillus megaterium* which had been pretreated with a bactericidal concentration of polymyxin; preparation not fixed. Lysis did not result on repeated washing with distilled water. × 38,500.

MEMBRANE PENETRATION AND THE THERAPEUTIC VALUE OF CHEMICALS

P. MITCHELL

Zoology Department, University of Edinburgh

The effectiveness of chemicals for the selective destruction of the parasites of man depends upon features of the tissues of man and parasite that may be visualized in two ranges of dimensions: first, the structural features of the tissues that determine the distribution of the chemicals; and second, the molecular features that initiate and specify the disruptive action of the chemicals on the metabolism and structure of the parasite. The line of demarcation between the dimensions of the structural and molecular features is not, of course, sharp, but it lies in the region of 10 mμ. Although the dimensions of the structural and molecular features merge, they may have qualitatively different effects upon the activity of a given chemotherapeutic agent; for, certain structural features of the tissues of the host or the parasite may be such as to promote or oppose the access of the chemotherapeutic agent to the reactive molecular sites that constitute both the target components at which the chemotherapeutic agent is aimed in the parasite, and the reactive molecular components through which undesirable toxicity may be caused in the host.

The structural features that affect the toxicity of chemotherapeutic agents by influencing their distribution in the tissues may be divided into two broad types: first, what we may call the place or locus type, in which the agent is attracted or repelled by the material (e.g. lipid) or state of the medium (e.g. pH) in the immediate neighbourhood of the molecular sites that react with the agent (e.g. Bailey & Cavallito, 1950); and second, the envelope type, in which the reactive molecular sites are enclosed in compartments, access to which is controlled by surrounding membranes (e.g. the membranes of the nucleus, the endoplasmic reticulum, mitochondria or the cell). In this paper, attention is to be focused upon the structural features of the second type, and for the sake of simplicity I propose to restrict attention to bacterial parasites. I have to consider how selective penetration may cause the destructive activity of a chemotherapeutic agent to be comparatively high to the parasite but low to its host: and I am also asked to speculate about the possibility that the knowledge of the differences in the permeability (or transport) properties of the membranes of host and parasite may be used for the development of efficient chemotherapeutic agents.

There are two circumstances that make my task particularly difficult to accomplish except in the most general and vague way: the recent advances in the knowledge of the compartmentalization of mammalian tissue cells (e.g. into mitochondrial inner and outer chambers and internal and external phases of the endoplasmic reticulum) has greatly complicated considerations of the 'permeability' of mammalian tissue cells even under well-defined conditions; and the notion that natural membranes are relatively inert lipoprotein films which act mainly as osmotic barriers through which a chemical may or may not diffuse according to its charge, size and lipid solubility, is now being supplemented by the view that, by containing enzymes and carriers, the natural membranes act as highly specific links through which chemical and osmotic contact is regulated and maintained by movements of their substrates between the phases on either side (Mitchell, 1954; Mitchell & Moyle, 1956a, b; Rickenberg, Cohen, Buttin & Monod, 1956; Mitchell, 1957a, b; Ernster, 1957). These circumstances, while of great interest in themselves and most salutary in revealing the depths of our ignorance in the past, are depressing from the point of view of the present Symposium. They show that in the field of membrane transport and permeability such is the paucity of detailed information that the natural direction for the diffusion of knowledge is not at present towards but away from the field of practical chemotherapy. On the other hand, we may be heartened by the circumstance that 'on the whole, the position of antimicrobial agents in medical therapy is highly satisfactory. The majority of bacterial infections can be cured simply, effectively and cheaply. The mortality and morbidity from bacterial diseases has fallen so low that they are no longer among the important unsolved problems of medicine' (Jawetz, 1956).

I suggest that we should not be surprised, in view of the basic similarities in the organization of host and parasite, and the complication and subtlety of the differences upon which successful chemotherapy depends, that the great chemotherapeutic advances have resulted from chance observations and from the intelligent application of trial and error methods, and that the fundamental research on the mechanism of action of chemotherapeutic agents at the subcellular level has contributed practically nothing to medical therapy. It would, I think, be unrealistic to believe that this situation will change in the foreseeable future although, of course, one hopes that it may. Therefore, in this paper, I propose to describe what is known of the main similarities in and differences between the membrane systems of mammals and bacteria and to consider some of the possible ways in which selective penetration may affect the therapeutic activity of several well-tried, efficient chemotherapeutic agents, namely: sulphonamides, penicillins, streptomycin, tetracyclines, chloramphenicol, and polymyxins. I hope that this treatment of the problem will show, as objectively as possible, the relation between the knowledge of the mechanism of action of chemotherapeutic agents and the advance of medical therapeutic practice.

MEMBRANE SYSTEMS OF HOST AND PARASITE

The dictum of Claude Bernard concerning the necessity for the maintenance of a regulated internal medium has been shown to be as true for bacteria as for other more complex organisms (Mitchell, 1949; Mitchell & Moyle, 1956a; Davis, 1956). There is, however, an important difference between the 'milieu interne' as considered by Claude Bernard and that which we describe in bacteria; for the 'milieu interne' of an organism with a closed circulatory system is the circulating medium that bathes the cells, but the 'milieu interne' of a bacterium is the intracellular medium that bathes the molecules and molecular complexes of the protoplasm. The contact between the internal chemical systems of a bacterium and the nutrient and toxic substances of the environment is entirely under the control of the osmotic barrier and osmotic linkage (specific transport) systems of the plasma-membrane; while in an organism with a closed circulatory system the organs of absorption and excretion coupled by the circulatory fluid are largely responsible for the contact of the organism with the environment and for the regulation of the nutrition of its tissue cells. Important differences in function or specialization of the osmotic systems of the plasma-membranes of bacteria from those of tissue cells are thus implicit: I have suggested that such differences may offer a useful type of idiosyncrasy of which the future inventors of chemotherapeutic agents may perhaps take advantage, and upon which the effectiveness of some of the chemotherapeutic agents now in use may be found to depend (Mitchell, 1956).

The recent electron microscopical studies of ultrathin sections of mammalian tissue cells and of bacteria have shown that, while there is probably only one major compartment in bacteria, namely, the whole protoplasm limited by the plasma-membrane (see Mitchell & Moyle, 1956a; Mitchell, 1957b), there are probably some five major compartments in mammalian cells (see Sjostrand, 1956; Palade, 1956; Porter & Palade, 1957). The compartments of a mammalian tissue cell and their limiting membranes are illustrated very diagrammatically in Fig. 1. Several of the membranes, particularly the inner mitochondrial membrane and the membrane of the endoplasmic reticulum, tend to be much infolded and may lie close to the neighbouring membrane system; so that the ratio of the area of the membranes to the volume of the spaces that they enclose may be high. This ratio may be comparable to that of the area to volume of bacteria which, it must be remembered, are some one thousand times less in volume than most mammalian cells, and correspond roughly in size to mitochondria. The membranes of both bacteria and mammalian cells appear to consist of lipoprotein films about 5 mμ thick.

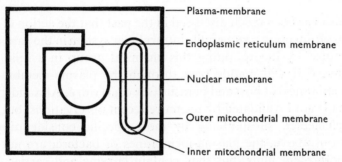

Fig. 1. Diagram of membranes and compartments of mammalian tissue cell.

It would not be appropriate in the present paper to attempt to evaluate the evidence for the distribution of different chemical components and biochemical activities between the different membranes and compartments of mammalian cells. Suffice it to say that the ribonucleoprotein particles, which are probably involved in protein synthesis, lie in the medium between the plasma-membrane and the membrane of the endoplasmic reticulum (Porter & Palade, 1957) and are thus osmotically protected from the outer medium only by the plasma-membrane; while the cytochrome and associated respiratory systems are largely concentrated in the mitochondrial membranes and chambers (Watson & Siekevitz, 1956), so that certain components of these latter systems may be protected not only by the plasma-membrane but also by the outer mitochondrial membrane or possibly by both mitochondrial membranes. In bacteria, the ribonucleoprotein particles appear to be situated in the cytoplasm, while the cytochrome system and other enzyme and carrier systems form part of the plasma-membrane and are responsible for coupling the uptake of nutrients and essential ions, etc. with the release of metabolic end-products to respiration and intermediary metabolism (see Mitchell, 1957b).

The passive permeability characteristics of the plasma-membranes of bacteria and most mammalian cells do not differ fundamentally. Solutes of small molecular weight generally permeate either type of cell with difficulty if they carry more than four water molecules, and positively charged solutes permeate somewhat more readily than negatively charged ones although the reverse is true of erythrocytes. In general lipid solubility is the property which allows a chemical to permeate the plasma-membranes of bacteria and mammalian cells alike. Very little is known in the case of the inner membranes of mammalian cells, but one or both of the mitochondrial membranes appears to behave similarly to bacterial and mammalian plasma-membranes (Tedeschi & Harris, 1955).

The idea has been much discussed in the past that the action of a given chemical group upon a vulnerable intracellular system in the parasite may be promoted by incorporating this chemical group in a lipid-soluble compound that will readily pass through the plasma-membranes (or other membranes) of host and parasite (see e.g. Trim & Alexander, 1949). This idea is not invalidated by the more recent observations, but it must be supplemented substantially by more specific considerations. As pointed out above, the plasma-membranes of bacteria are not simple inert lipo-protein films, but they contain enzyme and carrier systems that are responsible for linking the chemical reactions of metabolism to the transport of specific chemicals. It is likely that the membranes of mammalian cells are likewise active participants in metabolism and transport, and do not behave only as lipoprotein films (Mitchell, 1957a, b; Ernster, 1957). It follows that, since the membranes of host and parasite behave alike as lipoprotein films, the characteristic of being penetrated by lipid-soluble substances cannot be used directly as a differential for causing a chemical to discriminate against the parasite: on the other hand, the relatively complex specific chemical and osmotic linkage systems of the membranes of host and parasite would be likely to display idiosyncrasies that might be exploited chemotherapeutically. The relative therapeutic value of lipid-solubility (that confers non-specific membrane permeation) and the more subtle structural characteristics (that confer the specificity for facilitated diffusion or active transport through the membrane) depends on the location of the reactive molecular sites through which the chemotherapeutic agent exerts its lethal effect on the parasite, and upon the presence-and-location or absence of corresponding sites through which the agent may exert toxic effects on the host. Following this train of thought, we can recognize two possible classes of cause for the selective action of chemotherapeutic agents against the parasite; class A where the reactive molecular sites through which the agent exerts its disruptive effect are present only in the parasite, and class B where the reactive molecular sites are present both in the parasite and in the host, but only in the parasite are they accessible to the agent.

Class A. Reactive site only occurs in the parasite. In this case the efficiency of the agent does not depend upon differential penetration through the membranes of host and parasite. If the vulnerable molecular sites are situated outside or in the plasma-membrane of the parasite, the agent (appropriately administered) need not penetrate the membranes of either host or parasite to destroy all except those parasites which have penetrated into the cells of the host. On the other hand, if the vulnerable molecular sites are enveloped by the plasma-membrane of the parasite, the agent must penetrate this membrane, but may or may not also penetrate the membranes of the host. It would, of course, be advantageous if the agent were to penetrate the membranes of the host since this would allow access to intracellular parasites and would also allow more uniform distribution of the agent in the host tissues (particularly penetration into the cerebrospinal fluid) and absorption from the gastro-intestinal tract.

Of the six types of chemotherapeutic agent that we are to consider in this paper, it is probable that four, namely, chloramphenicol, the tetracyclines, the sulphonamides, and the polymyxins fall into class A, and penicillin may also fall into this class.

Chloramphenicol, the tetracyclines and the sulphonamides are appreciably lipid-soluble and, as one might have expected, they are readily absorbed from the alimentary canal, pass easily through the blood-brain barrier and are well distributed throughout the tissues (see e.g. Baron, 1950; Lawrence & Francis, 1953; Hussar & Holley, 1954; Welch, 1954). The passage of these substances through the membranes of both host and parasite may partly be determined by specific mechanisms, but it is unlikely that these mechanisms predominate over the non-specific permeation mechanism that depends upon the solubility of these substances in the membrane material.

The polymyxins are surface-active substances of high water solubility. Polymyxin B is not readily absorbed from the gastro-intestinal tract and does not pass into the cerebrospinal fluid when given parenterally. It is evident that it passes through the membranes of the host cells less readily than chloramphenicol, the tetracyclines and the sulphonamides. This is in keeping with the fact that the polymyxins do not need to enter the cytoplasm of susceptible bacteria to exercise their lytic effect, for their site of action is in the bacterial plasma-membrane (Newton, 1956, and this Symposium).

The salts of the penicillins are only very sparingly soluble in organic solvents at physiological pH values. They are absorbed slowly from the gastro-intestinal tract, do not diffuse significantly into the cerebrospinal fluid unless the meninges are acutely inflamed and are not reabsorbed through the membranes of the kidney tubule cells. Penicillin G was believed not to pass through the plasma-membrane of mammalian tissue cells because intracellular bacteria appeared to be protected. However, penicillin G may enter mammalian cells in tissue culture (see Eagle & Saz, 1955). It is possible, therefore, that the very low toxicity of penicillin to man is due entirely to the lack of essential reactive molecular sites in the tissues and that it is not determined by penetration factors. This is consistent with the knowledge that penicillin inhibits the synthesis of a polyglycerophospho-compound that is found only in the cell envelopes of penicillin-sensitive bacteria (Mitchell, 1956). However, it is also possible that the low toxicity of penicillin to man is due in part to its low lipid solubility and consequent exclusion from potentially vulnerable sites by certain of the membrane systems of mammalian cells; there is evidence that the reactive molecular sites through which penicillin exerts its disruptive effect are situated in the plasma-membrane of susceptible bacteria and may not involve penetration into the protoplasm (Cooper, 1956). If penetration of penicillin into susceptible bacteria does occur, it is probably by a specific mechanism.

Class B. Reactive site only accessible in the parasite. In this case the reactive sites of the host must be protected by one or more membranes, and the efficiency of the chemotherapeutic agent may or may not depend upon differential permeability of the membranes of host and parasite according to the location of the vulnerable molecular sites in the parasite. If the reactive sites of the parasite were superficial, an agent designed to be excluded alike by the plasma-membranes of host and parasite would discriminate against the latter. If, on the other hand, the reactive sites were protected by membranes both in host and parasite, discrimination against the parasite must depend upon a specific mechanism for the penetration of the agent into the parasite, and an effective agent would therefore have to be designed accordingly.

Streptomycin is a highly polar and water-soluble substance of very low lipid-solubility. It is not absorbed from the alimentary canal and passes through the blood-brain barrier only when the meninges are inflamed. It is not reabsorbed by the kidney tubule cells and is not evenly distributed throughout the tissues, the concentration in the liver, for instance, being very low in relation to that in the plasma; and it has been concluded that streptomycin is largely excluded from the tissue cells (see Welch, 1954). This factor has been cited as the reason for the resistance of brucellosis to streptomycin treatment (Magoffin & Spink, 1951) and for the resistance of intracellular tubercle bacilli (Mackaness & Smith, 1953). Studies of the action of streptomycin on tissue homogenates have shown that streptomycin-sensitive systems do indeed occur in the mitochondria. These systems appear to be protected not only by the mitochondrial membrane but also by the plasma-membrane of the tissue cell in which the mitochondria are situated (Umbreit & Tonhazy, 1949; Umbreit, 1955). It has usually been assumed that the site of action of streptomycin on bacteria is intracellular, but in view of the recent work that shows the presence of enzymes and carriers in the bacterial plasma-membrane, it may well be that the reactive molecular sites through which streptomycin exerts its disruptive effect lie in the plasma-membrane and are accessible from outside. At all events, the physical properties of streptomycin are such that even if the essential system that is blocked by combining with streptomycin is intracellular, it is very likely that the streptomycin must first pass through the plasma-membrane by a specific mechanism, that is to say, by combining reversibly with a component of the membrane. Thus, while the activity of streptomycin is very likely to depend upon specific combination with a component of the bacterial plasma-membrane, it is not known whether this combination is part of a permeation reaction that must precede access to a vulnerable intracellular site—the therapeutic effectiveness of streptomycin therefore being dependent upon a specific permeability differential between host and parasite—or whether the combination with the site in the membrane is directly responsible for the disorganizing activity of streptomycin—a permeability differential not being involved.

CONCLUSION

It is not certain that the chemotherapeutic efficiency of any of the six important types of agent considered in this paper is affected by differential permeability factors, although there is a possibility that such factors may be involved in the case of the penicillins and streptomycin. The polymyxins fall into a special class because their disruptive action on the plasma-membrane of sensitive bacteria depends upon a specific 'penetration' of the membrane; but the word 'penetration' has a different sense in this case, meaning entry into and not passage through.

Those agents that are appreciably soluble in lipids have the general advantage over the lipid-insoluble ones of being more uniformly distributed throughout the host tissues, more easily absorbed and less rapidly excreted. In particular cases, however, uniform distribution may not be desirable. Among the sulphonamides sulphathiazole, for instance, is chiefly of value in urinary infections because it is relatively rapidly excreted and concentrated by the kidney.

It does not appear to be possible to suggest any new general principles that would be of practical value for the development of chemotherapeutic agents. The permeability and transport factors which seem in the past to have been regarded as simpler than the biochemical factors, and therefore perhaps more easily susceptible to exploitation for chemotherapeutic purposes, are in fact quite as complex as the biochemical factors and in many cases are probably indistinguishable from them.

Successful chemotherapy depends upon the exploitation of subtle differences between the structure and reactivity of components of the tissues of the host and parasite. In view of the differences between the organization and specialization of the functions of the membranes of bacteria and of man, one might expect that a high proportion of the biophysical and biochemical differences would be concentrated in the membranes, and that they would therefore be a relatively rewarding target at which to aim a logical attack (Mitchell, 1956). However, the logical development of such agents can hardly be regarded as a practical possibility until much more is known of the biology of host and parasite.

The differences between the structure and reactivity of the components of host and parasite upon which the specific action of an efficient chemotherapeutic agent depends are so subtle, and the number and complexity of the essential chemical and physical processes of the host tissues with which the agent may interfere are so great that at present one can hardly expect chemotherapy to advance by any other method than by intelligent trial and error.

I would like to thank the Scottish Hospital Endowments Research Trust for a personal grant.

REFERENCES

BAILEY, J. H. & CAVALLITO, C. J. (1950). The effect of aliphatic acids on the activity of certain antibacterial agents. *J. Bact.* **60**, 269.

BARON, A. L. (1950). *Handbook of Antibiotics.* New York: Reinhold Publ. Co.

COOPER, P. D. (1956). Site of action of radiopenicillin. *Bact. Rev.* **20**, 28.

DAVIS, B. D. (1956). Relations between enzymes and permeability (membrane transport) in bacteria. In *Enzymes: Units of Biological Structure and Function. Henry Ford Hosp. Symp.* **4**, 509.

EAGLE, H. & SAZ, A. K. (1955). Antibiotics. *Annu. Rev. Microbiol.* **9**, 173.

ERNSTER, L. (1957). Distribution and interaction of enzymes within animal cells. *Symp. biochem. Soc.* **16** (in the Press).

HUSSAR, A. E. & HOLLEY, H. L. (1954). *Antibiotics and Antibiotic Therapy.* New York: Macmillan.

JAWETZ, E. (1956). Antimicrobial chemotherapy. *Annu. Rev. Microbiol.* **10**, 85.

LAWRENCE, J. S. & FRANCIS, J. (1953). *The Sulphonamides and Antibiotics in Man and Animals.* 2nd ed. London: H. K. Lewis & Co. Ltd.

MACKANESS, G. B. & SMITH, N. (1953). The bactericidal action of isoniazid, streptomycin and terramycin on extracellular and intracellular tubercle bacilli. *Amer. Rev. Tuberc.* **67**, 322.

MAGOFFIN, R. L. & SPINK, W. W. (1951). The protection of intracellular brucella against streptomycin alone and in combination with other antibiotics. *J. Lab. clin. Med.* **37**, 924.

MITCHELL, P. (1949). The osmotic barrier in bacteria. In *The Nature of the Bacterial Surface. Symp. Soc. gen. Microbiol.* **1**, 55.

MITCHELL, P. (1954). Transport of phosphate through an osmotic barrier. In *Active Transport and Secretion. Symp. Soc. exp. Biol.* **8**, 254.

MITCHELL, P. (1956). Penicillin and the logic of chemotherapy. *G. Microbiol.* **2**, 440.

MITCHELL, P. (1957*a*). A general theory of membrane transport from studies of bacteria. *Nature, Lond.* **180**, 134.

MITCHELL, P. (1957*b*). Structure and function in micro-organisms. *Symp. biochem. Soc.* **16** (in the Press).

MITCHELL, P. & MOYLE, J. (1956*a*). Osmotic function and structure in bacteria. In *Bacterial Anatomy. Symp. Soc. gen. Microbiol.* **6**, 150.

MITCHELL, P. & MOYLE, J. (1956*b*). Permeation mechanisms in bacterial membranes. *Disc. Faraday Soc.* **21**, 258.

NEWTON, B. A. (1956). The properties and mode of action of the polymyxins. *Bact. Rev.* **20**, 14.

PALADE, G. E. (1956). Electron microscopy of mitochondria and other cytoplasmic structures. In *Enzymes: Units of Biological Structure and Function. Henry Ford Hosp. Symp.* **4**, 185.

PORTER, K. R. & PALADE, G. E. (1957). Studies on the endoplasmic reticulum. III. Its form and distribution in striated muscle cells. *J. biophys. biochem. Cytol.* **3**, 269.

RICKENBERG, H. V., COHEN, G. N., BUTTIN, G. & MONOD, J. (1956). La galactoside-perméase d'*Escherichia coli. Ann. Inst. Pasteur*, **91**, 829.

SJÖSTRAND, F. S. (1956). The ultrastructure of cells as revealed by the electron microscope. *Int. Rev. Cytol.* **5**, 455.

TEDESCHI, H. & HARRIS, D. L. (1955). The osmotic behaviour and permeability to non-electrolytes of mitochondria. *Arch. Biochem. Biophys.* **58**, 52.

TRIM, A. R. & ALEXANDER, A. E. (1949). Surface activity and permeability as factors in drug action. In *Selective Toxicity and Antibiotics. Symp. Soc. exp. Biol.* **3**, 111.

UMBREIT, W. W. (1955). Mode of action of antibiotics. *Amer. J. Med.* **18**, 717.

UMBREIT, W. W. & TONHAZY, N. E. (1949). The action of streptomycin. III. The action of streptomycin in tissue homogenates. *J. Bact.* **58**, 769.

WATSON, M. L. & SIEKEVITZ, P. (1956). The isolation and analysis of a mitochondrial membrane fraction. *J. biophys. biochem. Cytol.* **2**, Suppl. *Tissue Fine Structure*, 379.

WELCH, H. (1954). *Principles and Practice of Antibiotic Therapy.* New York: Interscience Publ. Inc.

INHIBITORS OF ENERGY-SUPPLYING REACTIONS

H. A. KREBS

Medical Research Council Unit for Cell Metabolism,
Department of Biochemistry, University of Oxford

Since the supply of energy is a prerequisite of all life, it might be thought that a chemotherapeutic attack on the energy-supplying reactions of infective organisms would be a means of eliminating an invader. In practice, however, this idea has not so far proved particularly successful, because of the striking similarity between the energy-supplying processes of the host and those of infective organisms. By and large, host and invader employ much the same mechanisms and, as chemotherapy rests on differences in the chemical make-up of host and invader, the prospects of devising a differential attack on the energy-supplying reactions of the invader do not seem good. But they are not hopeless because differences do exist. Some of these are of a qualitative, others of a quantitative character. It is the object of this contribution to examine these differences.

Differences are here referred to as qualitative when substrates or intermediates undergo entirely different reactions in host and invader. Quantitative differences refer to situations where the reactions are identical but where quantitative differences exist in the properties of the enzymes catalysing these reactions. The most relevant differences are those of the relative affinity for inhibitors.

QUALITATIVE DIFFERENCES IN THE ENERGY-SUPPLYING REACTIONS BETWEEN HOST AND INVADER

Major qualitative differences in the energy-supplying reactions are very infrequent. When energy is released by the degradation of carbohydrate, fat or amino acids, there are over a hundred identifiable intermediate steps in animal tissues. Pathogenic micro-organisms may vary in the complexity of their energy-supplying mechanisms in that some, such as strict anaerobes, are more limited than animal tissues; but, in general, micro-organisms have the same type and range of intermediary steps as animal tissues. All micro-organisms share the basic arrangement with the energy-supplying systems of higher animals. Before the energy set free in the breakdown of nutrients can be utilized by the living cell, it must be transformed into that special form of chemical energy which is stored in the pyrophosphate bonds of adenosine triphosphate (ATP).

ATP is generated either by anaerobic reactions (chiefly the degradation of sugars or of α-ketonic acids) or by oxidative reactions, which in the last resort represent in most cases an oxidation of reduced pyridine nucleotide ($DPNH_2$) by molecular oxygen:

$$DPNH_2 + O_2 \rightarrow DPN + H_2O$$

a reaction which is coupled, in some unknown fashion, with the synthesis of three molecules of ATP from ADP (adenosine diphosphate) and inorganic phosphate.

There are only six reactions in animal tissues by which ATP is generated from ADP and inorganic phosphate (Table 1), and the same reactions are also widespread in micro-organisms.

Table 1. *The six reactions by which ATP can be generated in animal tissues and micro-organisms*

(Each of these reactions consists of several component steps, some of which cannot yet be fully formulated)

Anaerobic reactions (phosphorylation at substrate level)
1. Triosephosphate reaction of glycolysis.
2. Phosphopyruvate kinase reaction of glycolysis.
3. Oxidative decarboxylation of α-ketonic acids.

Oxidative phosphorylation
4. Reduced pyridine nucleotides + flavoprotein + ADP + P $\rightarrow$ pyridine nucleotide + reduced flavoprotein + ATP.
5. Reduced flavoprotein + 2 ferricytochrome + ADP + P $\rightarrow$ flavoprotein + 2 ferrocytochrome + ATP.
6. 2 ferrocytochrome + $\frac{1}{2}O_2$ + ADP + P $\rightarrow$ 2 ferricytochrome + ATP.

A distinct qualitative difference in the series of intermediary reactions of foodstuff degradation occurs at the stage of pyruvate under anaerobic conditions. In animal tissues there is only one major anaerobic reaction of pyruvate, namely, the reduction to lactate. In many micro-organisms pyruvate can be oxidized anaerobically, by coupled oxido-reductions, to form acetate (which arises in the form of acetyl coenzyme A). Acetyl coenzyme A can react further to form butyric acid, other fatty acids and various related compounds. Most of these reactions can also occur in the animal, but not under anaerobic conditions. This means that the obligatory coupling with other systems differs in detail, but not in principle, in animals and micro-organisms.

Another major qualitative difference between animal tissues and some micro-organisms exists in respect of the reactions which lead directly to the synthesis of ATP. In addition to the commonly occurring reactions listed in Table 1, micro-organisms may possess a special reaction, or type of reaction, not found in animal tissues. This is the 'acyl-phospho-kinase' reaction (Stern & Ochoa, 1951; Stadtman, 1952):

$$\text{acyl phosphate} + \text{ADP} \rightarrow \text{fatty acid} + \text{ATP}. \tag{1}$$

The most important representation of a reaction of this type is the 'acetokinase' reaction involving acetic acid:

$$\text{acetyl phosphate} + \text{ADP} \rightarrow \text{acetic acid} + \text{ATP}. \tag{2}$$

This reaction, as well as the 'phosphotransacetylase' reaction preceding it:

$$\text{acetyl coenzyme A} + \text{phosphate} \rightarrow \text{acetyl phosphate} + \text{coenzyme A} \tag{3}$$

are absent from animal tissues. To what extent they play a role in pathogens is uncertain. They are probably the main source of ATP in clostridia when growing in the absence of sugar, e.g. in a medium in which lactate is the main source of carbon, or when the 'Stickland re-action' is a source of energy. All types of Stickland reactions (coupled oxido reductions between pairs of amino acids) lead to the formation of an α-ketonic acid (see Nisman, 1954) which can react with coenzyme A according to the general scheme:

$$\text{R.CO.COOH} + \text{coenzyme A} + \text{DPN} \rightarrow$$
$$\text{R.CO.coenzyme A} + CO_2 + DPNH_2. \tag{4}$$

The acyl coenzyme A formed can yield acetyl coenzyme A by a transfer reaction catalysed by 'coenzyme A transphorase' (Stadtman, 1952):

$$\text{acyl coenzyme A} + \text{acetate} \rightarrow \text{acetyl coenzyme A} + \text{fatty acid}. \tag{5}$$

Whether acyl coenzyme A formed by reaction (4) yields ATP via re-actions (5), (3) and (2), or via a phosphotransacetylase reaction ana-logous to (3) followed by reaction (1), is an open question.

Other ATP generating reactions may occur in special organisms under special conditions. A known example is the fission of citrulline (Knivett, 1952; Slade & Slamp, 1952) in *Streptococcus faecalis*:

$$\text{citrulline} + \text{ADP} + \text{P} \rightarrow \text{ornithine} + \text{ATP} + NH_3 + CO_2$$

But this reaction is merely a modification of a reaction which occurs in liver tissue, and it is not likely to be relevant to chemotherapeutic considerations.

A third qualitative difference concerns the overall metabolism. Some pathogenic organisms, e.g. certain strains of *Escherichia coli*, unlike the host, may derive all their carbon requirements from 2-carbon compounds such as acetic acid or ethanol. But whilst this may help the organism to survive and to multiply outside the host, it is not likely to be of importance in the infected organism, where the invader is offered rich nutrient medium with almost all amino acids and many other basic cell constituents readily available.

No specific inhibitors of chemotherapeutic value can as yet be based on the qualitative metabolic differences mentioned. The differences are nevertheless discussed here, because the strategy of chemotherapy must concern itself with pinpointing potentially weak spots in the invader's chemical organization. In so far as invaders employ the same enzymes as the host, they are largely (though not necessarily completely) protected against the chemotherapeutic use of inhibitors. Where they employ other enzyme systems not required by the host, they lay themselves open to a differential attack.

QUANTITATIVE DIFFERENCES IN THE ENERGY-SUPPLYING REACTIONS BETWEEN HOST AND INVADER

As already mentioned, the enzymes which catalyse identical processes in host and invader may show in some cases major quantitative differences, for example, in the relative affinities of inhibitors for the enzyme. Quantitative kinetic studies of enzyme inhibition should therefore be expected to assist in the development of a rational chemotherapy.

Since each step of metabolism requires a different catalyst, the number of enzymes to be considered is very large. However, the enzymes of the various stages are by no means of equal interest from the point of view of chemotherapy. The potential activity of many enzymes is far in excess of requirements, and a considerable inhibition of their activity does not necessarily cause a significant disturbance of cell metabolism. Fumarase is an example. Whether a change of enzyme activity is of major consequence depends on whether the enzyme concerned plays a role in the rate control of metabolism, a consideration which leads to an examination of the factors governing the rate of intermediary processes of the energy supply.

The fact that intermediary products of metabolism do not as a rule accumulate shows that the amount of enzyme activity is not the main factor controlling the rate of the intermediate steps. The limiting factor in these cases is the amount of available substrate. The average half-life of the acids of the tricarboxylic acid cycle in a rapidly respiring tissue is of the order of only a few seconds. This means that the amount of enzyme in the tissue is sufficient to deal with the intermediate as soon as it arises, and that inhibitors which reduce enzyme activity substantially do not necessarily upset cell metabolism. It is true that the amounts of enzyme, together with those of substrates, determine the maximum rate of the process under any given conditions, but maximum rates are exceptional under physiological conditions.

However, this does not apply to all steps of metabolism. There are some reactions, probably small in number in comparison with the total number, where the rates depend not only on the amount of substrate supplied by the preceding stage, but on factors which are relatively easily upset.

These reactions are the pace-makers of metabolism (Krebs, 1957). The pace-makers are the steps of metabolism which are especially vulnerable to extraneous agents, because any decrease in activity is liable to show itself in a diminished overall rate of metabolism. Pace-makers are therefore the enzyme systems towards which chemotherapeutic efforts should be primarily directed.

Pace-makers occur at various stages of the long sequence of reactions by which energy is made available from foodstuffs. Since intermediates do not accumulate, those steps which initiate the degradation of the primary substrates, e.g. of glucose, amino acids, fatty acids and also of molecular O_2, must be pace-makers. Other pace-makers occur at the intermediary stages where, after a partial degradation, more than one pathway is open. It is decided at such 'branching points', for example, whether glucose is broken down to supply energy or stored in the form of glycogen; whether glucose via acetyl coenzyme A is converted into fat or whether fat is broken down to give energy; whether ketone bodies are formed from fatty acids or disposed of via the tricarboxylic acid cycle (see Krebs, 1957; Krebs & Kornberg, 1957).

The following examples illustrate the thesis that inhibitors of cell respiration interfere with pace-makers rather than with other intermediate steps. Inhibitors of respiration may be said to fall into three main classes according to the type of pace-maker which they inhibit. Substances of class I inhibit the rate of oxygen consumption because they interfere with the reactions initiating the utilization of oxygen. Members of this group are hydrocyanic acid, azide, carbon monoxide or sulphide, which all stop the interaction between molecular oxygen and reduced iron porphyrins.

Substances of class II interfere with the initiation of the reaction of the substrates of respiration, i.e. with the dehydrogenase reactions. If an inhibitor is specific for one dehydrogenase, or one type of dehydrogenase, it does not necessarily alter the overall rate of oxidations, because other substrates may take the place of that which is prevented from reacting. Thus cells exposed to malonate, which are prevented from oxidizing succinate at the normal rate, may still consume oxygen at the usual level if another substrate, such as fumarate, is available. Different dehydrogenase systems are known to vary in complexity. In most cases the initial substrate degradation involves a more or less direct transfer of hydrogen atoms to a pyridine nucleotide. There are two major exceptions to this rule. One of these is the dehydrogenation of α-ketonic acids, where the mechanism is much more complex in that various additional cofactors take part: coenzyme A, α-lipoic acid, cocarboxylase. It has long been known that the oxidation of α-ketonic acids is sensitive to reagents, for example arsenite (Krebs, 1933), which do not affect other dehydrogenases. Arsenite reacts with SH groups, and the semi-specific action of arsenite on the oxidation of α-ketonic acids can be understood on the basis of the special role played by sulphydryl catalysts in the dehydrogenation of α-ketonic acids. The second exception is the succinic dehydrogenase system, which does not require pyridine nucleotides or any other water-soluble cofactors. The relative simplicity of this system explains the fact that the oxidation of succinate is more stable towards inhibitors and environmental changes than the oxidation of other substrates.

Substances of class III interfere with the mechanism controlling the branching points of metabolism and can therefore divert metabolism from one pathway to another. Examples of inhibitors acting at such branching points are agents which induce the formation of ketone bodies ('ketogenesis') in the liver. Ketogenesis seems to depend on the supply of oxaloacetate, and those agents which reduce the supply of oxaloacetate are in fact ketogenic. Thus malonate, which prevents the conversion of succinate to oxaloacetate, or ammonium chloride which diverts metabolism of α-ketoglutarate to glutamate, are both ketogenic.

The factors which control the overall rate of glycolysis are by no means fully known, but there are two steps which have been identified as pace-makers. The first is the initiating reaction: the hexokinase reaction or the penetration of glucose into the cell; the second is the triosephosphate dehydrogenase system. Many inhibitors of glycolysis are substances which react with the two known pace-maker systems. Thus bromo- and iodoacetate inhibit triosephosphate dehydrogenase, by combining with the sulphydryl group which probably acts as the prosthetic group of the enzyme. The hexokinase reaction is inhibited by various hexosephosphates, in particular by the product of the reaction, glucose-6-phosphate (Weil-Malherbe & Bone, 1951) and by L-sorbose-1-phosphate (Lardy, Wiebelhaus & Mann, 1950). This inhibition is non-competitive. The two pace-makers are also the points of attack of glyceraldehyde, a powerful inhibitor of glycolysis (Mendel 1929; Rudney, 1949). L-Glyceraldehyde is transformed in glycolysing material into L-sorbose-1-phosphate under the influence of aldolase. D-Glyceraldehyde probably inhibits triosephosphate dehydrogenase (Needham, Siminovitch & Rapkine, 1951).

The pace-maker steps of the energy-supplying reactions must be essentially identical in host and invader and if they are the vulnerable stages of energy metabolism, any chemotherapy concerned with this aspect of metabolism must rest on the chance that weak spots are weaker in the invader than in the host.

SUMMING UP

The energy-supplying reactions of host and invader show a striking similarity, and the task of devising a rational strategy of chemotherapy directed against the energy-supplying reactions of the invader is therefore a difficult one. There are a few qualitative differences in that some reactions take place in micro-organisms which are absent from the host. In addition, there are differences between host and invader of a quantitative character in that enzymes may show different affinities for inhibitors. It is pointed out that some stages of the energy-supplying processes—the pace-maker reactions—are likely to be more vulnerable to a chemotherapeutic attack than other stages.

In the past, much of the successful chemotherapy has arisen from a hit-and-miss strategy rather than from a rational approach, based on the knowledge of the chemical make-up of host and invader, for the simple reason that such knowledge has been far too patchy. Previous failures of the rational approach, however, should not discourage fresh attempts, as the patchiness of our understanding is being reduced. It is in the spirit of this conviction that this contribution is offered.

REFERENCES

KNIVETT, V. A. (1952). Citrulline as an intermediate in the breakdown of arginine by *Streptococcus faecalis*. *Biochem. J.* **50**, xxx.
KREBS, H. A. (1933). Untersuchungen über den Stoffwechsel der Aminosäuren im Tierkörper. *Hoppe-Seyl. Z.* **217**, 191.

KREBS, H. A. (1957). Control of metabolic processes. *Endeavour*, **16**, 125.

KREBS, H. A. & KORNBERG, H. L. (1957). A survey of the energy transformations in living matter. *Ergebn. Physiol.* **49**, 212.

LARDY, H. A., WIEBELHAUS, V. D. & MANN, K. M. (1950). The mechanism by which glyceraldehyde inhibits glycolysis. *J. biol. Chem.* **187**, 325.

MENDEL, B. (1929). Krebszelle und Glycerinaldehyd. *Klin. Wschr.* **8**, 169.

NEEDHAM, D. M., SIMINOVITCH, L. & RAPKINE, S. M. (1951). On the mechanism of the inhibition of glycolysis by glyceraldehyde. *Biochem. J.* **49**, 113.

NISMAN, B. (1954). The Stickland reaction. *Bact. Rev.* **18**, 16.

RUDNEY, H. (1949). Studies on the mechanism of the inhibition of glycolysis by glyceraldehyde. *Arch. Biochem.* **23**, 67.

SLADE, H. D. & SLAMP, W. C. (1952). The formation of arginine dihydrolase by streptococci and some properties of the enzyme system. *J. Bact.* **64**, 455.

STADTMAN, E. R. (1952). The net enzymatic synthesis of acetyl coenzyme A. *J. biol. Chem.* **196**, 535.

STERN, J. R. & OCHOA, S. (1951). Enzymatic synthesis of citric acid. I. Synthesis with soluble enzymes. *J. biol. Chem.* **191**, 161.

WEIL-MALHERBE, H. & BONE, A. D. (1951). Studies on hexokinase. 1. The hexokinase activity of rat-brain extracts. *Biochem. J.* **49**, 339.

METAL-BINDING AGENTS IN CHEMOTHERAPY: THE ACTIVATION OF METALS BY CHELATION

A. ALBERT

*Department of Medical Chemistry,
Australian National University, Canberra*

Heavy metals, in traces, are essential for the proper functioning of all living cells; they are present in the form of cations. A remarkable specificity is shown by the fact that seldom can an excess of one essential metal remedy the deficiency of another; in fact in many cases such an excess has been found to increase the injurious effect of deprivation.

CHEMISTRY OF METAL-BINDING

The essential metals are: copper, cobalt, zinc, iron, manganese and molybdenum, and also lighter metals such as magnesium and calcium. All are essential for animals, although the role of molybdenum has only recently been discovered; and all except cobalt are essential for plants. It is quite possible that other metals will have to be added to this list, at least for certain species. For example the animals known as chordates, which stand just under vertebrates in the phylogenetic tree, are accumulators of vanadium which may well be essential for their metabolism. Indications have been obtained of the importance of aluminium, and of gallium (a common impurity in aluminium), for certain enzymes and species, but confirmation is required. A cadmium protein has been isolated from equine kidney cortex (Margoshes & Vallee, 1957).

The response to heavy metals is known to be biphasic: given too little the organism suffers severely, as is understandable from our knowledge of the large number of enzymes which cannot function without the appropriate trace-metal. But if the organism is given too much metal, a second phase of injury is seen, due to the toxic action of the excess. This biphasic response is well illustrated by the action of copper on oat plants (Piper, 1942). Piper's paper should be read by all who are interested in micronutrients, particularly for the photograph which shows so graphically that too much copper is as injurious as too little. These oat plants are seen growing in a series of vessels in which concentrations of copper vary from 0 to 3000 μg./l.: growth is seen to reach a maximum at 500 μg., and to fall away on either side of this figure.

Metal-depleted media

Such figures, 0–3000 μg./l., are not absolute, because there is no known way of removing every trace of a metal from a medium. Thus we should not speak of a 'metal-free medium' but of a 'metal-depleted medium'. Piper made his metal-depleted medium as follows: the required nutrient salts were dissolved in water, and shaken out with a solution of dithizone in chloroform. This operation was repeated many times, and finally the solution was shaken out with chloroform (to remove the dithizone), and then aerated (to remove the chloroform). In our work with oxine (8-hydroxyquinoline) (see below) we used oxine itself to remove metals in the same way (Rubbo, Albert & Gibson, 1950). Other substances with a high avidity for metals could be used similarly. Actually there is not much choice, because very few types of substance with a really high avidity for metals are known and, of these, several, such as ethylene-diaminetetra-acetic acid (EDTA), are not soluble in a water-immiscible solvent. Thirty-eight methods of metal depletion have been compared by Donald, Passey & Swaby (1952).

Newcomers to the trace-metal field are often surprised that it is necessary to deplete the medium before beginning experiments. Unfortunately 'Chemically Pure' and 'Analytical Grade' reagents are rich sources of the heavy metals. This is inevitably so, because a substance that is 99·99 % pure would have 600,000,000,000,000,000 foreign molecules in each gram (calculated from the Avogadro number (6×10^{23} particles/mole of any substance) and assuming an average molecular weight of 100). Actually, the makers of analytical reagents do not claim their products to be even as pure as 99·99 %. Moreover, the metallic content of bacteriological media is high (Society for General Microbiology, 1956). Thus eight much-used makes of peptone, upon spark-spectrographic analysis, were found to contain (in parts/million), 3–940 parts of copper, 20 to > 300 parts of iron, < 0·03–15 parts of cobalt, 0·1–6 parts of molybdenum, 2 to > 300 parts of vanadium, 0·1 to > 400 parts of aluminium, 0·6–9 parts of manganese, up to 300 parts of zinc (a difficult metal to estimate by this method), and several per cent of calcium, magnesium, sodium and potassium (taken together).

Ion-exchange resins, mixed bed type, of the high grade used for purifying distilled water can also be used for metal removal (Healy, Morgan & Parker, 1952). Water purified in this way should be stored in polythene, because it can dissolve substantial amounts of heavy metals from glass within a week, even from a borosilicate glass such as Pyrex. If glass vessels are used for an experiment, they should be rinsed in 2 %

ethanolic potassium hydroxide followed by water twice distilled in all-glass apparatus, then filled with aqua regia (diluted 1 : 3), and finally rinsed six times with the twice distilled water (cf. Waring & Werkman, 1942).

As a check on the amount of depletion required and obtained, the co-operation of a spark-spectroscopist is sometimes enlisted. However, this technique is time-consuming, and particularly troublesome where the saline ash (NaCl, etc.) vastly exceeds the amount of heavy metals present.

As an alternative, chemical determinations may be made. By such means Healy *et al.* (1952) were able to report as little as 0·001 parts/ million of copper, zinc, lead, iron and aluminium, but these are quantities in excess of an unknown background of these metals which escapes determination.

Complex-formation. Chelation

The chemical significance of heavy metals in biology arises from their ability to form, with certain anions (and amines), bonds which are tighter than ordinary ionic bonds, i.e. bonds which have a degree of covalent nature like the bonds between oxygen and hydrogen in water, or in acetic acid. Cupric sulphide and ferrous hydroxide have bonds of this kind; but of greater biological interest are the complexes which heavy metals form with organic substances. Some of these, particularly those involving sulphur, are linear in character, e.g. (I), whereas in others, particularly those involving oxygen or nitrogen or both, a ring is formed, e.g. (II). Those complexes having the metal in a ring are said to be *chelate*, and their one chemical peculiarity is that they are more stable than closely related substances in which the metal does not form part of a ring. Only 5- and 6-membered chelate rings are stable. Often a linear sulphur-containing complex is found to hold a given metal more firmly than a nitrogen-containing ring: for example, the copper in (I) is bound about 10^{12} times more tightly than in (II). The biological significance of a complex depends (*inter alia*) on the tightness with which the metal is bound, not on whether it is chelate.

$(CH_3)_2N \cdot \overset{..}{\underset{..}{C}}S-Cu^+$

Cupric dimethyldithiocarbamate (1:1)

(I)

Cupric-glycine (1:1)

(II)

Quantitative aspects

What substances bind essential heavy metals in the living cell? First, there are the porphyrins (also the porphyrin-like vitamin B_{12}) which bind iron (or cobalt) so avidly that it does not exchange with free ions of the same metal. This has been determined by using radioactive ions (e.g. Hahn, Bale, Ross, Hettig & Whipple, 1940; and see Atkins & Garner, 1952), but the experiments do not cover all known examples, nor do they explore the situation at other degrees of oxidation.

The majority of cell-constituents do not bind metals so tightly as the porphyrins: in fact many of them bind less avidly than 8-hydroxy-quinoline (oxine) and EDTA. But these synthetic substances do not bind metals so tightly as to preclude exchange.

Thus already we can distinguish three degrees of tightness of binding. It is evident that this discussion cannot be profitably continued without some measure of the varying degrees of avidity which one substance displays for different metals, or different substances for the one metal. For this purpose 'Stability Constants' are used: the greater the avidity, the higher the constant. The equilibria between metals and the complexes which they form are, in most cases, almost instantaneous in both directions: hence simple thermodynamic (rather than kinetic) equations can be used. These take the familiar form of mass-action equations.

Usually K_1 is first determined. This is the constant governing the equilibrium between one ion of metal and one molecule of metal-binding substance. Thus, for glycine and cupric ions,

$$K_1 = \frac{\left[\; H_2C \overset{CO_2}{\underset{N \atop H_2}{\diagup}} Cu^+ \;\right]}{[Cu^{++}]\left[\; H_2C \overset{CO_2^-}{\underset{N \atop H_2}{\diagup}} \;\right]} . \qquad (1)$$

For this combination $\log K_1$ has been found to be 8·5 (cf. 12·2 for 8-hydroxyquinoline, which thus binds *antilog 3·7 times* as firmly, i.e. 5000 times as firmly).

Although the reaction between EDTA and copper ceases with the formation of such a 1:1 complex, most divalent metals add two molecules of the metal-binding agent. This second addition corresponds to the equation,

$$K_2 = \frac{\left[\begin{array}{c} H_2C \diagdown \;\; CO_2 \diagup \;\; Cu \;\; \diagdown CO_2 \diagup CH_2 \\ N \qquad\qquad N \\ H_2 \qquad\qquad H_2 \end{array}\right]}{\left[\begin{array}{c} H_2C \diagdown \;\; CO_2 \diagup \;\; Cu^+ \\ N \\ H_2 \end{array}\right]\left[\begin{array}{c} H_2C \diagdown \;\; CO_2^- \\ N \\ H_2 \end{array}\right]} . \qquad (2)$$

This new equation resembles the earlier one: the substance undergoing formation is in the top line in each case, and the components with which it is in equilibrium are in the bottom line. The log K_2 for the 2:1-complex of glycine is 6·9, and hence the overall log stability constant (log K_s) is 15·4 (i.e. the equilibrium between glycine and the 2:1-complex).* Thus the overall constant is the *product* of the individual constants. Trivalent cations (and some divalent cations in certain circumstances) form 3:1 complexes, which are similarly dealt with.

Mixed complexes are also known. Thus small molecules can be bound to albumin by a metallic cation (Klotz & Loh Ming, 1954); copper binds ethylenediamine to iminodiacetic acid (Bennett, 1957) or to mannosan (Segal, Jonassen & Reeves, 1956).

Before 1941, the measurement of stability constants was seldom undertaken, for lack of a convenient method. The potentiometric method, which had been awaiting the discovery of a suitable mathematical treatment, was then successfully applied to the problem (Bjerrum, 1941). This is still the most practicable method, and depends on the displacement of the normal titration curve of a metal-binding substance when a heavy metal cation is present. This displacement is to lower pH values, because each metal cation upon combination with the agent liberates one hydrogen (cat)ion. The greater the displacement, the greater the stability constant.

The calculations for the potentiometric method are arduous, and require prior determination of two functions. First, $\bar{n}$ (pronounced

* Caution: different symbols are used by different authors.

en-bar), which is the average number of molecules of agent in combination with one ion of metal (at various stages of the titration of
glycine and copper, $\bar{n}$ may be any number between 0 and 2, and is
usually taken to two places of decimals). Secondly, [L], the concentration of unbound ligand. The ligand is the complex minus the metal,
and hence is the metal-binding substance minus a hydrogen ion. When
a metal is held between two nitrogen atoms, the 'metal-binding substance' is a cation, and hence the ligand is a neutral molecule. In other
cases, the ligand is an anion, as with glycine (see equation 1, above).

The necessary calculations (and their derivations) have been clearly
set out, and approximations devised (Albert, 1950, 1952), together with
simple tests to find if the approximations are applicable to the data in
hand.

Other methods available are (a) exchange, usually of a competitive
character, of two ligands for one metal, or two metals for one ligand,
often measured by one of the components being isotopic (e.g. Schubert
& Lindenbaum, 1952), (b) polarography (e.g. Li, White & Doody, 1954),
(c) spectroscopy (e.g. Ågren, 1954). For copper, the copper electrode
has been used with success (e.g. Dobbie & Kermack, 1955).

The potentiometric method is preferred so long as the complex is more
soluble in water than 0·0005 M. Polarography permits operation at a
tenfold greater dilution, but often does not yield all the required
constants. For excessively insoluble substances, the exchange method is
best. Spectroscopy depends upon each species having a characteristic
and intense spectrum: in practice its use generally has to be confined to
determining one constant when another is known. Spectroscopy is
particularly useful for the highly acid solutions produced by the first
step in the union of copper with a highly avid binding agent.

Binding of metals by cell constituents

After this discussion into quantitative aspects of the subject, it is convenient to return to the question of what binds metals in cells. Porphyrins, as we saw on p. 115, appear to hold metals with an avidity so
great that it is at present beyond measurement. Not so with the amino
acids, of which a comprehensive survey (Albert, 1950, 1952) has revealed
that all but two have very much the same constants as glycine (see
Table 1). Histidine and cysteine, however, are more avid than glycine.
The peptides have slightly lower constants than the amino acids, but
they bind metals differently, the —CO.NH— group being brought into
play (Dobbie & Kermack, 1955; Datta & Rabin, 1956). Proteins, in

general, seem to have still less avidity, and it would seem that in them cysteine and histidine groups make the greatest contribution to metal-binding, at least in albumin (Tanford, 1952; Gurd & Goodman, 1952). Nevertheless, the fact that oxine can enter the cell without causing harm (see below) suggests that *vital* enzymes bind their relevant metals with greater avidity than the studies on albumin would indicate.

In 1950 further heterocyclic cell-constituents (pteridines, purines and riboflavine) were found to be metal-binding (see Albert, 1953a). These have stability constants similar in magnitude to those of the amino acids, the principal difference being that ferrous iron tends to be promoted above its usual place in the 'avidity series'. This avidity series, which holds for most combinations, runs as follows:

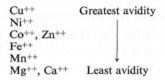

A place has not been assigned to trivalent iron, or to molybdenum which is hexavalent in biology. Those substances which can combine with trivalent iron (e.g. tetracycline, pyrophosphate, oxine) hold it with an avidity exceeding that with which they bind copper.

The only other substances in cells known to bind metals are phosphoric acid derivatives, and the acids of the tricarboxylic acid cycles. The work that has been done on adenosine triphosphate (Martell & Schwarzenbach, 1956) and polyphosphoric acids (van Wazer & Holst, 1950) leaves the major part of the subject, including nucleic acids, unexplored. Similarly the constants obtained for the carboxylic acids (Schubert & Lindenbaum, 1952) need expansion.

Future development of the chemical aspect

The discovery of a connexion between structure and stability constants would enable the constants of a given substance to be approximately known in advance of its synthesis (as is the case with ionization constants). Much has been written along these lines, but reliable rules are not yet known, and so a great deal of time is wasted in synthesizing substances which turn out to have only low or medium affinity for metals.

As will have been gathered, the known metal-binding agents have little specificity, in fact far less than would be imagined from reading the analytical literature. A few substances (e.g. folic acid and *o*-phenanthroline) are known which thrust copper down the avidity series (see p. 118) for steric reasons, and a few others (e.g. riboflavine and dipyridyl) which promote ferrous iron by bringing new orbitals into play. The variable position of ferric iron has been mentioned above. In spite of these modest advances, the discovery of metal-binders with different, and greater, specificity is a task for which few clues exist. A natural phenomenon, which may later be adapted to biological uses, is that a plot of stability constant against atomic weight for the transition metals (manganese, iron, cobalt, nickel and copper, in that order) rises much more steeply for ligands which chelate by two nitrogen atoms than for those which chelate by two oxygen atoms. Given such a pair of substances, e.g. ethylenediamine and salicylaldehyde, it often happens that the curves cross one another. Thus in a solution containing both these substances, all the manganese would be bound by salicylaldehyde, the iron divided equally between both, and the heavier metals held mainly by the ethylenediamine (Irving & Williams, 1953, fig. 4).

The above problems will most likely be solved by a more profound study of molecular orbitals. Such a study should also shed light on what Bjerrum terms robust complexes, i.e. those which are not in thermodynamic equilibrium with their components. The nickel complex of EDTA is an example (the other complexes of EDTA are fairly normal). Both the nickel and the ferrous 3:1 complexes of *o*-phenanthroline are formed only after an indirect (although fairly rapid) hydrogen-ion catalysed reaction; moreover the ferric complex is formed from the components only at a negligible rate and is quite stable when formed, yet not so stable as the more rapidly formed ferrous complex.

Thus the formation of these robust complexes needs to be described in terms of a rate constant as well as a stability constant, for an energy barrier obviously has to be overcome. It is possible that the porphyrins are robust complexes of this kind.

Finally, the biologist cannot simply leave chemistry to the chemist but must ask himself whether in his particular experiment K_s or $\bar{n}$ (see p. 116) is the more important. If at a given pH, all metal-binding agents were equally well ionized, their success in competing for traces of metals would be in proportion to their stability constants only. However, at any given pH, two substances are most often ionized to different extents: thus it can easily happen that the one with less affinity for metals (i.e. with the lower K_s) produces a hundred times as much anion as the other and hence achieves a higher $\bar{n}$ value. In such a case, the substance with the less affinity for the metal may well be the one that gets by far the greater part of it. Thus K_a (the ionization constant) as well as K_s (the stability constant) determine the outcome ($\bar{n}$) of competition for a metallic ion.

Table 1. *Stability constants (as log K_s) of some familiar metal-binding agents (water, 20–25°)*

Ligand	No. of molecules bound/atom of metal	Cu^{++}	Ni^{++}	Zn^{++}	Co^{++}	Fe^{++}	Mn^{++}	Fe^{+++}
Glycine	2	15	11	9	9	8	5·5	—
Cysteine	2	*	19	18	16	11	7	—
Histidine	2	19	16	12	13	9	?	—
8-Hydroxyquinoline (oxine)	3	—	—	—	—	—	—	36
	2	23	18	15	17	15	11·5	—
Ethylenediamine	3	—	18	12	14	9·5	—	—
	2	20	—	—	—	—	5	—
Ethylenediamine-tetra-acetic acid	1	18	18	16	16	14	13·5	24
o-Phenanthroline	3	18	24	17	?	21	—	14
	2	—	—	—	—	—	8	—
Dipyridyl	3	18	?	13	?	17	—	?
	2	—	—	—	—	—	7	—
Pteroylglutamic acid ('folic acid')	2	8	9	7·5	8	8	6	—
Oxalic acid	1†	6	5·5	5	4·5	4·5	4	10

* The cysteine reduces the Cu^{++} to Cu^{+}.
† The corresponding figure for calcium is 3.

INHIBITION OF CELLULAR GROWTH

The biphasic response of organisms to metals, so neatly illustrated by Piper's oats (see p. 113), suggests two distinct methods for inhibiting cells, (*a*) by the removal of metals essential for normal growth or metabolism, and (*b*) by supplying metals in greater quantities than the cell can tolerate.

(a) *Removal of metals from an organism by metal-binding agents*

Very few cases are known where a metal-binding agent is *of itself* injurious to an organism, and this immunity is probably due to the tightness with which vital metals are bound. The best investigated example of this kind of injury is that caused by hydrogen cyanide, which binds the free valencies of the iron in cytochrome oxidase without detaching it from its four-bonded contact with the porphyrin nucleus. Thus, this enzyme is prevented from uniting with its substrate, and so respiration comes to a standstill. In most forms of animal life, this causes immediate death of the organism.

The metal-binding *antidotes* form a contrast to the toxic and unselective action of hydrogen cyanide. They have all been discovered since 1940. The first of these was dimercaprol, formerly called BAL or British Antilewisite (III) (Peters, Stocken & Thompson, 1945). This can remove arsenic, antimony, gold or mercury (inorganic or organic) from the bloodstream of people poisoned with these substances, and it does so without injury to the patient. The poisonous element is tightly bound, as in (IV). Dimercaprol does not penetrate into cells. Calcium ethylenediaminetetracetate (V) is similarly effective against lead, and large doses of salicylic acid have proved successful in beryllium poisoning. The use of 2-mercaptoethylamine (VI) in preventing radiation injury (Bacq, Hervé & Fischer, 1953) appears to be similar in that it can sequester the traces of iron and copper which apparently propagate the destructive chain reaction of hydroxyl radicals. DL-Penicillamine is an excellent antidote for copper poisoning, including Wilson's disease (Walshe, 1956).

This demonstration that several metal-binding agents can circulate in the blood without injury to the host holds out special hope to those who would expand the practice of chemotherapy by chelation.

(b) Intensification of the toxic action of metals by metal-binding agents

Attempts to kill organisms in the blood-stream by injecting inorganic substances such as mercury, bismuth, copper and gold represent the second phase of the biphasic action of metals in cells, as discussed on p. 113 for Piper's oats. These inorganic treatments have lost favour because they are insufficiently selective. Even iron can cause serious acute poisoning from oral ingestion of large doses, particularly in

children: death follows upon shock and cardiovascular collapse
(Goodman & Gilman, 1955).

There are, however, more subtle ways in which the second phase can
operate. This came to light as my colleagues and I pursued our studies
on oxine (8-hydroxyquinoline). No other substance with this type of
action has been studied so intensively, hence it seems best to describe
the biological action of oxine in detail.

(i) *The mode of action of oxine*

Proof that oxine acts by combining with heavy metals. Oxine (VII) was
introduced sixty years ago as a fungicide and bactericide for surface use
in human medicine, and it has been remarkably successful for these

8-Hydroxyquinoline (oxine)	8-Methoxyquinoline	Oxine methochloride	The 1:1-ferric complex of oxine
(VII)	(VIII)	(IX)	(X)

The 3:1-ferric complex of oxine
(XI)

purposes. The suggestion that its antibacterial action was due to a
metal-binding action (Albert, 1944) was confirmed as follows (Albert,
Rubbo, Goldacre & Balfour, 1947). The six isomers of oxine cannot
chelate because they cannot form 5- or 6-membered rings including the
metal, for obvious spatial reasons. All of these isomers were prepared
and found, as expected, not to chelate. They were also without antibacterial action. But oxine chelates very avidly (Table 1) and prevents
the growth of staphylococci and streptococci at M/100,000 (2 parts/

million). For confirmation, the molecule of oxine was methylated in two different places to give respectively (VIII) and (IX). Neither of these substances can chelate, and neither is antibacterial. Thus the connexion between chelation and antibacterial action was established. It remained to show whether the toxic action of oxine was due to the withdrawal of essential metals, as had been suggested (Zentmyer, 1944), or whether it was actually increasing the toxic action of metals normally present in the medium. The latter proved to be the case for both the bacteriostatic and bactericidal actions (Rubbo *et al.* 1950; Albert, Gibson & Rubbo, 1953), the first clue coming from a phenomenon known as 'concentration quenching'.

Table 2. *The effect of increasing concentration on the bactericidal action of oxine in broth ('concentration quenching')*

(*Staphylococcus aureus* in meat broth at pH 7·0–7·3 (20°))

Concentration of oxine 1/M	Growth after exposure (hr.)			
	0	1	3	24
800	+++	+++	+++	+
1,600	+++	+++	+++	+
3,200	+++	+++	+	+
6,400	+++	+++	+	−
12,800	+++	+	+	−
25,000	+++	+	−	−
50,000	+++	+	−	−
100,000	+++	−	−	−
200,000	+++	+++	+++	+++

The bactericidal test in this, and the following tables, is based on that of Miles & Misra (1938). At the end of the given time, samples were withdrawn, diluted, and inoculated on a dried blood-agar plate. The plates were read after 48 hr. at 37°. Symbols: −, no growth; +, up to 50 colonies; + +, 50–150 colonies; + + +, uncountable.

Concentration quenching. Who would expect the effect of any biologically-active substance to decrease as the concentration is increased? However, a few instances have been found where this does occur, an effect known as 'concentration quenching'. Oxine shows this phenomenon to an unprecedented degree. As will be seen from Table 2, staphylococci which are killed in an hour by M/100,000 oxine, are not killed (even in 3 hr.) by M/1600 oxine (in fact, even a saturated solution, which is M/200, will not kill them). There is, however, a degree of toxicity after 24 hr. (Albert *et al.* 1953). Streptococci behave similarly.

The meaning of this concentration quenching became evident when it was found that it occurred in broth, but not in distilled water.

Experiments with oxine in distilled water. The viability of staphylococci for at least 24 hr. in distilled water permits some decisive tests to

124   A. ALBERT

be made. It will be seen, from the distilled water experiments in Table 3, that oxine (M/100,000) is not bactericidal on its own, but becomes so in the presence of a similar quantity of iron, although the iron alone is not toxic. Clearly, the toxic agent is not oxine, but an oxine-iron complex.

  Experiments with oxine in broth. When broth is used instead of water, added iron is not necessary (Table 3), because a sufficient amount has been introduced from the meat. When the concentration of oxine was

Table 3. *The innocuousness of oxine in the absence of iron*
(bactericidal test)

(*Staphylococcus aureus*: pH 6–7 (20°))

Oxine 1/M	FeSO₄, or Fe₂(SO₄)₃ 1/M	Growth after 1 hr. exposure	
		Glass-distilled water	Untreated meat broth
nil	nil	+ + +	+ + +
100,000	nil	+ + +	−
nil	100,000	+ + +	+ + +
100,000	100,000	−	−
800	nil		+ + +
nil	800		+ + +
800	800		−

increased to M/800, the bactericidal action disappeared (concentration quenching). It seemed evident to us that the toxic action was caused by the 1:1-complex (X) or the 2:1-complex, but not by the 3:1-complex (XI) which must be the only form present when oxine was in excess. Therefore we added iron in sufficient amount (M/800) to equal that of the oxine, and thus restore the 1:1-complex. As expected, this combination proved as highly bactericidal as the earlier one (see Table 3). It should be noted that M/800 iron is not toxic on its own, but the oxine has made it so.

  The metals co-toxic with oxine. It is noteworthy that experiments with two different radioactive oxines have shown that oxine enters the cell of the fungus *Aspergillus niger* without causing any harm (Great-house *et al.* 1954). Damage to fungi and yeasts occurs only when cupric ions are present in the medium (Anderson & Swaby, 1951; Nordbring-Hertz, 1955; Block, 1956). The nature of the co-toxic metals varies from species to species: for Gram-positive bacteria, ferrous, ferric and cupric (see Table 4) ions are equally toxic, whereas nickel, zinc, cobalt, cadmium, manganese and calcium have no co-toxicant action.

  Antagonism by cobalt of the toxic action of oxine-iron. It is evident that the addition of a large excess (200 equivalents) of an inert metal could prevent the toxic action of oxine iron, if the stability constant of the new complex was greater than, or not much less than, that of oxine-iron; thus, by the law of mass action, the oxine should almost entirely combine with the inert metal. As expected, experiments showed that cadmium, cobalt, zinc and nickel were protective under these conditions, and manganese, magnesium and calcium were ineffective (see Table 1 for stability constants).

Cobalt, however, has a unique position. Not only is it protective in large amounts, but in traces also. As little as $M/25,000$ cobaltous sulphate completely prevents the *bacteriostatic* effect of $M/100,000$ oxine (Rubbo

Table 4. *Protective action of cobalt against the bactericidal action of iron-oxine and copper-oxine*

(*Staphylococcus aureus* in metal-depleted broth at pH 7·3 and 20°)
$M/25,000$ oxine present in every tube

Tube	Conc. of metal added, $1/M$			Growth after exposure (hr.)			
	$FeSO_4$	$CuSO_4$	$CoSO_4$	0	2	4	24
1	nil	nil	nil	+++	+++	+++	+++
2	50,000	nil	nil	+++	−	−	−
3	50,000	nil	50,000	+++	++	++	+++
4	nil	50,000	nil	+++	−	−	−
5	nil	50,000	50,000	+++	−	−	−
6	nil	50,000	10,000	+++	+++	+++	+++

et al. 1950; this paper should be consulted for a photograph of a series of cultures showing clearly that cobalt is the only metal with this protective action). Cobalt is just as (or even more) effective in preventing the *bactericidal* action of iron-oxine, as Table 4 shows. It is only a little less effective against copper-oxine. Cobalt also protects yeasts against copper-oxine (Nordbring-Hertz, 1955). Molybdenum (but not cobalt) has a slight protective effect for fungi against copper-oxine (Block, 1956; Anderson & Swaby, 1951), but molybdates are copper precipitants.

What is the explanation of this protective action of cobalt? At first it might seem that the cobalt combined with the oxine and thus denied it to iron. But if this were so, nickel would be still more effective because the stability constant of nickel-oxine is much higher than that of cobalt-oxine (Table 1, also Albert, 1953 a). But nickel has no protective action at low concentrations.

A better clue, perhaps, comes from knowledge that several cell constituents, particularly mercapto-compounds and ascorbic acid are easily oxidized by atmospheric oxygen if traces of iron or copper are present. These oxidations lead to the formation of hydrogen peroxide which in turn oxidizes more substrate: the combination of metal and hydrogen peroxide produces a fulminating chain reaction so that a very small amount of metal can catalyse a widespread destruction. In some reactions of this kind, traces of cobalt can act as an efficient chain-breaker which greatly moderates the destruction (see Fig. 1).

The state of oxidation of iron in iron-oxide. When a metal capable of existence in two valence states is chelated, its oxidation-reduction potential is changed. Thus ferrous iron becomes harder to oxidize after chelation with *o*-phenanthroline, but after chelation with oxine it is more

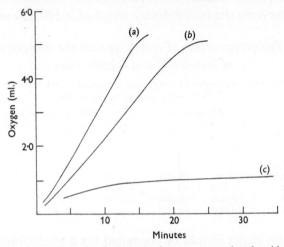

Fig. 1. The protective action of cobalt upon the copper-catalysed oxidation (by O_2) of cysteine (M/40) (20°). (*a*) M/10,000 cupric sulphate. (*b*) M/100,000 cupric sulphate. (*c*) As (*b*), but with M/500 cobaltous sulphate. Modified from Baur & Preis (1936).

easily oxidized. Although broth is a medium of low E_H, the E_0' of oxine-iron appears to be so much lower that it seems certain that iron-oxine is in the ferric form.* In practice it was found that the toxic action of oxine on staphylococci in distilled water was quantitatively identical, whether the iron was added as ferrous, or as ferric, sulphate.

It might be thought that a substance so prone to remain in the ferric state as iron-oxide would not be a good catalyst of oxidation. This is not so, because a mixture of inorganic iron and oxine catalyses the aerial

---

* E_H may be defined as the oxidation-reduction potential as recorded by a galvanometer under the conditions of the test. It is not a constant.

$$E_0 = E_H - \frac{RT}{nF} \, \mathit{In} \, \frac{[\text{ox}]}{[\text{red}]}$$

where R is the gas constant, T is the absolute temperature, F is the faraday, n the number of electrons concerned, In is the natural logarithm, [ox]/[red] is the ratio of concentrations of oxidized to reduced forms. E_0 (pronounced e-zero) is a constant provided the pH is 0. At any other pH, the sign E_0' is used, and the pH is specified, giving a series of pH-dependent constants.

oxidation of the —SH groups in nucleoproteins from rat liver and from fish eggs, whereas inorganic iron is ineffective on its own (Bernheim & Bernheim, 1939). The superior catalytic powers of iron-oxide probably spring from the rearrangement of the orbitals of the ferric cation caused by chelation (the unusual colours, red for ferrous-oxine and green for ferric-oxine are evidence of rearrangement). It is fair to assume that the toxic forms are the 1:1- or 1:2-ferric complexes because these are 'unsaturated', i.e. they have the residual combining power so necessary in a catalyst. The 1:3-complex (XI) is, on the other hand, saturated and unlikely to be a catalyst.

The site of action of iron-oxine is unknown, but any hypothesis must be consistent with the following facts. Derivatives of oxine having a low oil/water partition coefficient are not antibacterial. Thus oxine-5-sulphonic acid has the same stability constants as oxine (Albert, 1953a), but, unlike oxine, it does not tend to pass from water into lipids: also, it is without any antibacterial properties whatsoever. Now it is known (Davson & Danielli, 1952) that the penetration of non-metabolites through the semipermeable membrane that surrounds cells is small for ions, but considerable for unchanged molecules; small for substances with a low oil/water partition coefficient, but high if the coefficient is high. Thus oxine sulphonic acid should be excluded from cells on both counts, whereas oxine is likely to be admitted rapidly because it is not ionized and its partition coefficient is high (see Table 5).

To find if the high partition coefficient of oxine was essential for its antibacterial action, a series of *un*charged derivatives of oxine having low partition coefficients was synthesized and tested (Albert, Hampton, Selbie & Simon, 1954; Albert & Hampton, 1952, 1954). These are the aza-oxines which are dealt with under (ii) below. This series showed that antibacterial action fell and rose, as partition coefficients fell and rose in response to small changes in molecular structure. Thus a high partition coefficient plays a very important part in determining the action of oxine and related substances. It has been suggested that this is evidence that the action of oxine takes place *inside* the cell, although it is also possible that it takes place in the substance of the membrane. Finally, the factors which make for a high partition coefficient also confer some surface activity, so that it cannot quite be excluded that the action is on the outer surface of the cell membrane or even on the porous cell walls.

Any hypothesis of the site of action must be consistent, too, with the facts that the rapid bactericidal action of iron-oxine (3 min. often suffices) is much delayed if either an excess of iron is present or an excess of oxine (as in Table 3). For a hypothesis of action outside the semipermeable membrane, these facts would be consistent with the 2:1-ferric complex being toxic, and the 1:1- and 3:1-complexes non-toxic. For a hypothesis of action inside the membrane, the highly probable assumption is made that the unsaturated (1:1- and 2:1-) complexes are toxic but cannot penetrate, whereas the saturated (3:1-) complex can penetrate, but is non-toxic. In that case, death is brought about by the breakdown of the 3:1-complex inside the cell, giving a toxic 1:1- or 2:1-complex or even free ferric ions. (This extreme form of the hypothesis implies that the role of oxine has been to transport the iron into the cell, in larger amounts than its normally carefully regulated entry may permit.) In the presence of excess iron, only the 1:1-complex can be present; in the presence of excess oxine only the 3:1-complex, the breakdown of which would be prevented by oxine entering the cell at the same time (see p. 124).

Miscellaneous facts about oxine. In spite of its strong antibacterial action *in vitro*, and in wounds, oxine is useless in general chemotherapy, because it is inactivated by red blood cells (Rubbo *et al.* 1950). This is also true of substituted oxines, and other substances with an oxine-like action (Albert *et al.* 1954; Albert, Rees & Tomlinson, 1956). This phenomenon has been investigated further, and it would seem that the red cells produce a thermolabile substance, 'erythrochelatin', which binds the oxine loosely (Beckett & Smith, 1956, 1957).

Although the methyl ether of oxine (VIII) is not antibacterial, some of the higher ethers are active (Pershchin & Vichkanova, 1952). This seems to be the usual membrane-disrupting action of substances with long aliphatic side-chains.

The assimilation of glutamic acid by washed suspensions of *Staphylococcus aureus* is inhibited by oxine ($M/250$) and restored by manganese ($M/500$) (Gale, 1949). However, these concentrations are far higher than those concerned in the antibacterial action of oxine.

Oxine prevents the germination of spores of *Bacillus subtilis*. It remains on the outside, and can be removed by washing. After washing proliferation is as free as in untreated controls (Keilin & Hartree, 1947).

(ii) *Substances related to oxine in structure*

The antibacterial action of several substituted oxines has been examined and found to be high, so long as no substituent was permitted in the 2-position (a steric effect, apparently). Similarly a pyridine or benzene ring could be annelated on to oxine without loss of activity provided the 2:3-face was avoided (Albert *et al.* 1947). Work on the partition coefficient of substituted oxines shows that a fourfold increase over that of oxine does not improve the action (Albert *et al.* 1956). Many derivatives and analogues of oxine have been tested against the tubercle bacillus, mainly *in vitro*, where a potentiating action of copper (but not of iron), usually antagonized by cobalt, has been found (Erlenmeyer, Baümler & Roth, 1953).

(XII)   (XIII)   (XIV)

$$(CH_3)_2N.CSSC.N(CH_3)_2$$
(XV)

$$NaS_2C.NHCH_2CH_2NH.CS_2Na$$
(XVI)

The aza-oxines are a series of oxine analogues in which each $=CH-$ group has been replaced in turn by $=N-$; thus (XII) is 3-aza-oxine (8-hydroxyquinazoline), and so on. Other aza-oxines are hydroxy-naphthyridines, -cinnolines and -quinoxalines. It is evident from Table 5 that inserting an extra ring-nitrogen atom has lowered the partition coefficient,* and with this the antibacterial action has fallen to vanishing point. However, without removing the extra nitrogen atom, the partition coefficient has been raised (by inserting a small

Table 5. *The fall and rise of bacteriostatic action with fall and rise of partition coefficient*

(*Streptococcus pyogenes* in meat broth at pH 7·3 and 37°)

Substance	Partition coefficient oleyl alcohol/water	Lowest inhibitory dilution 1/M	Log first stability constant (Ni++)
Oxine	67	200,000	9·8
5-Aza-oxine	<0·02	<800	5·8
7-Aza-oxine	0·1	<800	6·7
6-Aza-oxine	1	<800	5·9
3-Aza-oxine	5	13,000	7·6
2-Aza-oxine	6	13,000	7·8
4-Aza-oxine	8	6,400	7·6
4-Methyl-2-aza-oxine	16	25,000	8·1
4-Methyl-3-aza-oxine	17	50,000	7·9
4-Propyl-3-aza-oxine	135	100,000	7·9
7-Allyl-3-aza-oxine	310	100,000	7·9

* Nitrogen and oxygen atoms lower (halogens and alkyl-groups raise) the partition coefficients.

9

alkyl-group, never exceeding three carbon atoms) up to, and even beyond, that of oxine. When this is done, the antibacterial action rises also, up to a maximum value (see Table 5) (Albert *et al.* 1954).

It will be observed that, although the high stability constant of oxine is not quite reached (namely, by one twofold serial dilution), the last seven substances in Table 5 all have stability constants of the same order. For these seven substances, the antibacterial action runs parallel to the partition coefficient, which establishes the correlation.

(iii) *Substances acting like oxine, but of a different structure*

Aspergillic acid, an antibiotic derived from pyrazine-*N*-oxide, is mildly antibacterial. The *N*-oxides of pyridine, quinoline, and benzoquinoline are similarly antibacterial provided that, as in aspergillic acid, a hydroxy-group is in the 2-position to make chelation possible. A mercapto-group has been found much better for this purpose: 2-mercaptopyridine oxide (XIII) is as intensely antibacterial as oxine. Although the chelated complex, e.g. (XIV), has an entirely different structure from that of oxine, e.g. (X), the mode of action is the same. The grounds for this conclusion are as follows: both substances are bactericidal only in the presence of iron; this action is prevented by cobalt, and also by an excess of the substance itself (Albert *et al.* 1956).

The fungicide dimethyldithiocarbamic acid ((I) is the copper complex) is much used in agriculture in the form of its sodium (NaDDC), iron, and zinc salts. In laboratory tests on *Aspergillus niger*, a triphasic effect is seen. The first zone of inhibition occurs at 1 part/million, but only if a trace of cobalt, or preferably copper is present (iron is ineffective). Increasing the concentration of NaDDC to 10 p.p.m. abolishes the action, due to the conversion of all the toxic 1:1-complex (I) to a saturated 2:1-complex. The third phase, which appears in concentrations of 50 p.p.m. or more, is again a toxic one, and is believed to be an intrinsic toxicity of the substance, unconnected with metal-binding. When it is recalled that copper, but not iron, is a co-toxicant of oxine for this same fungus (p. 124), and that cobalt does not antagonize copper-oxine in this fungus, the action of NaDDC is seen to be close to that of oxine (Goksøyr, 1955*a*, *b*; Sijpesteijn, Janssen & van der Kerk, 1957). The apparently anomalous action of cobalt-NaDDC may be explained after measurement of oxidation-reduction potentials.

Tetramethylthiuram disulphide (XV), the product of oxidation of NaDDC, is also widely used as an agricultural fungicide. It is believed to act after reduction to NaDDC. However, the apparently related fungicide, dithane (disodium ethylene-*bis*dithiocarbamate) (XVI), acts in a quite different way, namely by conversion to ethylene*bisiso*thiocyanate.

Ethylenediaminetetra-acetic acid (EDTA) is incapable of penetrating bacterial and mammalian cells, alone, or in combination with metals; moreover, it is not in the least antibacterial. Nevertheless, ferric-EDTA has the property of being able to penetrate the roots of plants, and is widely used to correct iron-deficiency chlorosis in fruit and vegetable crops (Weinstein, Robbins & Perkins, 1954).

The organic portion of ferric-EDTA, isotopically labelled in the nitrogen atoms, was found to be oxidized in maize plants so that inorganic iron was liberated. Sunlight helps to break down this iron complex (Krugers & Agterdenbos, 1957).

(iv) *Further examples of the co-operative effect*

That metal complexes can be chemically more vigorous than the metals themselves has been exemplified by oxine (p. 127). Even apart from the porphyrin enzymes, this is quite a common phenomenon. Hence the practice of adding metal-binding substances to sequester a metal may often aggravate the very effect that it is desired to suppress. The offending metals are usually, but not always, those with more than one valency state, particularly copper and iron. The co-operative effect is most likely to be encountered if insufficient metal-binding agent is added, so that the complex is unsaturated (see p. 116).

The earliest recorded instance of the co-operative effect concerns the proteolysis of calves' pancreatic protein by cathepsin at pH 4 (Michaelis & Stern, 1931). This process is accelerated by zinc and ferrous ions, and still more if these metals are first bound to dipyridyl; on the other hand, the iron complex of acetylacetone inactivates the enzyme, the very reverse of a co-operative effect.

Other examples will now be given. The oxidative blackening of dihydroxyphenylalanine in the presence of cupric sulphate is greatly accelerated if *o*-phenanthroline is added (Isaka, 1957). The oxidation of glutathione in an extract of ocular lens tissue is accelerated in the presence of EDTA (Pirie & van Heyningen, 1954). Both *o*-phenanthroline and dipyridyl increase the rate of iron-catalysed decomposition of hydrogen peroxide by a hundredfold: these are, in fact, models for catalase, and perhaps other haemoprotein enzymes. Both peroxidase and catalase are imitated by manganese, cobalt and iron in the presence of pyridoxalphosphate-ethylenediamine or disulphosalylidene-ethylenediamine (Langenbeck & Oehler, 1956). Disalicylidene-ethylenediamine retards the autoxidation of *cyclo*hexene when it is catalysed by copper, accelerates it greatly when it is catalysed by iron, and does not influence the considerable catalysis of cobalt or manganese ions (Chalk & Smith, 1954).

The copper-catalysed hydrolysis of di*iso*propyl fluorophosphate is much accelerated by amino acids, ethylenediamine, *o*-phenanthroline and dipyridyl. The best proportions are those which give a 1:1-complex (Wagner-Jauregg, Hackley, Lies, Owens & Proper, 1955). EDTA does not show this effect, indeed it is not a co-operator for copper.

(c) *Substances whose biological action may not be due entirely to their metal-binding action*

Isoniazid (the hydrazide of *iso*nicotinic acid) (XVII, R = H), which is used with great success in the treatment of human tuberculosis, has an affinity for the ions of heavy metals. This affinity is of the same order as that of glycine (Albert, 1953*b*). In order to form complexes, isoniazid must first form the anion (XVIII). Because an anion cannot be formed from 1-*iso*-nicototinyl-1-methylhydrazine (XVII, R = CH$_3$), the inactivity of this substance *in vitro* is good evidence that isoniazid acts in tuberculosis through chelation (Cymerman-Craig, Rubbo, Willis & Edgar, 1955; Cymerman-Craig & Willis, 1955).

However, its action can hardly be due to chelation alone, because neither of its two isomers has any notable action against *Mycobacterium tuberculosis*, even *in vitro*, although their stability constants are as high, or higher (Albert, 1956). Other hypotheses of the mode of action of this drug (that it combines with pyridoxal, that it displaces nicotinamide from diphosphopyridine nucleotide) have helped understanding of the toxic side-effects of isoniazid on patients; but its action on the bacterium, so plainly tied to chelation, remains to be fully explained.

Strains of *Mycobacterium tuberculosis*, made highly resistant to isoniazid, are still fully sensitive to 'Tibione' (*p*-acetamidobenzaldehyde thiosemicarbazone) which cannot, therefore, act by exactly the same mechanism. This substance is metal-binding, but nothing is known about its constants.

The tetracycline family of antibiotics (tetracycline, terramycin, and aureomycin) chelate divalent metals with about the same avidity as glycine. The principal difference is their strong affinity for trivalent metals, so that high K_s values (25 and 19) are reached for Fe^{+++} and Al^{+++} respectively (Albert & Rees, 1956). The action of the tetracyclines on bacteria is much slower than that of oxine; moreover they are active in iron-depleted media. Hence the mode of action must be different from that of oxine. Yet chelation is likely to play a part in it, because substances with constants of this magnitude could not fail to compete for metals in the tissues.

(XVII)   (XVIII)

DISCUSSION

The phenomena that have been outlined above fall into three distinct classes. The first class, discussed under (*a*) (p. 120), covers effects obtained by the inactivation of a metal in its biological setting, e.g. hydrogen cyanide or sodium azide poisoning. This inactivation is followed, in some cases, by the removal of the metal from that setting, e.g. the use of such antidotes as dimercaprol (BAL) to counteract mercury poisoning, and the calcium salt of ethylenediaminetetra-acetic acid (EDTA) in lead poisoning.

The second class, discussed under (*b*) (pp. 121–132), covers effects obtained by *increasing the activity* of a metal. This may take the form of increasing its local concentration by acting as a carrier. The use of EDTA to ferry iron from the soil into plants is a well authenticated example of this (p. 131). In this connexion it may be recalled that the toxic action of encephalomyelitis virus, which is rich in iron, has been ascribed to transporting ferrous ions across the blood-brain barrier which normally is impervious to them (Racker & Krimsky, 1947). Alternatively the activation of the metal can take place in a chemical sense, either by changing the oxidation-reduction potential, or by altering the distribution of electrons even to the point of making hidden orbitals available. (Several examples of this chemical activation (termed the 'co-operative effect'), are described on p. 131.) Of substances belonging to this second class, none has been more thoroughly investigated than 8-hydroxy-quinoline (oxine). The story of how and why it is bactericidal and fungicidal in dilute, but not in concentrated, solution (pp. 123–124) might profitably be re-read at this stage, because it brings to light some important facts which have to be taken into account in any further development of the second class of metal-binding agents. The specific antagonism by cobalt, apparently the result of breaking a destructive chain reaction, is particularly noteworthy.

A third type of metal-binding drug is discussed under (c) (p. 132), namely, those which avidly bind metals, but whose therapeutic action has not been shown to depend entirely on this phenomenon. Isoniazid and the tetracyclines are examples. The evidence for chelation being involved in the action is very strong for isoniazid. It is not known whether these substances work by activation, or by inactivation of metals.

Looking at the most useful members of each of the three classes, we may be excused for thinking that many other good metal-binding drugs will be discovered, including some superior to those in use today. But how is that goal to be reached? Most of the chelating agents used in analytical work lack antibacterial properties (Albert *et al.* 1947; Schraufstätter, 1950); hence it is evident that the mere possession of metal-binding properties is not enough to ensure success. Obviously for a substance to be a successful metal-binding drug, the stability constants must exceed certain critical values. It seems likely that these critical values are the stability constants of the common amino acids, in so far as the drug will be competing with these for metals (free or combined), in the medium and tissues. The constants for glycine (see Table 1) are typical of all but two of the common amino acids, and afford a clue as to the minimal values to be aimed at. Unfortunately, it is not yet known how to predict the stability constants of substances in advance of synthesis and measurement, so that much effort will be wasted at this stage until better rules for prediction are evolved.

Another desideratum for a metal-binding antiparasitic drug may well be ease of penetration of the cell that it is required to injure. There are indications that this is so in the oxine series (see p. 127, and Table 5) from the fact that a high partition coefficient (i.e. one that favours leaving water for lipids) made all the difference between high activity and inactivity. The raising of the partition coefficient to a given value is not a difficult task for the chemist, provided that the substance is not ionized. There are, of course, other ways of persuading a substance to enter a cell, e.g. it may be made to resemble a nutrient or a metabolite. In this connexion, it seems important to find out whether isoniazid and the tetracyclines penetrate bacterial cells and, if so, does the high therapeutic index (i.e. the selectivity) depend on their not being able to enter mammalian cells, or even on their being excluded by the mito-chondrial membrane. There is no doubt that improvement of specificity requires studies of distribution, and of the comparative biochemistry of parasite and host.

These are, perhaps, the principal signposts for the biologist and bio-chemist, but special problems exist for the chemist, too. The possibility that some of the oxine in iron-oxine must be destroyed in the cell in order to unmask the true antibacterial agent (p. 128), may have a wider application. In discussing 2-mercaptopyridine-*N*-oxide, which is more readily oxidized than oxine, this point has been further emphasized (Albert *et al.* 1956). If there is anything in this concept, it would be profitable to examine (*inter alia*) substances which are readily meta-bolized, or which are likely to be partly consumed in any chain reaction which they initiate. Although it is not suggested that all metal-binding drugs initiate chain reactions, or exert the 'co-operative effect', the study of oxidation-reduction potentials of chelated complexes is likely to provide one of the most important chemical contributions to defining the biological limitations of the subject. An equally important contri-bution from chemists will be the investigation of the orbitals concerned in metal-binding substances of therapeutic value.

REFERENCES

ÅGREN, A. (1954). The complex formation between iron (III) ion and some phenols. II. Salicylic acid and *p*-aminosalicylic acid. *Acta chem. scand.* **8**, 1059.

ALBERT, A. (1944). Kationic chemotherapy with special reference to the acridines. *Med. J. Aust.* i, 245.

ALBERT, A. (1950). Quantitative studies of the avidity of naturally occurring sub-stances for trace metals. I. Amino-acids having only two ionizing groups. *Biochem. J.* **47**, 531.

ALBERT, A. (1952). Quantitative studies of the avidity of naturally occurring sub-stances for trace metals. II. Amino-acids having three ionizing groups. *Biochem. J.* **50**, 690.

ALBERT, A. (1953*a*). Quantitative studies of the avidity of naturally occurring sub-stances for trace metals. III. Pteridines, riboflavin and purines. *Biochem. J.* **54**, 646.

ALBERT, A. (1953*b*). The affinity of *iso*nicotinic hydrazide for metals. *Experientia*, **9**, 370.

ALBERT, A. (1956). Mode of action of isoniazid. *Nature, Lond.* **177**, 525.

ALBERT, A., GIBSON, M. I. & RUBBO, S. D. (1953). The influence of chemical constitution on antibacterial activity. Part VI. The bactericidal action of 8-hydroxyquinoline (oxine). *Brit. J. exp. Path.* **34**, 119.

ALBERT, A. & HAMPTON, A. (1952). Analogues of 8-hydroxyquinoline having additional cyclic nitrogen atoms. Part I. Preparative. *J. chem. Soc.* p. 4985.

ALBERT, A. & HAMPTON, A. (1954). Analogues of 8-hydroxyquinoline having additional cyclic nitrogen atoms. Part II. Further preparations, and some physico-chemical properties. *J. chem. Soc.* p. 505.

ALBERT, A., HAMPTON, A., SELBIE, F. R. & SIMON, R. D. (1954). The influence of chemical constitution on antibacterial activity. Part VII. The site of action of 8-hydroxy-quinoline (oxine). *Brit. J. exp. Path.* **35**, 75.

ALBERT, A. & REES, C. W. (1956). Avidity of the tetracyclines for the cations of metals. *Nature, Lond.* **177**, 433.

136   A. ALBERT

ALBERT, A., REES, C. W. & TOMLINSON, A. J. H. (1956). The influence of chemical constitution on antibacterial activity. Part VIII. 2-Mercaptopyridine-N-oxide and some general observations on metal-binding agents. *Brit. J. exp. Path.* **37**, 500.

ALBERT, A., RUBBO, S. D., GOLDACRE, R. J. & BALFOUR, B. G. (1947). The influence of chemical constitution on antibacterial activity. Part III. A study of 8-hydroxy-quinoline (oxine) and related compounds. *Brit. J. exp. Path.* **28**, 69.

ANDERSON, B. & SWABY, R. J. (1951). Factors influencing the fungistatic action of 8-hydroxyquinoline (oxine) and its metal complexes. *Aust. J. sci. Res.* B, **4**, 275.

ATKINS, D. C. & GARNER, C. S. (1952). Isotopic exchange reactions of zinc chelate complexes. *J. Amer. chem. Soc.* **74**, 3527.

BACQ, Z.-M., HERVÉ, A. & FISCHER, P. (1953). Rayons X et agents de chelation. *Bull. Acad. Méd. Belg.* Sér. VI, **18**, 226.

BAUR, E. & PREIS, H. (1936). Über die Oxydationshemmung von Cystein und Ascorbinsäure. *Z. phys. Chem.* B, **32**, 65.

BECKETT, A. H. & SMITH, W. G. (1956). Erythrocytin: an inhibitor of 8-hydroxy-quinoline ('oxine') derived from erythrocytes. *Nature, Lond.* **178**, 742.

BECKETT, A. H. & SMITH, W. G. (1957). 'Erythrocytin' and 'erythrochelatin'. *Nature, Lond.* **179**, 54.

BENNETT, W. E. (1957). Stepwise mixed complex formation. *J. Amer. chem. Soc.* **79**, 1290.

BERNHEIM, F. & BERNHEIM, M. L. C. (1939). The effect of various metals and metal complexes on the oxidation of sulfhydryl groups. *Cold Spr. Harb. Symp. quant. Biol.* **7**, 174.

BJERRUM, J. (1941). *Metal ammine formation in aqueous solution. Theory of the reversible step reactions.* Copenhagen: Haase.

BLOCK, S. S. (1956). Reversal of fungitoxicity of copper-8-quinolinolate. *J. agr. food chem.* **4**, 1042.

CHALK, A. J. & SMITH, J. F. (1954). Effect of chelating agents on heavy metal catalysis. *Nature, Lond.* **174**, 802.

CYMERMAN-CRAIG, J., RUBBO, S. D., WILLIS, D. & EDGAR, J. (1955). Mode of action of *iso*nicotinic hydrazide. *Nature, Lond.* **176**, 34.

CYMERMAN-CRAIG, J. & WILLIS, D. (1955). The chemotherapy of tuberculosis. Part VI. Some derivatives of *iso*nicotinic acid. *J. chem. Soc.* p. 4315.

DATTA, S. P. & RABIN, B. R. (1956). The chelation of metal ions by dipeptides and related compounds. *Biochem. biophys. Acta*, **19**, 572.

DAVSON, H. & DANIELLI, J. F. (1952). *The Permeability of Natural Membranes*, 2nd ed. Cambridge: The University Press.

DOBBIE, H. & KERMACK, W. O. (1955). Complex-formation between polypeptides and metals. 2. The reaction between cupric ions and some dipeptides. *Biochem. J.* **59**, 246.

DONALD, C., PASSEY, B. I. & SWABY, R. J. (1952). A comparison of methods for removing trace metals from microbiological media. *J. gen. Microbiol.* **7**, 211.

ERLENMEYER, H., BAÜMLER, J. & ROTH, W. (1953). Metallkomplexe und tuber-kulostatische Aktivität. *Helv. chim. acta*, **36**, 941.

GALE, E. F. (1949). The assimilation of amino-acids by bacteria. 8. Trace metals in glutamic acid assimilation and their inactivation by 8-hydroxyquinoline. *J. gen. Microbiol.* **3**, 369.

GOKSØYR, J. (1955a). Reversal of the fungicidal effect of dithiocarbamyl compounds. *Nature, Lond.* **175**, 820.

GOKSØYR, J. (1955b). The effect of some dithiocarbamyl compounds on the metabolism of fungi. *Physiol. Plant.* **8**, 719.

GOODMAN, L. S. & GILMAN, A. (1955). *The Pharmacological Basis of Therapeutics*, 2nd ed. New York: Macmillan.

GREATHOUSE, G., BLOCK, S., KOVACH, E., BARNES, D., BYRON, C., LONG, G., GERBER, D. & McLENNY, J. (1954). Research on chemical compounds for inhibition of fungi. U.S. Corps of Engineers, Fort Belvoir, Virginia.

GURD, F. R. N. & GOODMAN, DE W. S. (1952). Preparation and properties of serum and plasma proteins. XXXII. The interaction of human serum albumin with zinc ions. *J. Amer. chem. Soc.* 74, 670.

HAHN, P. F., BALE, W. F., ROSS, J. F., HETTIG, R. A. & WHIPPLE, G. H. (1940). Radio-iron in plasma does not exchange with haemoglobin iron in red cells. *Science*, 92, 131.

HEALY, G. M., MORGAN, J. F. & PARKER, R. C. (1952). Trace metal content of some natural and synthetic media. *J. biol. Chem.* 198, 305.

IRVING, H. & WILLIAMS, R. J. P. (1953). The stability of transition-metal complexes. *J. chem. Soc.* p. 3192.

ISAKA, S. (1957). Effects of some copper complexes upon the formation *in vitro* of melanin. *Nature, Lond.*, 179, 578.

KEILIN, D. & HARTREE, E. F. (1947). Comparative study of spores and vegetative forms of *Bacillus subtilis*. *Antonie van Leeuwenhoek J. Microbiol. Serol.* 12, 115.

KLOTZ, I. M. & LOH MING, W.-C. (1954). Mediation by metals of the binding of small molecules by proteins. *J. Amer. chem. Soc.* 76, 805.

KRUGERS, J. & AGTERDENBOS, J. (1957). Photosensitivity of the iron (III) ethylene-diaminetetra-acetate complex. *Nature, Lond.* 179, 45.

LANGENBECK, W. & OEHLER, K. (1956). Organische Katalysatoren, XLII. Chelat-katalysen III. *Chem. Ber.* 89, 2455.

LI, N. C., WHITE, J. M. & DOODY, E. (1954). Cadmium and copper complexes of imidazole and 1-methylimidazole. *J. Amer. chem. Soc.* 76, 6219.

MARGOSHES, M. & VALLEE, B. (1957). A cadmium protein from equine kidney cortex. *J. Amer. chem. Soc.* 79, 4813.

MARTELL, A. E. & SCHWARZENBACH, G. (1956). Adenosinphosphate und Triphosphat als Komplexbildner für Calcium und Magnesium. *Helv. chim. acta*, 39, 653.

MICHAELIS, L. & STERN, K. G. (1931). Über den Einfluss von Schwermetallen und Metallkomplexen auf proteolytische Vorgänge. *Biochem. Z.* 240, 192.

MILES, A. A. & MISRA, S. S. (1938). The estimation of the bactericidal power of the blood. *J. Hyg., Camb.* 38, 732.

NORDBRING-HERTZ, B. (1955). Studies on growth and inhibition of *Candida albicans*. *Physiol. Plant.* 8, 691.

PERSHCHIN, G. & VICHKANOVA, S. (1952). Action of 8-hydroxy-quinolines and their derivatives on acid-fast bacteria. *Pharmakologiya i Toxocologiya*, 15, 38 (in Russian).

PETERS, R. A., STOCKEN, L. A. & THOMPSON, R. H. S. (1945). British anti-lewisite (BAL). *Nature, Lond.* 156, 616.

PIPER, C. S. (1942). Investigations on copper deficiency in plants. *J. agric. Sci.* 32, 143.

PIRIE, A. & VAN HEYNINGEN, R. (1954). Oxidation of glutathione in extracts of lens in the presence of ethylenediaminetetra-acetate. *Nature, Lond.* 173, 873.

RACKER, E. & KRIMSKY, I. (1947). Relation of iron salts to inhibition of glycolysis by Theiler FA virus of mouse encephalomyelitis. *J. exp. Med.* 85, 715.

RUBBO, S. D., ALBERT, A. & GIBSON, M. I. (1950). The influence of chemical constitution on antibacterial activity. Part V. The antibacterial action of 8-hydroxyquinoline (oxine). *Brit. J. exp. Path.* 31, 425.

SCHRAUFSTÄTTER, E. (1950). Schwermetallkomplexbildung und antibakterielle Wirkung. *Z. Naturf.* 5b, 190.

SCHUBERT, J. & LINDENBAUM, A. (1952). Stability of alkaline earth-organic acid complexes measured by ion exchange. *J. Amer. chem. Soc.* **74**, 3529.

SEGAL, L., JONASSEN, H. & REEVES, R. E. (1956). The reaction between the copper (II)-ethylenediamine complexes and D-mannosan. *J. Amer. chem. Soc.* **78**, 273.

SIJPESTEIJN, A. K., JANSSEN, M. J. & VAN DER KERK, G. J. M. (1957). Investigations on organic fungicides. XI. The role of metals and chelating agents in the fungitoxic action of sodium dimethyldithiocarbamate (NaDDC). *Biochim. biophys. Acta.* **23**, 550.

SOCIETY FOR GENERAL MICROBIOLOGY (1956). *Constituents of Bacteriological Culture Media.* Cambridge: University Press.

TANFORD, C. (1952). The effect of pH on the combination of serum albumin with metals. *J. Amer. chem. Soc.* **74**, 211.

WAGNER-JAUREGG, T., HACKLEY, JUN., B. E., LIES, T. A., OWENS, O. O. & PROPER, R. (1955). Model reactions of phosphorus-containing enzyme inactivators. IV. The catalytic activity of certain metal salts and chelates in the hydrolysis of di-isopropyl fluorophosphate. *J. Amer. chem. Soc.* **77**, 922.

WALSHE, J. (1956). Penicillamine, a new oral therapy for Wilson's disease. *Amer. J. Med.* **21**, 487.

WARING, W. S. & WERKMAN, C. H. (1942). Growth of bacteria in an iron-free medium. *Arch. Biochem.* **1**, 303.

VAN WAZER, J. R. & HOLST, K. A. (1950). Structure and properties of the condensed phosphates. 1. Some general considerations about phosphoric acids. *J. Amer. chem. Soc.* **72**, 639.

WEINSTEIN, L. H., ROBBINS, W. R. & PERKINS, H. F. (1954). Chelating agents and plant nutrition. *Science*, **120**, 41.

ZENTMYER, G. A. (1944). Inhibition of metal catalysis as a fungistatic mechanism. *Science*, **100**, 294.

THE DESIGNING OF ANTIMETABOLITES

D. W. WOOLLEY

The Rockefeller Institute for Medical Research, New York

Because antimetabolites have proved so useful both for the study of metabolic reactions and for chemotherapy, an increasing number of people has wished to learn how to design them. Despite numerous statements that the antimetabolite approach to chemotherapy is a hopeless pursuit, and that we must put our efforts into chance discoveries of useful drugs, the successes which have attended the application of the antimetabolite concept attract more and more investigators to it. Consequently, one must now inquire into the basic principles involved in the designing of these compounds.

The plan to be followed in this discussion is first to summarize some of these basic principles, and then, lest you should feel that these are only hypotheses, to show how, by application of them, two classes of useful therapeutic agents have been discovered. These two classes are not the only ones which have been so discovered, but time is short, and the art is long. A somewhat more comprehensive discussion can be found in a book published in 1952 entitled *A Study of Antimetabolites* (Woolley, 1952 a).

GENERAL PRINCIPLES

Structural changes needed to convert a metabolite into an antimetabolite

Given a vitally essential compound (i.e. a metabolite) of known chemical structure, how are we to change this structure so that it will act as an antimetabolite? Here we should recall the way in which antimetabolites act. They take the place of the essential metabolite in an enzymic or semi-enzymic reaction; they do this because they are shaped much like the essential metabolite. The metabolite acts as substrate for some specific protein which is usually an enzyme; the antimetabolite, because it resembles the metabolite, combines with the active centre of this protein, but, because it is slightly different from the metabolite, it does not undergo the usual reaction to form products. This usual reaction is impeded or completely stopped with the result that a specific deficiency of the metabolites is created. Our problem then is to inquire into the structural changes which will convert a metabolite into an antimetabolite, that is into a compound which will still combine with the active centre of the specific protein.

In 1944 some general principles were deduced as to how this was to be done (Woolley, 1944). The experience of the succeeding fourteen years has proved their soundness and also provided us with additional generalizations, some of which may be summarized as follows:

(*a*) If a metabolite is a carboxylic acid, it may be converted into an antimetabolite by replacement of the carboxyl group with some other

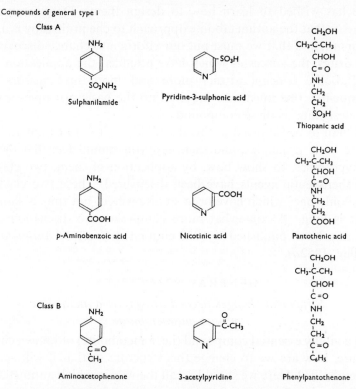

Fig. 1. Analogues of carboxyl-containing metabolites. Class A, sulphonic acid analogues; class B, substitution with alkyl- or aryl-group.

acidic group; sulphonic acid or sulphonamide radicals or sufficiently negative ketonic groups are usually employed. A few examples may be seen in Fig. 1. The nature of the grouping to be substituted for the carboxyl depends on the particular living systems for which the anti-metabolite is intended, because special requirements greatly influence the choice of the new group to be employed. Some of the points to be taken into consideration will be discussed later.

(*b*) If the metabolite contains a ring (and many of them do) the exchange of one atom in this ring for another frequently gives rise to very potent antimetabolites. Thus, a carbon atom may replace a nitrogen, or an oxygen a sulphur. A particularly useful change is to replace a sulphur atom in the ring with —C=C—, converting, for example, thiamine into pyrithiamine. The converse (the replacement of —C=C— by S) leads from the metabolite phenylalanine to the potent antimetabolite thienylalanine. A few other examples of this class are shown in Fig. 2. This type of change has been a fruitful one for the development of antimetabolites, and consequently there are scores of examples.

(*c*) If a metabolite contains a hydroxyl or amino group attached to an aromatic ring the replacement of the one by the other frequently yields highly active antimetabolites. Thus, if the —NH$_2$ in thiamine, is replaced by —OH we obtain oxythiamine, a rather good antithiamine. Conversely, when the —OH group of folic acid is replaced by —NH$_2$ we get the powerful antimetabolite of folic acid called aminopterin. There are many more examples of this class which cannot be mentioned now; however, it is worth noting that this type of change frequently confers on the antimetabolite a certain degree of irreversibility which, as we shall see, is a desirable character in a compound to be used in chemotherapy.

(*d*) The replacement of hydrogen atoms or methyl groups in a metabolite with halogen atoms frequently gives rise to good anti-metabolites. If a hydrogen atom is to be replaced, the halogen of choice is fluorine, as it has usually been found to give the most active compound, whereas chlorine or bromine atoms yield less potent analogues. However, if a methyl group in the metabolite is to be replaced, a chlorine atom is usually the best choice; bromine or iodine analogues are usually less potent. Well-known examples of this class are 5-bromouracil, a thymine antagonist, and *p*-fluorophenylalanine, an antimetabolite of phenylalanine. A recent member of the series which has shown chemo-therapeutic promise is 5-fluorouracil, a powerful uracil antagonist (Heidelberger *et al.* 1957). It is of some interest that the physical sizes of —Cl and —CH$_3$ and of —F and —H are comparable.

(*e*) Replacement of a hydrogen atom in the metabolite by a fluorine atom is not the only way of making potent antimetabolites; exchange of hydrogen for a methyl group or for a hydroxyl group frequently gives rise to very powerful antimetabolites. In fact, Nature has taken advantage of this fact because we find that several of the naturally occurring antimetabolites differ from their corresponding metabolites in just this way. Cases in point are threonine and serine or testosterone and estrone. In the laboratory this rule has been very useful in the production of such potent antiserotonins as 2:5-dimethylserotonin and of ω-methylpantothenic acid.

(*f*) Rather than to list more types of structural alteration that will convert a metabolite into an antimetabolite, it will be better to point out some of the changes which were not successful. One of these is inversion

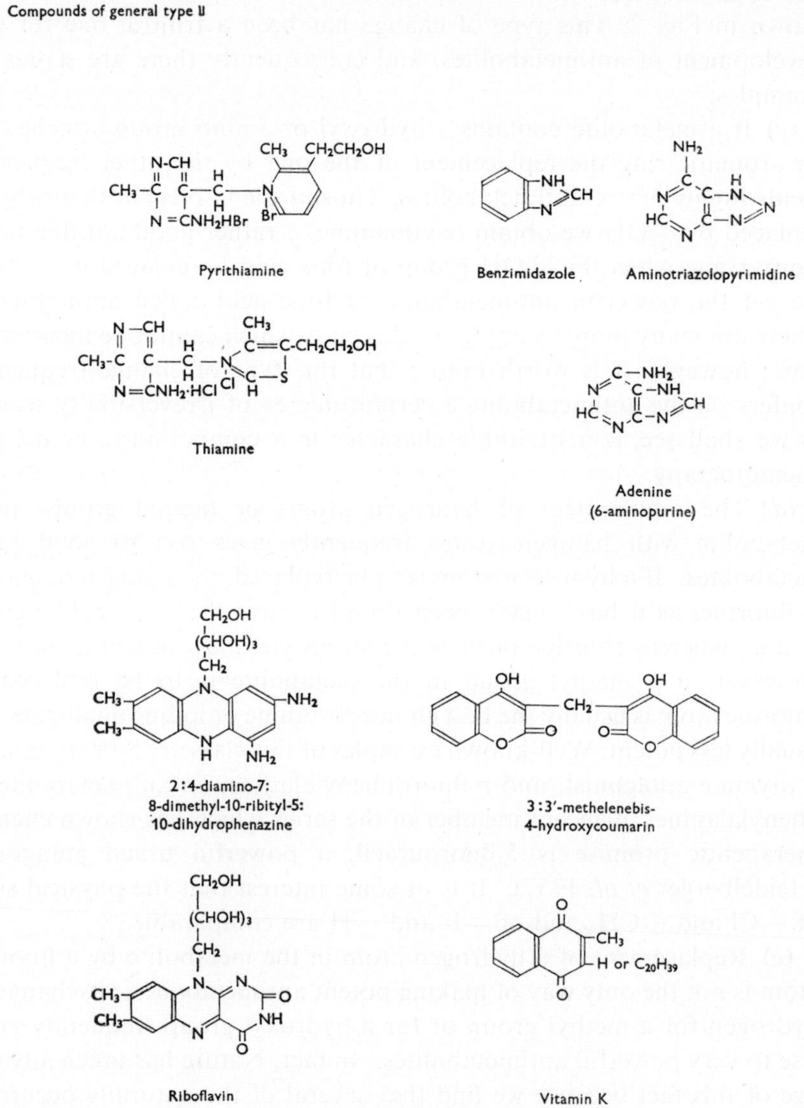

Compounds of general type II

Pyrithiamine

Benzimidazole

Aminotriazolopyrimidine

Thiamine

Adenine
(6-aminopurine)

2:4-diamino-7:
8-dimethyl-10-ribityl-5:
10-dihydrophenazine

3:3'-methelenebis-
4-hydroxycoumarin

Riboflavin

Vitamin K

Fig. 2. Analogues with atoms in the ring changed.

of the optical centre of a metabolite; the optical isomers have in general proved to be inert as antimetabolites, although there have been a few exceptions to this generalization. Furthermore, the importance of the optical configuration for union to the specific protein is shown by the fact that although (+)-pantoyltaurine is an antipantothenic acid, (−)-pantoyltaurine is not. Pantothenic acid is (+). When one reflects upon the mode of action of antimetabolites as outlined above, it is not surprising that there should be this preference for the optical configuration of the metabolite.

The optimal magnitude of change in structure

If we wish to convert a metabolite into a potent antimetabolite, is it better to make a small change in structure or a large one? Should we make as many changes as we know how, or should we make the least possible number? There are many qualifications to be discussed subsequently, but in general the answer is that the most potent antimetabolites are the ones which involve the smallest structural change from the metabolite. This basic fact is frequently obscured because the testing of the biological activity of an antimetabolite is conducted in a complex organism, in which extraneous factors such as penetration to the site of action and protection from destruction en route to this site are important considerations. It is enlightening to see how, in so many instances, the truth of the generalization becomes evident as the test system is simplified. Thus, in the sulphonamide drugs, we may be misled by the fact that sulphadiazine is more potent as a chemotherapeutic agent than sulphanilamide itself, and assume that the more complicated sulphadiazine is the more active at the enzyme site. Sulphadiazine is less like the metabolite p-aminobenzoic acid (p-AB) in structure than is sulphanilamide, but it has been shown that its therapeutic superiority is merely a reflexion of a secondary property. Sulphadiazine, at pH 7·4 (the pH value of blood), penetrates the bacterial cell more readily than does sulphanilamide; when a pH value is chosen at which both sulphadiazine and sulphanilamide are equally ionized, and hence can penetrate the bacterial cell equally, the superiority of sulphadiazine disappears. The structural feature of sulphadiazine which confers on it its chemotherapeutic superiority over sulphanilamide is the substituted sulphonamide grouping; this gives sulphadiazine a dissociation constant more favourable than that of sulphanilamide, so that at pH 7·4 the former can pass into the bacterial cell to a greater extent. There is reason to believe that at the actual site of action (the specific enzyme site) sulphanilamide is more active as an antagonist to *p*-AB than is sulphadiazine, sulphanil-amide appearing to fit the enzyme site more closely and tightly. If this be true and we could provide sulphanilamide with a temporary grouping to allow easy passage of the molecule into the bacterial cell at pH 7·4 which would be removed by some metabolic reaction inside the cell once it had entered, we might reasonably expect such a derivative to be much more potent than sulphadiazine, and in fact to exceed the limit of potency set up by Bell & Roblin (1942) for compounds of the sulphanil-amide class. This greater potency would result from the greater ability of sulphanilamide itself, once it has reached its site of action, to combine with the *p*-aminobenzoic acid site on the enzyme. Being closer in chemical shape than sulphadiazine to *p*-AB, one would expect this greater activity.

This discussion should bring out the point that the most active anti-metabolites are those which differ only slightly in structure from the related metabolite, provided that barriers to passage into cells and similar extraneous matters do not enter the picture. However, such extraneous matters are a very large part of the chemotherapeutic picture, and for this reason we must now turn our attention to the ways in which structural features can be built into a molecule so that it will survive passage through the blood stream, and be able to reach its site of action easily. We may then be able to make the smallest structural change in order to convert the metabolite into the most active antimetabolite, and then to provide the minimal number of additional structural features so that the drug will reach its site of action safely and will persist there once it has reached it.

Irreversible action and some ways to achieve it

The question of irreversible action of an antimetabolite is a very sore one among devotees of these compounds. The purists among us refuse even to speak of the matter; to them, the action of a structural analogue must be freely and competitively reversible by the metabolite if it is to be considered an antimetabolite at all. To illustrate this point, let us say that we have a poisonous compound, the structure of which looks much like that of biotin; suppose too that it causes symptoms which look like those of biotin deficiency. But suppose that these symptoms are not overcome by increasing the amount of biotin in the system; shall we call this compound an antimetabolite of biotin? The purists say no. To them, the ability to reverse the action of the analogue by increases in the concentration of metabolite is the *sine qua non* of antimetabolites. Much controversy has raged on this point. The arguments for and against can be found in *A Study of Antimetabolites*, ch. 3 (Woolley, 1952 *a*). However, for the present discussion the point at issue is a very real one; it is that many of the most potent analogues of metabolites are the ones with an irreversible action. We might say that the irreversibly active analogues are good for the practice but bad for the theory of antimetabolites.

Actually, however, there is no theoretical difficulty posed by these irreversibly active compounds; they may be regarded as antimetabolites which are attracted to the specific site on the enzyme or semi-enzyme with which the metabolite reacts. Like the orthodox (reversible) antimetabolites they are attracted to that site because of their structural resemblance to the metabolite. However, once there they combine irreversibly, and cannot be removed merely by an increase in the concentration of the metabolite. Because of the irreversible nature of the combination, these antimetabolites are frequently remarkable for their high potency and prolonged action. In an organism there is usually a considerable quantity of the metabolite free to counteract the effect of a conventional (reversible) antimetabolite. For the irreversibly acting analogues this poses no problem; they do not compete with the metabolite, they just exclude it completely.

Several ways are known for making irreversibly active antimetabolites. One of these is to provide the molecule with some chemically reactive groups. Phenolic- or imino-groups have been used with great effect, as in aminopterin. Another useful method is to provide halogen atoms in the antimetabolite; even though the halogens may be chemically unreactive, as in the dichloro-analogue of riboflavin, they can still confer an irreversible character. However, when they are chemically reactive they almost always give an irreversible character. Another useful way is to provide a nitro-group in the antimetabolite in place of an amino-group or even of a methyl-group or hydrogen atom. Chloramphenicol (chloromycetin), which has been shown to act as an antimetabolite of phenylalanine (Woolley, 1950 *a*) has not only the nitro group but also two chemically reactive chlorine atoms. Its action is characterized by irreversibility in all but a limited range of concentration.

A second way of achieving irreversibility deserves attention, because it has provided us with some very potent and useful compounds; this is to make what have been termed aggregate analogues (Woolley, 1952 *b*). Two metabolites which are known to participate in a connected chain of metabolic reactions are selected and then converted into antimetabolites which are united into one single molecule. The belief is that one end of this aggregate analogue unites with the active site for one metabolite, and the other end with the active site for the second metabolite; the two sites being postulated to be physically close together in the cell. Even though the arrival of one of the metabolites displaces one end of the aggregate it is still attached by the other end and hence does not become dislodged completely. Compounds of this sort have been made which are directed at both *p*-aminobenzoic acid and dimethyldiaminobenzene. This latter metabolite has been indicated to be a precursor for the synthesis of vitamin B_{12} and of riboflavin. Two of these aggregate analogues, the more active of which is DCDNS, are shown in Fig. 3.

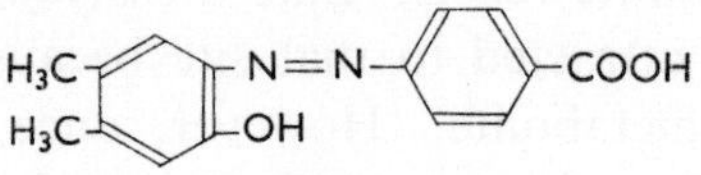

Fig. 3. Aggregate analogues. CPA = 1:2-dimethyl-4-carboxyphenylazo-5-hydroxybenzene. DCDNS = 1:2-dichloro-4-(*p*-nitrobenzenesulphonamido)-5-nitrobenzene.

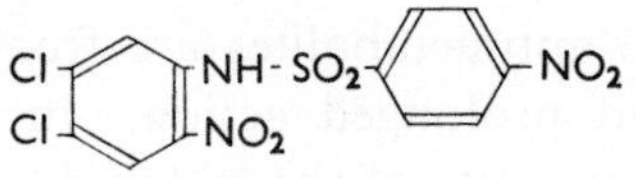

We shall see presently that these have some chemotherapeutic import- ance in the treatment of spontaneous mammary cancers. The aggregate analogue called DCDNS is a derivative both of sulphanilamide and of dichlorodiaminobenzene. Sulphanilamide is of course an antimeta- bolite of *p*-aminobenzoic acid, and dichlorodiaminobenzene of di- methyldiaminobenzene. The activity of DCDNS is not overcome by either or both of these metabolites, and this was the result sought. In other words, this aggregate analogue is an irreversible agent, the action of which is not antagonized by the metabolites to which it is related.

Selective action and some ways to achieve it

Unless the action of a chemotherapeutic agent is selective it will be useless. In other words, unless it harms the disease parasite far more than the host animal the new agent will be of little value. If it is poisonous to the host, even though it is more poisonous to the parasite, it will be too dangerous for widespread use unless the divergence between these two toxicities is very large.

Attempts to understand the basis of selective action and thus to learn how to be able to predict and control it have been rare indeed. In fact, with one or two notable exceptions, the universal practice has been to trust to luck for this essential aspect of chemotherapy. The almost universal attitude has been to search for toxic agents (antimetabolites and others) and to hope that some will be markedly less toxic to the host than to the parasite. I believe that a reliance on chance for this important property is one of the chief reasons why there have been so many failures in efforts at the so-called rational approach. Any rational approach must take account of selective action, but this has generally not been done. Let us therefore ask whether anything is known about how to make antimetabolites which will act on living things selectively.

A few beginnings have been made in the understanding of this problem. Time will allow mention of only two of them, but these will serve to emphasize the fact that there is no unique solution to the problem. Rather, there seems to be a variety of ways to achieve selective action.

One way is to take advantage of the fact that certain antimetabolites act reversibly on some cells or tissues and irreversibly on others. Consequently if the whole system is flooded with the metabolite at the time the antimetabolite is administered, only those parts will be poisoned in which the antimetabolite acts irreversibly; the parts in which it acts reversibly will be protected by the excess of metabolite. This mode of achieving selective action has been studied consciously in only a few model systems. One of these is the selective poisoning of yeasts in the presence of lactobacilli by phenyl pantothenone (Woolley, 1952a), an antimetabolite of pantothenic acid which is injurious both to yeasts and to bacteria; its harmful action on bacteria is overcome by excess of the vitamin, but for yeasts it is irreversibly poisonous. Consequently, if an excess of the vitamin is added at the same time as the antimetabolite, lactobacilli are not harmed whilst yeasts are prevented from growing. It is unknown whether some of the common antibacterial chemotherapeutic agents owe their selective action to such a mechanism, but it is an aspect which should be given more study.

A second mode of achieving selective action in an antimetabolite is to choose the target metabolite in such a way that in the host animal it is unessential whilst in the parasite it is vital. This may seem an impossible task, but in fact it has proven not to be. The nutritional requirements of host and parasite give the necessary clues. This seems to be the reason why sulphanilamide and its congeners exhibit a selective toxicity for certain bacteria, and are not markedly harmful to higher animals. The bacteria use p-aminobenzoic acid as a precursor of folic acid and of certain other essential compounds, and it is the synthesis of these compounds which is specifically blocked by the antimetabolite. The fact that the bacteria use p-aminobenzoic acid is shown by the fact that they carry out the synthesis of folic acid, which is a conjugate of *p*-amino-benzoic acid. Higher animals, on the other hand, exhibit a dietary need for folic acid; they lack the metabolic machinery with which sulphanil-amide reacts, and are thus not poisoned by it. What they would get from the functioning of this machinery they receive from their food, i.e. folic acid.

This, however, is only half of the story. If it is only the inhibition of folic acid synthesis that sulphanilamide causes, one immediately asks why the folic acid circulating in the blood and tissues of an animal infected with streptococci does not supply the needs of these bacteria for folic acid and thus obliterate the harmful action of the drug. Obviously there is something about sulphanilamide which avoids this difficulty.

We think that we understand what there is about sulphanilamide which gives it this desirable property of being able to act even in the presence of the products of the reaction which it specifically inhibits (Woolley, 1951). As we see it, *p*-aminobenzoic acid is the precursor, not only of folic acid, but also of some other essential compound the passage of which into the cell is linked with the function of folic acid. Space does not permit a full discussion of the evidence for such a view. Con-sequently, let us note now merely that there is such a body of evidence; it is considerable, although not conclusive. Rather, let us point to the fact that the pursuit of this idea has led directly to the development of a class of antimetabolites which have chemotherapeutic usefulness. One of the principal reasons why they do is that just as with the sulphon-amides, they are not rendered inoperative by the products of the meta-bolic reactions which they inhibit. This practical success is perhaps a strong reason for giving credence to the basic postulate.

These agents are antimetabolites of dimethyldiaminobenzene (DMDA), a common precursor both of riboflavin and of vitamin B_{12}. The anti-metabolites have been shown to inhibit the synthesis of these two vitamins in living cells; thus they are harmful to all of those organisms without a nutritional need for riboflavin and vitamin B_{12} (i.e. those which make their own supplies of these vitamins), but are not poisonous to those which show such nutritional needs. Furthermore, these two vitamins are no more capable of reversing the poisonous action of these antimetabolites on susceptible cells than folic acid is of overcoming the toxic action of sulphanilamide on pneumococci. Some of these anti-metabolites will be mentioned in the last section of this paper. The fact that they were produced by a conscious effort to understand and to manipulate the basis of selective action indicates that this branch of chemotherapy is not a hopeless pursuit.

The considered use

If we wish to control a disease, whether an infection or an endocrine disturbance, through the use of antimetabolites we must give much thought to the proper choice of the metabolite at which to aim. A frequent cause of failure in past attempts to invent antibacterial or antiviral therapeutic agents has been to start with the assumption that any metabolite which occurs in the parasite is a good target. If experience has taught us anything it is that this is not necessarily true. There is first the consideration of selective action which has been indicated above; to achieve the necessary selective action we are frequently much limited in our choice of metabolites at which to aim. It is regrettable that the choice of so many candidates for chemotherapy has depended on finding an antimetabolite by observation of which compounds are poisonous to normal animals. Instead, we must look for compounds which are not poisonous to normal animals.

There are many other considerations in the choice of a metabolite as target. One of these may be illustrated as follows. The major source of energy in bacteria is usually the breakdown of carbohydrate; in this breakdown there are a number of well-known compounds each of which may be viewed as a metabolite in the sense in which we have been using the term. However, to aim at these in an effort to achieve a chemotherapeutic agent would seem ill advised. Apart from the fact that the host is also using most of these same compounds (and hence might also be susceptible to the attack of the antimetabolite), the concentration and turnover of these major sources of fuel are so large that unless the antimetabolite were extraordinarily potent, very large doses of it would be required. The Krebs cycle would not seem to be a happy hunting ground for the chemotherapeutically-minded antimetabolitist.

In order to make a judicious choice of metabolite at which to aim, we must make use of the entire body of existing knowledge about the biochemistry of the systems with which we have to deal. Frequently this knowledge can give us direct indication of a useful choice, even though our present lack of understanding often defeats our aims.

SOME PRACTICAL RESULTS

To appreciate that the foregoing discussions have not been just a mental exercise, let us examine briefly three practical examples of the development by the use of these principles of new classes of drugs. These examples do not exhaust the list, but will serve to illustrate that the sole dependence on chance for the finding of new classes of pharmacological agents may be nearing an end.

A new treatment for high blood-pressure

One of the newest hormones to be discovered is that known as serotonin or 5-hydroxytryptamine, the structure of which is shown in Fig. 4. This compound causes smooth muscle to contract, and so increases blood pressure when it is injected into an animal. When the nature of this substance was first established (Rapport, 1949; Hamlin & Fischer, 1951) it seemed to be a good choice of a metabolite from which to derive anti-metabolites. We considered that an excess of this hormone might well be

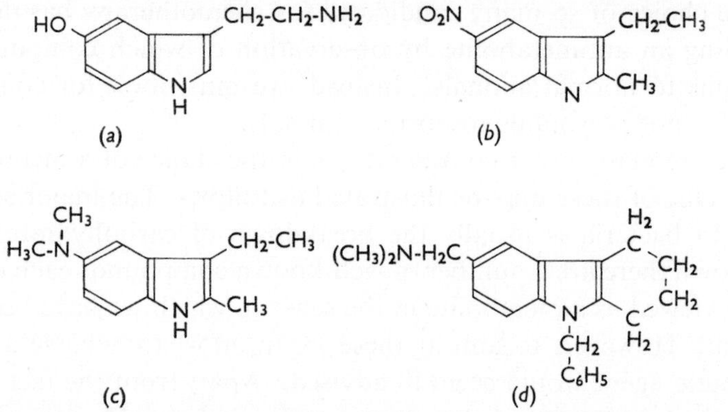

Fig. 4. Sequence in the development of antiserotonins. (a) = serotonin; (b) = nitroindole analogue (2-methyl-3-ethyl-5-nitroindole); (c) = medmain (2-methyl-3-ethyl-5-dimethyl-aminoindole); (d) = dimethylbenzylthamca (1:2:3:4-tetrahydro-6-dimethylaminomethyl-9-benzylcarbazole).

related to the cause of hypertension (high blood-pressure) and that certain other diseases of obscure origin might also be related to it (Woolley & Shaw, 1952). Recent findings have justified these views. The problem was how to make a good antimetabolite of serotonin.

Following our general rules it seemed wise to make the least possible change in structure; we therefore replaced the hydroxyl-group with an amino-group. This was not a large enough change, because the 5-amino-tryptamine so formed still showed serotonin-like potency when tested on smooth muscles (Woolley & Shaw, 1953a). The next step was to retain the 5-amino-group, but to eliminate the amino-group in the side chain; this yielded an antimetabolite of serotonin. The further introduction of a methyl group at position 2 of the indole ring gave a substance of increased potency, and also one much easier to synthesize. The alkylation of the indole ring at position 2 blocked one of the many ways in which indoles may be degraded in living organisms (i.e. by reaction with aldehydes) and presumably for this reason the increase in potency resulted. The 2-methyl-3-ethyl-5-aminoindole so produced was quite active *in vitro* as an antiserotonin, but when tested *in vivo* it was only slightly active. It was effective in doses of 20 mg./kg. by the intravenous route, but by the oral route it was almost inert (Woolley & Shaw, 1953*b*).

This compound was found to be readily destroyed by animal tissues, presumably by the same enzymes which attack other *p*-phenylene-diamines, and it seemed wise to protect it; this was done by methylation of the amino-group to give medmain (Fig. 4). Although the product so obtained was highly potent in some tissues it was unsuitable for use *in vivo* (Shaw & Woolley, 1954) because the blood globulins adsorbed and inactivated it. The next step was to insert a CH_2-group between the methylated amino-group and the ring; the compound so formed was the most potent produced to that time for use *in vivo*. The attachment of a benzyl-group to the indole nitrogen gave it a further prolonged and irreversible action (see Fig. 4) (Shaw & Woolley, 1957). This substance was given the trivial name of dimethylbenzylthamca. Although it contained a cyclohexyl ring fused to the indole system instead of the 2-methyl-3-ethyl side chains, it could be compared directly to the preceding members of the series because earlier studies had shown that no significant difference in activity could be detected when the tetrahydro-carbazole ring system was used in place of a 2:3-dialkylindole.

Activity when taken by mouth is of first importance if one envisions an antiserotonin as a practical chemotherapeutic agent for the treatment of hypertension. The nature of the disease is such that one must think of daily administration of the drug for long periods, perhaps for the entire remainder of the patient's life. It is totally unrealistic to assume that a patient will submit to intravenous, or even subcutaneous inoculations for such protracted periods; he would rather suffer from the disease. For these reasons therefore, it is essential to produce an anti-serotonin effective by mouth. The last compound shown in Fig. 4 was orally effective in protecting animals against pressor action of serotonin, but we were not yet at the end of the trail.

Although we had been able to develop potent antiserotonins which were active even when given orally a new problem now presented itself; many of these compounds caused mental disturbances. Many and varied naturally occurring drugs were shown to be specific antimeta-bolites of serotonin (Shaw & Woolley, 1953) and these as well as some of the synthetic compounds caused profound mental changes (Woolley & Shaw, 1954*a*, *b*); some so severe that they could be recognized even in animals. Thus, the ergot alkaloids, especially lysergic acid diethylamide (LSD), the harmala alkaloids such as harmine, and drugs related to yohimbine (e.g. the recently discovered reserpine) were naturally occurring antiserotonins which markedly affected the mind. Some of these compounds cause excitement (e.g. lysergic acid diethylamide and harmine) whilst others cause profound depression (reserpine). Both types of mental aberration can be produced by a single compound if dosage and conditions of administration are manipulated. The same kinds of mental disturbances were also produced by the synthetic anti-metabolites; thus, 2-methyl-3-ethyl-5-nitroindole (Fig. 4) caused profound mental depression in man, and a noticeable change in character of mice, which became savage and attacked those who fed them. The benzyldimethylaminomethyl indole of Fig. 4 was especially active in its psychotogenic effects. For obvious reasons this compound has never been tested in man but in dogs it caused severe excitement, and behaviour which could readily be seen to result from visual hallucinations. The ramifications of this discovery will be discussed in more detail in the next section, but for the present we should note that the problem arose of creating an antiserotonin which would not have this property.

In our endeavour to develop an antiserotonin which would not cause mental disturbances we were greatly aided by finding that serotonin, injected peripherally, passed into the brain only with great difficulty (Woolley & Shaw, 1954a). Thus, when large doses of the hormone were given to mice, serotonin could not be found in the brain. This observation has recently been amply confirmed by other investigators. We thought that a battery of enzymes (amineoxidase, phenolsulphatase, and others) might be located in the capillary walls in the brain vessels, and that as serotonin passes through these walls it is destroyed by the enzymes. There is now a mounting body of experimental evidence to support such a view, but nevertheless, it must be regarded as a working hypothesis. It has, however, helped to lead us to a useful drug.

If serotonin is kept out of the brain by such a battery of enzymes, then we should be able to construct an antiserotonin which also would be kept out by this same means. We should want to retain the aliphatic primary amino-group as a site of attack for amineoxidase, and some of the other features of the serotonin molecule. A new series of compounds was prepared with these ideas in mind. 2:5-Dimethylserotonin (Fig. 5) was a very potent antiserotonin, but suffered from two defects; it was not as active by the oral as by the intravenous route, and it was competitively reversible by serotonin. Addition of a benzyl-group to give 1-benzyl-2:5-dimethylserotonin overcame these difficulties. This compound was called the benzyl analogue of serotonin, or BAS. Doses of 1 mg./kg./day by mouth protected dogs from the pressor action of serotonin. On smooth muscle preparations it was an irreversible and highly specific antagonist of this hormone. Its antiserotonin effect in dogs was long-lasting. Finally it did not cause changes in behaviour when fed to animals. However, when it was injected directly into the brain the marked excitement and other changes elicited by compounds such as lysergic acid diethylamide were produced. By oral or parenteral dosing the only evidence of an effect on the central nervous system was the appearance of some tranquillization in the animals (Woolley, Van Winkle & Shaw, 1957).

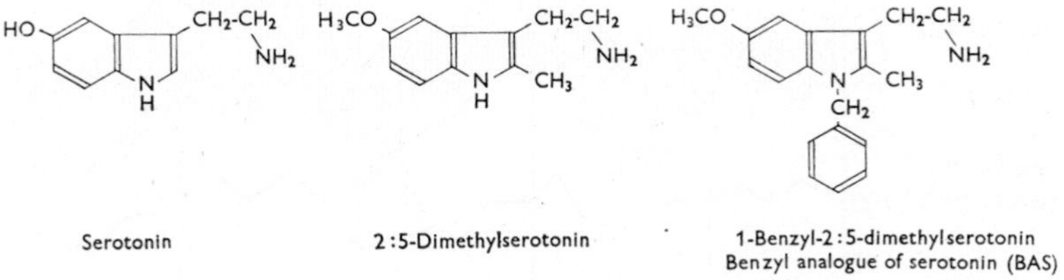

| Serotonin | 2:5-Dimethylserotonin | 1-Benzyl-2:5-dimethylserotonin
Benzyl analogue of serotonin (BAS) |

Fig. 5. Serotonin, dimethylserotonin and BAS
(1-benzyl-2:5-dimethylserotonin)

Clinical trials of BAS in patients suffering from hypertension have shown that it causes reduction in blood pressure in many of them (Woolley & Shaw, 1956). By contrast, blood-pressure was not reduced in the limited series of normals tested. BAS has not caused hallucinations or other undesirable mental effects in human beings. The effects on blood-pressure may be seen in Fig. 6 which has been taken from a paper by Wilkins (1956).

Probably BAS is not the best antiserotonin that can be produced for the treatment of hypertension; it is merely the first member of a series of new drugs. It is not capable of reducing the blood-pressure of all hypertensive patients, but improved members of the series may be found which will affect a larger percentage of patients, and which may be able to cause a greater reduction in blood-pressure. In the first group of patients on which Wilkins and his associates tested the drug, eighteen of twenty-five showed a response to BAS, and the average lowering of blood-pressure was about 25 mm. Hg. However, I believe that it is too much to expect all patients to be favourably affected by an antiserotonin, no matter how good it is. Hypertension is probably of different aetiology in different people. In some it seems to be concerned with an excess of serotonin, but in others it is known to be related to an excess of epinephrine.

The specificity of BAS as an antagonist of serotonin may be illustrated by the data in Table 1. These data have been obtained by the use of a derivative of BAS which was somewhat more active, but similar findings have been made with BAS itself. Note that not even tryptamine (which

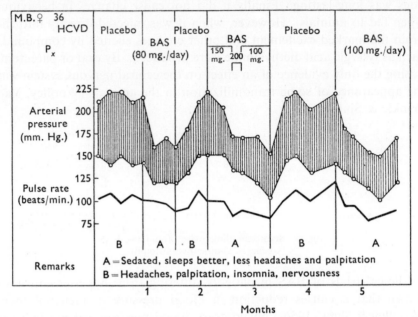

Fig. 6. Effect of BAS on blood-pressure and pulse-rate (from Wilkins, 1956).

Table 1. *Pressor responses in a dog before and after injection of BAS-phenol* (1-*benzyl*-2-*methyl*-5-*hydroxytryptamine hydrochloride*) (2·2 mg./kg.)

Pressor agent	Amount μg./kg.	Rise in pressure Before BAS-phenol mm. Hg	After BAS-phenol mm. Hg
Serotonin	30	36	6*
Tryptamine	220	46	68
Epinephrine	2	72	98
Norepinephrine	1	50	58

* The fall in pressure which accompanies injection of serotonin into a protected dog (Woolley & Shaw, 1957) was observed.

differs from serotonin merely by lacking a hydroxyl-group) was antagonized by this drug. Epinephrine and norepinephrine, of course, were not antagonized either.

We feel that antimetabolites of serotonin will be useful in conditions other than hypertension (Woolley & Shaw, 1953*b*); when we reflect on the variety of physiological effects of serotonin it will be surprising if the antiserotonins do not have numerous uses. This idea has been in our minds from the beginning of this quest.

The understanding and control of schizophrenia

The findings outlined above on the induction of mental disturbances by certain antimetabolites of serotonin indicated for the first time the possible nature of some mental diseases and means of their control. Antimetabolites act by causing a deficiency of the essential metabolite to which they are specifically related. If antimetabolites of serotonin, when they reach the brain, induce disturbances resembling those of schizophrenia, then perhaps the cause of schizophrenia is a deficiency of serotonin in the brain. This deficiency would arise, not necessarily from an antimetabolite, but merely from the metabolic failure to synthesize enough serotonin in the brain. Thus, it could arise from failure to decarboxylate enough 5-hydroxytryptophan, the natural precursor of serotonin. It could also arise from failure to form enough 5-hydroxytryptophan, or from other metabolic derangements related to serotonin. This idea was first proposed by Woolley & Shaw (1954a, b) and considerable supporting evidence has been accumulating.

You can appreciate that this hypothesis cannot be tested merely by peripheral injection of serotonin. The supposed deficiency in the brain cannot be overcome so easily, because, as was pointed out in the preceding section, serotonin does not readily pass from the blood into the brain; some sort of barrier stands in the way. The chemotherapeutic problem is how to get serotonin into the brain by peripheral medication. With this end in view we made several derivatives of the hormone but none proved to be successful.

Udenfriend, Bogdanski & Weissbach (1956) recently observed that 5-hydroxytryptophan, unlike serotonin, passes from the blood into the brain; consequently, the peripheral administration of this amino acid increases the cerebral serotonin. However, a serious problem attends the use of 5-hydroxytryptophan; not only does it increase cerebral serotonin, it also increases this hormone in many other organs. On these organs the excess serotonin exerts its pharmacological effects, shown by increases in blood-pressure, by severe diarrhoea, and by other signs of smooth muscle contraction.

These peripheral effects of serotonin can be prevented with an antiserotonin such as BAS. Since BAS, like serotonin, seems to have difficulty in passing from the periphery into the brain, we should be able, by the use of BAS + 5-hydroxytryptophan, to increase the functioning serotonin in the brain but not in the periphery. In the periphery the excess should be neutralized by the BAS. We have shown that this can be done; in mice and in dogs treated with this combination the peripheral effects (diarrhoea, increased blood-pressure) are prevented but the central effects of excess serotonin are plainly visible (Woolley *et al.* 1957). Data to illustrate these points are shown in Table 2.

Table 2. *Effects of BAS and 5-hydroxytryptophan on peripheral serotonin effects, cerebral serotonin content, and behaviour*

No. of mice	BAS (mg./mouse/ day)	5-Hydroxy- tryptophan (mg./mouse)	Peripheral serotonin effects (diarrhoea) (%)	Cerebral serotonin* (μg./gm.)	Change in behaviour
44	0	0	0	2·3	None
17	1·0	0	0	2·8	Slight
3	0	0·5	100	—	Slight
10	0	2·5	100	—	Slight
25	1·0	2·5	0	3·4	Marked
9	1·0	15·0	0	21·0	Severe

* Based on serotonin creatinine sulphate, not on the free base.

Clinical trial of BAS + 5-hydroxytryptophan in patients suffering from schizophrenia should show whether the disease is due to a deficiency of serotonin in the brain; these trials are now in progress. The first patient so treated responded most gratifyingly. Perhaps by the time this Symposium is held it will be clear whether or not patients will benefit from this treatment and how extensive the change may be.

We can look at mental disease in the simplified fashion just outlined, and hope that alleviation of the disease may be brought about in this way. Nevertheless I would not want to leave the impression that this is the whole story. Clearly it is not; let me very briefly indicate some of the complications. One is the fact that in many mental disorders there is alternation of depression and excitement; among the antiserotonins there are some which cause excitement and others which principally cause depression. Some produce both excitement and depression, depending on the dosage or the species of animal or on particular conditions of the experiment. Some of the more excitatory such as lysergic acid diethylamide, when tested on properly chosen isolated tissues or *in vivo*, can be shown to have a serotonin-like property as well as an antiserotonin effect. Perhaps the mental disturbances have an aspect of too much as well as too little serotonin, and it may be the control of the serotonin production which is at fault.

A second complication arises from the fact, demonstrable in several ways, that some other hormones of the nervous system have related actions to that of serotonin. Acetylcholine, histamine, epinephrine and norepinephrine are so implicated. The interplay of these hormones with each other is an important part of this problem; it is easy to show that agents which antagonize these other hormones can cause mental disturbances and changes in behaviour. Space does not permit discussion of this aspect of the problem, but we must not forget that it exists. Some critics of the serotonin concept have apparently forgotten this point.

Suppression of spontaneous mammary cancers

Although much has been said, and with considerable supporting evidence, about the treatment with aminopterin and mercaptopurine of leukaemia and a few other cancers, these antimetabolites suffer from a serious disadvantage; they are toxic to the host as well as to the cancer. Thus, aminopterin causes folic acid deficiency in man and laboratory animals and the antimetabolites of purines such as mercaptopurine also cause acute adenine deficiency. Consequently, the clinical treatment of cancers with these compounds is complicated by serious risk to the patient, who may show severe signs of deficiency disease brought about by the antimetabolite. Furthermore, the remissions of the cancers which occur in an appreciable percentage of the patients are usually of short duration; after a period of a few months to a few years, the cancer reappears in a form no longer susceptible to the drugs. It is, therefore, clear that some new approach is needed to yield really effective drugs which are not poisonous to the host. Let us consider some experiments carried out during the past ten years which have as their aim the development of a chemotherapy of cancers with antimetabolites so designed as to be selectively active, by which we mean compounds that will not harm the host animal unduly.

In the opening sections of this paper we saw how selective toxicity could be achieved by taking advantage of the differences of nutritional needs of various living things. The selective action of sulphanilamide was viewed as depending on this kind of mechanism by poisoning bacteria which make folic acid from p-aminobenzoic acid. On the other hand the host animal does not make folic acid, but gets this vitamin from its food. Since it seems to lack the machinery specifically attacked by sulphanilamide it is not poisoned by the drug. We saw also that a mechanism was needed to avoid the overcoming of the folic acid

158 D. W. WOOLLEY

deficiency (induced by the sulphanilamide in the bacteria) by the folic acid in the surrounding medium (the host tissue).

With these ideas in mind we undertook to produce antimetabolites of dimethyldiaminobenzene. Both riboflavin and vitamin B_{12} are derivatives of this substance (Fig. 7); an antimetabolite of it, if it is a precursor of these two vitamins, should inhibit their synthesis in organisms which carry out such syntheses and which consequently do not require vitamin B_{12} and riboflavin. It was readily demonstrated that such antimetabolites did in fact inhibit the synthesis of riboflavin and vitamin B_{12} (Woolley, 1950b, 1951), and we presume that the poisonous nature of these antimetabolites for such organisms was due to inhibition of these syntheses.

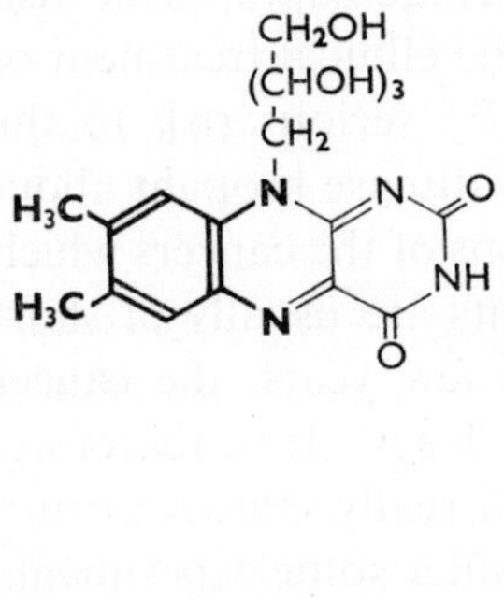

Riboflavin 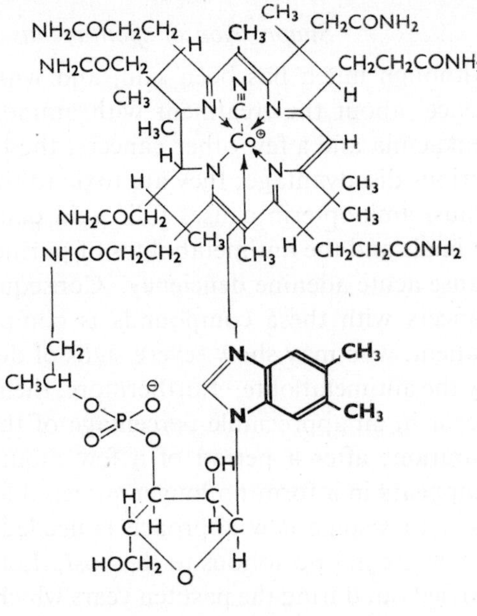   Vitamin B_{12}

Fig. 7. Riboflavin and vitamin B_{12} as derivatives of dimethyldiaminobenzene.

If the poisonous character of antimetabolites of dimethyldiaminobenzene depends on their ability to inhibit synthesis of riboflavin and vitamin B_{12}, we should be able to predict which living things will be poisoned by them, and which will not. All creatures which do not require these two vitamins should be susceptible while those which do need them should not be poisoned by the antimetabolites. This prediction proved to be true for the antimetabolite dichlorodiaminobenzene, and for some others (see Table 3).

A second prediction about the action of such antimetabolites also proved to be correct, namely that the poisonous character of the anti-metabolite should not be reversed by riboflavin and vitamin B_{12}. Thus, just as folic acid will not reverse sulphanilamide toxicity, so vitamin B_{12}

Table 3. *Toxicity of* 1:2-*dichloro*-4:5-*diaminobenzene correlated with nutritional requirements for riboflavin and vitamin* B_{12}

Toxicity is expressed as amount of the dihydrochloride which caused half maximal inhibition of growth in a synthetic medium containing all known nutrients

Organism	Amount of analogue γ/ml.	Riboflavin requirement	B_{12} requirement
Lactobacillus brevis	6	None	None
L. arabinosus	10	None	None
Saccharomyces cereviseae	6	None	None
Staphylococcus aureus	6	None	None
Streptococcus faecalis R	40	None	None
Bacillus tenuis	20	None	None
Chlorella vulgaris	10	None	None
Ophiostoma multiannulatum mutant strain 1671	20	None	None
Leuconostoc mesenteroides	4	None	None
Xanthomonas pelargonii	1	None	None
Corynebacterium fascians	1	None	None
C. michiganense	0·6	None	None
Pseudomonas angulata	100	None	None
P. tabaci	30	None	None
Agrobacterium tumefasciens	60	None	None
Escherichia coli	200	None	None
Proteus sp. strain 4	100	None	None
Shigella sonnei	200	None	None
Salmonella typhimurium	100	None	None
Lactobacillus casei	140	Required	None
Haemolytic streptococcus H69D	180	Required	None
Euglena gracilis	100	None	Required
Lactobacillus leichmannii strain 313	No effect at 300*	Required	Required
L. bifidus strain 4963	No effect at 300*	Required	Required
L. lactis Dorner strain 8000	No effect at 300*	Required	Required

* This was the largest concentration which could be dissolved in test media.

and riboflavin will not reverse the toxicity of these antimetabolites. We thus had compounds with selective and irreversible action which were suitable for chemotherapeutic trial when we could find host and parasite of the proper nutritional backgrounds.

Antimetabolites directed at some aspect of vitamin B_{12} seemed promising for attempts at chemotherapy of cancer and virus diseases. It is well known that vitamin B_{12} plays a role in the synthesis of deoxynucleosides and of methionine, compounds which have frequently been directly linked to the events of cell division.

For chemotherapeutic application of the antimetabolites of dimethyl-diaminobenzene we should have to find hosts with a nutritional need for vitamin B_{12} and riboflavin, and parasites without. Since most of the higher animals investigated nutritionally require these two vitamins, we should not lack for hosts. As for the parasite, we found considerable evidence that the spontaneous mammary cancers of mice actually synthesize vitamin B_{12}; whether they also form riboflavin is not yet clear. The change to neoplastic tissue is accompanied by acquisition of the ability to synthesize vitamin B_{12}, just as in the plant world cancerous growth is accompanied by ability to synthesize a vital compound (indoleacetic acid) (Woolley, 1953). If the ideas we have been following are correct, we should expect suitable antimetabolites of dimethyldiaminobenzene to suppress spontaneous mammary cancers of mice without at the same time poisoning the mice. This situation has been realized in part; the drugs are relatively harmless to the animals, and they can be given for long periods in large doses without noticeable harmful effects. They affect many of the cancers, and about two-thirds are made to recede, some of which disappear completely. With proper administration, some of the cancers are completely and permanently destroyed; others disappear, but return after several months.

The antimetabolites most studied for this effect are shown in Figs. 3 and 8. DCDNS is the irreversibly acting aggregate analogue discussed in the early section of this paper; a combination of DCDNS, CPA and DMAP has been found to cause decrease in size or complete disappearance of two-thirds of the spontaneous mammary cancers of one strain of mice (Woolley & Schaffner, 1954). Please note that these were spontaneous cancers and not transplants. With transplanted cancers of this kind it is possible to select a strain in which one can demonstrate complete and permanent cure of all of the neoplasms. However, it is the spontaneous disease and not the transplanted one with which we must deal in the final analysis.

It is not known why some of the spontaneous cancers fail to respond to these drugs. Neither is it understood why, after some of them have disappeared, they return again. These are the problems with which we now work, and we hope to be able to solve them.

There is some evidence to suggest that success along these lines would be greater if we had more potent antimetabolites of dimethyldiaminobenzene. Compounds such as DMAP have been shown to be rather rapidly metabolized by the host mice. An intensive effort to avoid such destruction of the active agents and to get the drugs to penetrate to the sites of action may possibly lead to sufficiently potent derivatives to permit complete suppression of the disease. A considerable number of such derivatives has now been tested but the net result has been to yield only two compounds of greater activity. Neither of these has proved capable of causing all spontaneous mammary cancers of the strain studied to decrease in size, and neither compound has been able to cure permanently more than a few of the animals. However, the dosage required with these new substances is small; consequently, it would seem that some progress has been made because these antimetabolites of dimethyldiaminobenzene are the only substances known which exert a therapeutic effect on these spontaneous cancers.

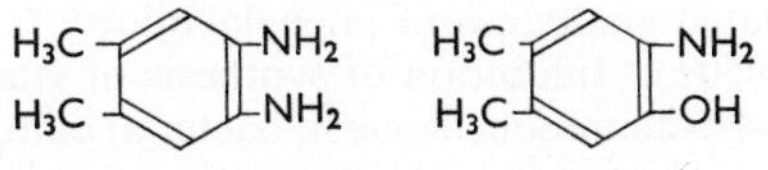

Dimethyldiaminobenzene   DMAP

Fig. 8. Dimethyldiaminobenzene and antimetabolite of it
(DMAP = 3:4-dimethyl-6-aminophenol).

Epilogue

The examples we have examined show clearly that a variety of metabolic happenings must be taken into account if we are to make progress in chemotherapy. There is no simple rule which will unerringly lead one to a useful agent. Even in the most considered plans of attack unforeseen problems constantly arise and a certain degree of luck must be credited to every right decision. Nevertheless, it is becoming clear that as we learn more about physiological and biochemical events, and, as we slowly distil the knowledge gained empirically into true general principles, our chances of achieving the practical goals seem steadily to increase. The designing of antimetabolites is an art that is slowly being built into a science.

REFERENCES

BELL, P. H. & ROBLIN, R. O. (1942). Studies in chemotherapy. VII. A theory of the relation of structure to activity of sulfanilamide type compounds. *J. Amer. chem. Soc.* **64**, 2905.

HAMLIN, K. E. & FISCHER, F. E. (1951). The synthesis of 5-hydroxytryptamine. *J. Amer. chem. Soc.* **73**, 5007.

HEIDELBERGER, C., CHAUDHURI, N. K., DANNEBERG, P., MOOREN, D., GRIESBACH, L., DUSCHINSKY, R., SCHNITZER, R. J., PLEVEN, E. & SCHEINER, J. (1957). Fluorinated pyrimidines, a new class of tumour-inhibitory compounds. *Nature, Lond.* **179**, 663.

RAPPORT, M. M. (1949). Serum vasoconstrictor (serotonin). V. The presence of creatinine in the complex. A proposed structure of the vasoconstrictor principle. *J. biol. Chem.* **180**, 961.

SHAW, E. & WOOLLEY, D. W. (1953). Yohimbine and ergot alkaloids as naturally occurring antimetabolites of serotonin. *J. biol. Chem.* **203**, 979.

SHAW, E. & WOOLLEY, D. W. (1954). Pharmacological properties of some antimetabolites of serotonin having unusually high activity on isolated tissues. *J. Pharmacol.* **111**, 43.

SHAW, E. & WOOLLEY, D. W. (1957). Indole carboxamidines and aminomethylindoles as antimetabolites of serotonin. *J. Amer. chem. Soc.* **79**, 3561.

UDENFRIEND, S., BOGDANSKI, D. F. & WEISSBACH, H. (1956). Increase in tissue serotonin by administration of its precursor, 5-hydroxytryptophan. *Fed. Proc.* **15**, 493.

WILKINS, R. W. (1956). Serotonin, antiserotonins, and hypertension. *New Engl. J. Med.* **255**, 115.

WOOLLEY, D. W. (1944). Some new aspects of the relationship of chemical structure to biological activity. *Science,* **100**, 579.

WOOLLEY, D. W. (1950a). A study of non-competitive antagonism with chloromycetin and related analogues of phenylalanine. *J. biol. Chem.* **185**, 293.

WOOLLEY, D. W. (1950b). Inhibition of synthesis of vitamin B_{12} and of riboflavin by 1,2-dichloro-4,5-diaminobenzene in bacterial cultures. *Proc. Soc. exp. Biol., N.Y.* **75**, 745.

WOOLLEY, D. W. (1951). Selective toxicity of 1,2-dichloro-4,5-diaminobenzene: its relation to requirements for riboflavin and vitamin B_{12}. *J. exp. Med.* **93**, 13.

WOOLLEY, D. W. (1952a). *A Study of Antimetabolites.* New York: John Wiley & Sons.

WOOLLEY, D. W. (1952b). Some aggregate analogs of *p*-aminobenzoic acid and dimethyldiaminobenzene possessing unusual biological properties. *J. Amer. chem. Soc.* **74**, 5450.

WOOLLEY, D. W. (1953). Evidence for the synthesis of vitamin B_{12} by spontaneous tumors. *Proc. nat. Acad. Sci., Wash.* **39**, 6.

WOOLLEY, D. W. & SCHAFFNER, G. (1954). Effects of analogs of dimethyldiaminobenzene on various strains of transplanted mammary cancers of mice. *Cancer Res.* **14**, 802.

WOOLLEY, D. W. & SHAW, E. (1952). Some metabolites of serotonin and their possible application to the treatment of hypertension. *J. Amer. chem. Soc.* **74**, 2948.

WOOLLEY, D. W. & SHAW, E. (1953a). Antimetabolites of serotonin. *J. biol. Chem.* **203**, 69.

WOOLLEY, D. W. & SHAW, E. (1953b). An antiserotonin which is active when fed. *J. Pharmacol.* **108**, 87.

WOOLLEY, D. W. & SHAW, E. (1954a). A biochemical and pharmacological suggestion about certain mental disorders. *Proc. nat. Acad. Sci., Wash.* **40**, 228.

WOOLLEY, D. W. & SHAW, E. (1954b). Some neurophysiological aspects of serotonin. *Brit. med. J.* ii, 122.

WOOLLEY, D. W. & SHAW, E. (1957). Differentiation between receptors for serotonin and tryptamine by means of the exquisite specificity of antimetabolites. *J. Pharmacol.* **121**, 13.

WOOLLEY, D. W. & SHAW, E. N. (1956). Antiserotonins in hypertension and the antimetabolite approach to chemotherapy. *Science,* **124**, 34.

WOOLLEY, D. W., VAN WINKLE, E. & SHAW, E. (1957). A method for increasing brain serotonin without incurring some of the peripheral effects of the hormone. *Proc. nat. Acad. Sci., Wash.* **43**, 128.

LETHAL SYNTHESIS

R. MARKHAM

*Agricultural Research Council Virus Research Unit,
Molteno Institute, University of Cambridge*

It is well known that many products of metabolism are toxic, and that this toxicity is not confined to substances produced from normal metabolites. Thus, for example, methanol, which is extremely toxic in mammals, has no obvious effect so long as its oxidation is prevented by the presence of ethanol: so one may conclude that the toxicity of methanol is due entirely to its oxidation products, formaldehyde and formic acid. The metabolism of one compound to give another having some pharmacological action is not necessarily confined to such simple cases. Perhaps the best known instance in medicine is the metabolism of the azo dye Prontosil which at one time was used as a bacteriostatic. This compound, in spite of its colour, is completely inert against bacteria *in vitro*, and its action *in vivo* depends entirely on its reduction by mammalian tissue enzymes to sulphanilamide.

A rather more sophisticated example, and one which has served as a model for further experimentation, is the metabolism in mammals of monofluoroacetic acid. For many years this substance has been known to be toxic in small doses to a number of mammals, and in fact has been employed as a poison against pests. Surprisingly enough, fluoroacetic acid is a compound which occurs in nature in the poisonous plants belonging to the genus *Dichapetalum*. The mechanism of action of fluoroacetic acid has been the subject of much controversy, and the study of its action has contributed much to our knowledge of intermediary metabolism. Poisoning by fluoroacetate leads, somewhat unexpectedly, to the accumulation of citrate in the tissues, and Peters and his colleagues have produced evidence which suggests that fluoroacetate is sufficiently like acetate to be metabolized along the same pathway. During this breakdown the fluoromethyl carbon atom enters the tricarboxylic acid cycle, and is found, together with its fluorine atom, in fluorocitrate. This substance inhibits the enzyme aconitase, causing an accumulation of citrate, the true toxic agent. This type of mechanism, in which the similarity of an unnatural compound to a naturally occurring metabolite induces the tissues to convert it to a substance having toxic effects, has been called 'lethal synthesis' by Peters (1952), who pointed out that the exploitation of this type of phenomenon could lead to a new and powerful approach to chemotherapy. This prediction has certainly been fulfilled, and although little control of disease has been achieved so far by this method, it is plain that this approach is well worth following. In particular, inducing viruses to incorporate unnatural substances into their somewhat limited structures seems to offer hopes for the control of these agents by chemical means, a possibility which would have been discounted a few years ago. Moreover, in the case of viruses, there is now good evidence which suggests that it is possible to cause the metabolism of certain unnatural substances to proceed in such a way as to damage the very genetic mechanism of the virus.

THE TYPES OF COMPOUND INVOLVED IN 'LETHAL SYNTHESIS'

The variety of substances which may be introduced into tissues and metabolized to compounds having some sort of pharmacological action is now known to be so large that certain generalizations can be drawn about their general structure compared with that of normal metabolites. Thus the design of antimetabolites is no longer entirely empirical, although, of course, substances which may appear possible antimetabolites on paper frequently have no effect *in vivo*. It almost goes without saying that these compounds must resemble quite closely a natural substrate for some enzyme system, and they are usually isosteric with such a substance, or they are substituted in such a way as not to interfere with the enzyme-substrate combination in the early stages of their metabolism. This limits the amount of alteration of the structures to a relatively small number of variations, examples of which are given below. These examples are not intended to be exhaustive but merely illustrative.

(*a*) Substitution of a small group by an atom of similar size, such as —Cl, —Br or —I substituting for —CH_3.

(*b*) The substitution of =N— for =CH—.

(*c*) The substitution of =CF— for =CH—.

(*d*) The substitution of —SH for —OH, =S for =O.

(*e*) Substitution of —S— for —HC=CH—.

(*f*) Modification of a side chain by putting —CH_3 in place of —CH_2OH, —CH_2—CH_2—CH_3 in place of —$CH(CH_3)_2$, etc.

Other possibilities are the substitution of Se for S, As for P, stereochemical alterations, variations in the substituents of aromatic rings, and so on.

Much of the information about the alterations which may be made to structures without preventing their use by enzymes as substrates has been obtained by experiments *in vitro*, and only in exceptional cases has any possibility of disease control been found. This is largely because the metabolic pathways in the host and the pathogen tend to be similar, and so it is only in those cases in which the metabolism of the latter is unusual in some respect that any effective control is possible. It is also only in exceptional instances that the mode of action of the antimetabolite is known with certainty, because many compounds found to be antagonistic towards micro-organisms may well exert their effects in a number of different ways. Examples of this will be given later.

In general most of the effective compounds exert their action in one of a few ways, which may be summarized as follows:

(*a*) By resembling one of a number of metabolites and being carried along a metabolic pathway until an enzyme system becomes blocked by the product. An example of this is fluoroacetate which has already been discussed.

(*b*) By having a structural similarity to a precursor of a coenzyme and being metabolized to an analogue of the latter.

(*c*) By resembling a naturally occurring amino acid and being incorporated into a protein, with effects on the biological activity of the latter.

(*d*) By resembling a nucleic acid constituent and causing the synthesis of an abnormal nucleic acid.

The last class of compounds seems to be the most promising at the moment, as well as the most fashionable, but many of the earlier investigations were carried out on the compounds of class (*b*). It is in fact often difficult to distinguish between classes (*b*) and (*d*).

Substances acting as coenzyme inhibitors

One of the earliest records of lethal synthesis was given by Umbreit & Waddell (1949) who investigated the action of deoxypyridoxine (I), which acts as an antagonist of pyridoxine (II), a precursor of pyridoxal phosphate (III), the coenzyme of tyrosine decarboxylase of *Streptococcus faecalis*.

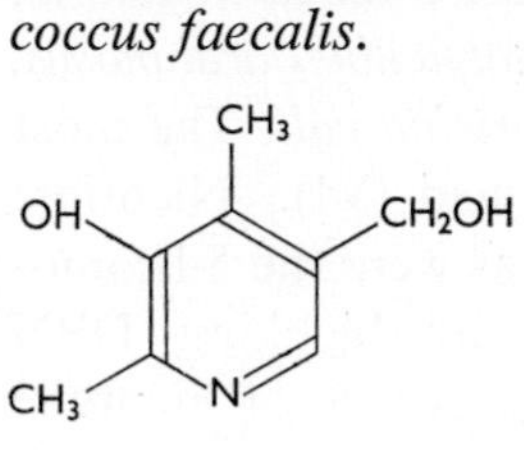

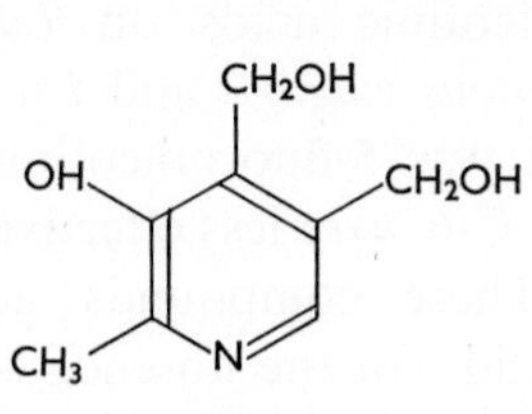

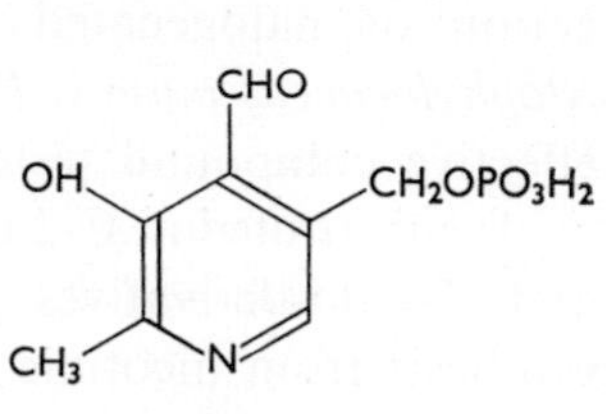

It will be noted that the formation of the coenzyme involves two steps, namely phosphorylation of the hydroxymethyl group on C-3, and oxidation of that on C-4 to give the corresponding aldehyde. Deoxypyridoxine readily undergoes phosphorylation, but the 4-methyl group cannot be oxidized. The resulting deoxypyridoxine phosphate resembles pyridoxal sufficiently closely to combine with the apoenzyme, which it does irreversibly to give an inactive compound.

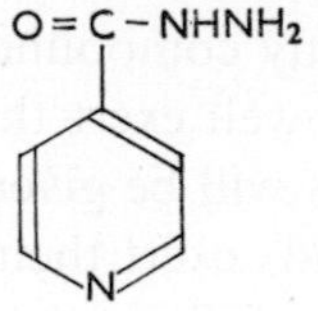

(IV) 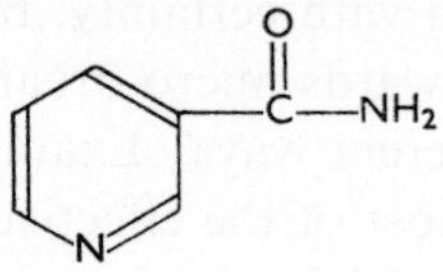   (V)

A very similar transformation has been studied by Zatman, Kaplan, Colowick & Ciotti (1953), who found that the diphosphopyridine nucleotidase of human spleen was able to catalyse the exchange of *iso*nicotinic acid hydrazide (IV) with nicotinamide (V) in diphosphopyridine nucleotide (DPN). Beef spleen, however, is unable to catalyse the exchange and is strongly inhibited by the *iso*nicotinic acid hydrazide analogue of DPN.

Humans are relatively insensitive to *iso*nicotinic acid hydrazide which is an effective agent in the chemotherapy of tuberculous infections and it seems possible, as Zatman *et al.* (1953) suggested, that enzymes in the tissues convert the drug to a DPN analogue, which is the substance inhibitory to the bacteria.

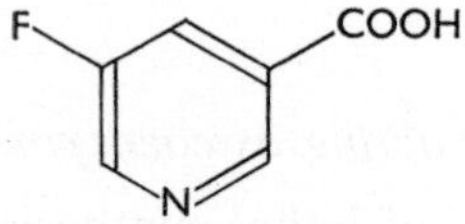

(VI)

A very interesting instance of lethal synthesis involving a coenzyme has been described by Hughes (1954), who investigated the antibacterial action of halogenated nicotinic acids on *Lactobacillus arabinosus*, *Staphylococcus aureus*, *Proteus vulgaris* and *Escherichia coli*. The most effective compound tested was 5-fluoronicotinic acid (VI). Nicotinic acids substituted at C-2 or C-6 were less effective, as were the 5-bromo- and 5-iodo-derivatives. These compounds act by blocking DPN synthesis from nicotinic acid. In the absence of a source of nicotinic acid, 5-fluoronicotinic acid is taken up by the cells, a process requiring concomitant glycolysis, and is metabolized along the same pathways as nicotinic acid:

$$\text{nicotinic acid} \rightarrow \text{nicotinamide} \rightarrow \text{nicotinamide riboside} \rightarrow$$
$$\text{nicotinamide nucleotide} \rightarrow \text{DPN}.$$

Synthesis of DPN from any of the first three compounds and to some extent from nicotinamide nucleotide is inhibited by 5-fluoronicotinic acid and the inhibition is greater if the bacteria are incubated with fluoronicotinic acid before the addition of the nucleotide precursor. The inhibitory step is largely the blocking of the phosphorylation of nicotin-amide riboside by the fluoronicotinamide formed. This particular case, of course, is only of academic interest, because the halogenated nicotinic acids are likely to be toxic to most organisms, all of which use nicotinic acid compounds in their metabolism.

Amino acid analogues as antimetabolites

Largely due to the fact that little is yet known about the function of the individual amino acids in protein molecules, the potential utility of amino acid analogues has not received as much attention as we might expect. It is well known that a number of amino acid analogues are incorporated into proteins, for example norleucine appears in the casein from cows fed with this unnatural amino acid, presumably replacing leucine or iso-leucine, and the quantity incorporated may be quite high (Black & Kleiber, 1955). It is also known that selenium-containing amino acids are to be found in plants growing in soils having a high selenium content.

As far as micro-organisms are concerned, a most interesting example of the incorporation of amino acid analogues has been investigated by Munier & Cohen (1956). These workers used the popular system for studying protein synthesis which is provided by the adaptation of strains of *Escherichia coli* to ferment lactose. If these organisms are grown in the presence of *p*-fluorophenylalanine (VII) in a glucose-salts medium, the growth rate becomes linear rather than exponential, suggesting that some limiting system is not increasing in amount, and the ability of the organisms to form β-galactosidase when presented with the inducer is decreased, but not prevented. The unnatural amino acid is incorporated into the proteins of the organisms, and this seems to be true incorpora-tion rather than reversible exchange with phenylalanine and/or tyrosine, analogues of *p*-fluorophenylalanine, both of which accumulate in the medium. We cannot exclude the possibility that *p*-fluorophenylalanine is acting in a number of different ways. Certainly the accumulation of the analogous amino acids in the medium suggests that the fluorophenylalanine itself is a competitive inhibitor of phenylalanine and tyrosine transport, but there is also no doubt that the substance is actually incorporated into the bacterial proteins. Another amino acid analogue incorporated into these organisms is β-2-thienylalanine (VIII), which is isosteric with phenylalanine.

$$CH_2.CHNH_2.COOH \qquad CH_2.CHNH_2.COOH$$

(VII)   (VIII)

Purine and pyrimidine analogues in lethal syntheses

Over the last ten years it has become obvious that purine and pyrimidine compounds, usually in the form of phosphorylated glycosides, play an important part in life processes. They are found in large numbers of coenzymes concerned with the transport of phosphate, amino acids, sulphate, sugars and other small molecules. They are also found in the nucleic acids, which are now regarded as the repository of hereditary characters and as the active agents controlling the synthesis of proteins. Nucleic acids, in fact, are to be found in any system requiring control by heredity, from the largest mammal to the smallest virus, and even down to the transforming principles of the bacteria. It is not surprising, therefore, that many attempts have been made to influence the course of disease by the modification of purine and pyrimidine compounds in such a way as to cause the production of 'ineffective' genetic material. This approach has a great deal to recommend it, because in general the rates of nucleic acid formation or turnover in an adult animal or plant are relatively small compared with that, say, in a virus during multiplication, a process which may only take minutes. It thus becomes feasible to cause more damage to the parasite than to the host, though, of course, some damage is inevitable, except in cases where the parasite may contain unusual compounds in its nucleic acids. At present the known instances of this are few but it should prove possible, for example, to combat infection of *Escherichia coli* by the T_2 bacteriophage with an analogue of 5-hydroxymethylcytosine. However, this achievement could hardly be regarded as a great therapeutic triumph.

The control of disease by the use of purine and pyrimidine analogues is made extremely difficult by the ubiquitous distribution of the latter in coenzymes, and indeed some of the compounds tested have been found extremely toxic to the hosts. There is also a remote possibility of inducing unfavourable genetic changes in the host, but at the moment this is of secondary importance. Work in this field is largely in the preliminary stages, but some of the compounds have been used in severe cases of cancer, with some degree of success.

It has been known for some time that analogues of those purines and pyrimidines found naturally in organisms could cause deleterious effects. Kalckar (1953) has attributed these effects to the sequestering of ribose-1-phosphate, but this is now known to be unlikely. The enzyme systems involved in nucleoside and nucleotide formation mostly act by exchanging a phosphoryl or a pyrophosphoryl group on C-1 of a ribose derivative for a purine or pyrimidine which is linked as an N-glycoside. These enzymes show a remarkable catholicism as far as the aglycone is concerned. Experiments *in vitro* have shown formation of a number of such compounds (Friedkin, 1954; Strominger & Friedkin, 1954; Lukens & Herrington, 1957; and others), and more recent studies have revealed their presence in nucleic acids of organisms treated with these compounds.

Pyrimidine compounds

The first extraneous compound to be shown to be incorporated into the nucleic acid of an organism was 5-bromouracil (IX) (Weygand, Wacker & Dellweg, 1952). This substance was already known to be bacteriostatic, and, using *Streptococcus faecalis* as a test organism, these authors demonstrated that the inhibition was reversed by thymine, and that if the bromouracil was labelled by ^{82}Br, some of the radioactivity was present in the nucleic acid fraction.

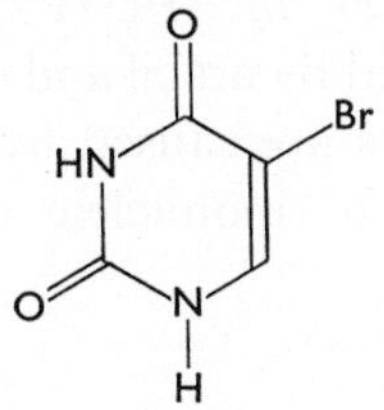

(IX) 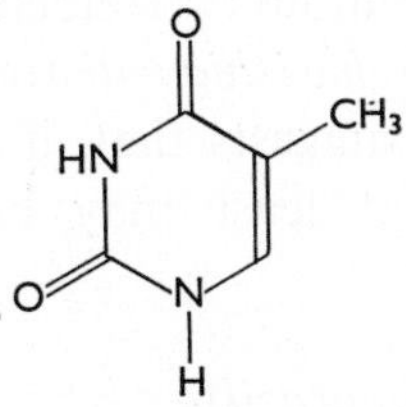   (X)

The effects of this compound, and of the analogous Cl and I derivatives, have been the subject of much study. Generally speaking such compounds have little effect if the organisms can obtain or synthesize thymine, so that the phenomena have been investigated with the use of organisms either having a requirement for thymine or inhibited in some way to prevent its synthesis from uracil by methylation (Dunn & Smith, 1954; Zamenhof & Griboff, 1954). All these authors were able to demonstrate that the compound accumulated in the deoxyribonucleic acid of the organisms used (strains of *Escherichia coli*) where, apparently, it replaces thymine (X), a compound having a very similar shape. From our point of view the most interesting observation was that of Dunn & Smith on the fate of T_2 bacteriophage particles infecting bacteria which had been treated with the halogenated pyrimidines. Lysis occurred normally and bacteriophage particles were liberated with the analogue replacing a large proportion of their thymine. Up to 98 % of such particles were non-infective. This constituted a clear demonstration that it is possible to cause a modification of the nucleic acid of a pathogen in such a way as to render it non-viable. It does not, of course, enable one to decide how the halogenated pyrimidine acts, or even to decide whether bacteriophage particles containing small numbers of halogenated pyrimidine residues are viable. The indication is that a certain amount of substitution is, in fact, tolerated.

Fluorouracil

It is interesting to note that while iodouracil, bromouracil and chlorouracil are to be found in the deoxyribonucleic acid of organisms treated with these compounds, only chlorouracil becomes incorporated into the ribonucleic acids (Dunn & Smith, 1957). This is presumably because the size of the Cl atom is small enough to mimic —H, and large enough to substitute for —CH_3. Going down the scale of sizes in the halogens we have fluoride, and 5-fluorouracil promises to be a very effective anti-tumour agent, incorporated exclusively into the ribonucleic acids of the tumours (Heidelberger *et al.* 1957). Its inhibitory effects against *Escherichia coli* are reversed by uracil and not by thymine. This work also suggests that, if tumours are caused by infection with a virus, some at least may be due to ribonucleic acid-containing viruses.

4-*Azauracil* (6-*azauracil*)

This compound (XI), which causes a certain amount of confusion by being numbered according to two alternative systems, acts as an antagonist of uracil in *Lactobacillus bulgaricus* and *Streptococcus faecalis*, and when labelled in position 2 by ^{14}C, may be detected as a constituent

of the ribonucleic acids (Handschumacher & Welch, 1956; Handschumacher, 1957).

2-*Thiouracil*

Thiouracil (XII) has been used in pharmacology for years as an anti-
thyroid agent. More recently it has been tried as an anti-virus agent.

(XI)   (XII)

This compound was first investigated by Commoner & Mercer (1952),
who hoped to prevent the synthesis of tobacco mosaic virus in plants by
depriving the system of uracil. In fact, thiouracil is extremely effective
against tobacco mosaic virus, as well as a few other plant viruses, but
its efficacy is somewhat impaired by the fact that it is also a strong
herbicide, and the relation between the effective dose and the lethal dose
for the host is such that it is only of use in exceptional circumstances.
An unusual genetic type of tobacco plant reacted in a hypersensitive way
to infection with the virus and thiouracil cured it of infection even after
local manifestations had become visible (Holmes, 1955).

The way in which thiouracil acts is doubtful. It almost certainly is an
inhibitor in uracil-containing coenzyme systems, and it certainly has the
effect of causing a reduction in the quantity of virus synthesized
(Commoner & Mercer, 1952; Jeener, 1954; Bawden & Kassanis, 1954),
and the plants may not become infected at all if the thiouracil is applied
before inoculation. Commoner & Mercer (1952) and Bawden &
Kassanis (1954) have both reported that the virus produced in the
presence of thiouracil is of normal infectivity, although data given by
the former authors suggest that on a weight basis the infectivity is much
less than that of control virus. Jeener (1954, 1957) has reported that
the infectivity may be reduced, but his most interesting claim is that
the growth rate of virus from thiouracil-treated plants is much lower
than that of control virus causing the same number of local infections.
He suggests that the number of infectious units per virus particle is
fairly large, and that some or all may be inactivated in any individual
particle, thus causing a change in the rate of virus multiplication. This

explanation seems improbable for a number of reasons, but the phenomenon is extremely interesting.

Thiouracil is incorporated into the virus ribonucleic acid, as has been
shown by experiments using ^{35}S-labelled thiouracil (Jeener & Rosseels,
1953; Matthews, 1956), and it is of interest that much of the compound
is found in a terminal position in the nucleic acid chains. This was
shown by the liberation of 2-thiouridine-3′:5′-diphosphate from the
nucleic acid of the virus by means of pancreatic ribonuclease (Mandel,
Markham & Matthews, 1957). It seems possible that some of the effect
of thiouracil on virus multiplication may be due to its preventing chain-
lengthening during nucleic acid synthesis. The tendency for an unnatural
base to be in a terminal position in ribonucleic acid chains is not
confined to thiouracil. Azaguanine, as we shall see later, is also found
in large amounts at chain ends, but in this case at the other end of the
chain. The end from which a pyrimidine nucleoside diphosphate can
be liberated by the action of pancreatic ribonuclease is that end of the
chain which is terminated by a primary ethanolic hydroxyl group, in
this case as a phosphate ester.

Purine analogues

A most fruitful field in chemotherapy in recent years has been the
investigation of purine analogues and of substituted purines in the
control of malignant tumours. One of the more successful classes of
compounds are those such as thioguanine (XIII) in which a mercapto
group replaces the oxygen at C-6 of the purine ring. The actual fate of
these compounds is not known, but a similar substance which has been
studied by a number of workers, and which is well known to substitute
for a normal metabolite is 8-azaguanine (XIV) in which C-8 of the
purine ring is replaced by a nitrogen atom.

(XIII)   (XIV)

8-Azaguanine was first investigated as a potential anti-tumour agent,
but much of the present interest in this compound has been the result of
work on plant viruses and bacteria. Its action on plant viruses was first

investigated by Matthews (1953), who found it quite effective in delaying or preventing infection in a number of virus diseases. Some time later he (Matthews, 1954) was able to show that the compound was incorporated into the nucleic acid of tobacco mosaic virus, where it replaced up to 3 % of the guanine residues. Since this time 8-azaguanine has been found to replace guanine in a number of nucleic acids from bacteria, tumours and viruses as well as from mammalian tissues (Lasnitzki, Matthews & Smith, 1954; Matthews & Smith, 1956; Mandel, Carló & Smith, 1954; Mandel, 1957).

The action of 8-azaguanine in plant virus infections is puzzling. Measurable quantities of the analogue are incorporated into tobacco mosaic and turnip yellow mosaic viruses, and in both infectivity is reduced (Matthews, 1954, 1955). In these cases if the analogue is distributed evenly several hundred residues of guanine are replaced in each virus particle. The infectivity is only reduced to about half, so one must assume either that half the particles contain none of the analogue, or that a virus may contain a considerable amount of the analogue and remain viable. However, the substance is very active in preventing virus multiplication, and it seems not unlikely that it acts in this case by inhibiting nucleic acid synthesis, either directly or by blocking guanine-containing coenzyme systems.

One of the main difficulties in the use of azaguanine as an antimetabolite is its ready deamination to the inactive azaxanthine by the enzyme guanase. In organisms such as *Bacillus cereus*, which have little or no guanase activity, relatively large quantities of azaguanine may be taken up and may be found in the organisms as free nucleosides, nucleotides and in the ribonucleic acids. A very small amount may also be found in the deoxyribonucleic acid fraction as well (Mandel, 1957). Under optimal conditions for uptake azaguanine may completely replace guanine in the ribonucleic acid which is being synthesized (Mandel & Markham, unpublished).

Incorporation of large amounts of the analogue is, of course, usually accompanied by a decreased rate of multiplication of the organisms, the formation of abnormal growth forms, and the ability of the organisms to produce adaptive enzymes may be reduced (Creaser, 1955). There appears to be no doubt, however, that the mere incorporation of the analogue into the nucleic acid of an organism is not an indication of the activity of the substance. Certain organisms will tolerate large quantities of the analogue while others will not, and it is also entirely possible that the main way in which the compound acts is in blocking a guanine-containing coenzyme system, rather than by making imperfect nucleic acids.

One of the most remarkable instances of 'lethal synthesis' is also connected with 8-azaguanine. The compounds of 8-azaadenine (XV) and 4-(5)-amino-1H-1:2:3-triazole-5-(4)-carboxyamide (XVI) are both converted by plants into 8-azaguanine and thus exercise anti-virus activity (Matthews & Smith, 1955).

(XV)   (XVI)

When azaguanine is incorporated into ribonucleic acids, a relatively large proportion of the substance may be released by the enzyme ribonuclease as azaguanosine-2′:3′-phosphate (Smith & Matthews, 1957; Mandel & Markham, unpublished). This means that the compound has a tendency to occupy a terminal position in the nucleotide chains adjacent to a pyrimidine nucleotide (XVII; R = pyrimidine nucleotide).

(XVII)

The abundance of such groupings suggests that one of the effects of azaguanine is to cause the shortening of the nucleic acid chains, and it may be in this way that it exerts its action.

CONCLUSION

This account covers many of the compounds which have been shown to act by being incorporated into metabolic systems, and then converted into substances which have blocked some essential system. There are, however, innumerable other compounds which resemble normal metabolites, and which have been shown to exert some biological effects. A complete discussion of such compounds, with special reference to the control of virus multiplication, is given by Matthews & Smith (1955), and others are to be found in the literature on cancer.

The modification of compounds of this type with intent to increase their activity is a field which is already flourishing, and which may produce spectacular results. On the other hand the results obtained may be quite unexpected. As an example of this, Wacker, Trebst, Jacherts & Weygand (1954) found that while 5-bromouracil inhibited *Lactobacillus leichmannii*, the deoxyriboside acted as growth stimulant. Such experiments are discouraging, but work of this type, while it may not solve all our outstanding problems with regard to the control of disease, is certainly giving us more insight into the way in which the normal organism functions, and it may even lead to a closer understanding of the way in which nucleic acids manage to exert their control over the various processes of life. Of all the possible methods of controlling virus infections the most promising does indeed seem to be the inducing of the virus to form inactive progeny by supplying some analogue of purines or pyrimidines, because the present indication is that virus particles so formed will be inactivated irreversibly. It is true that a certain amount of danger to the host is inevitable, but this may be slight, and, if not, there is every indication that the techniques of nucleic acid transfusion now being examined could well overcome this difficulty without any danger of reactivating the viruses.

REFERENCES

BAWDEN, F. C. & KASSANIS, B. (1954). Some effects of thiouracil on virus-infected plants. *J. gen. Microbiol.* **10**, 160.

BLACK, A. L. & KLEIBER, M. (1955). The recovery of norleucine from casein after administering norleucine-3-C^{14} to intact cows. *J. Amer. chem. Soc.* **77**, 6082.

COMMONER, B. & MERCER, F. L. (1952). The effect of thiouracil on the rate of tobacco mosaic virus biosynthesis. *Arch. Biochem. Biophys.* **35**, 278.

CREASER, E. H. (1955). Effect of 8-azaguanine on enzyme formation. *Nature, Lond.* **176**, 556.

DUNN, D. B. & SMITH, J. D. (1954). Incorporation of halogenated pyrimidines into the deoxyribonucleic acids of *Bacterium coli* and its bacteriophages. *Nature, Lond.* **174**, 305.

DUNN, D. B. & SMITH, J. D. (1957). Effects of 5-halogenated uracils on the growth of *Bacterium coli* and their incorporation into deoxyribonucleic acids. *Biochem. J.* **67**, 494.

FRIEDKIN, M. (1954). Enzymatic synthesis of azaguanine riboside and azaguanine deoxyriboside. *J. biol. Chem.* **209**, 295.

HANDSCHUMACHER, R. E. (1957). Metabolites of 6-azauracil formed by *Streptococcus faecalis. Fed. Proc.* **16**, 191.

HANDSCHUMACHER, R. E. & WELCH, A. D. (1956). Microbial studies of 6-azauracil, an antagonist of uracil. *Cancer Res.* **16**, 965.

HEIDELBERGER, C., CHAUDHURI, N. K., DANNEBERG, P., MOOREN, D., GRIESBACH, L., DUSCHINSKY, R., SCHNITZER, R. J., PLEVEN, E. & SCHEINER, J. (1957). Fluorinated pyrimidines, a new class of tumour-inhibitory compounds. *Nature, Lond.* **179**, 663.

HOLMES, F. O. (1955). Preventive and curative effects of thiouracil treatment in mosaic-hypersensitive tobacco. *Virology*, **1**, 1.

HUGHES, D. E. (1954). The inhibition of growth and cozymase synthesis in bacteria by halogen-substituted nicotinic acids. *Biochem. J.* **57**, 485.

JEENER, R. (1954). Influence of thiouracil incorporation in the ribonucleic acid moiety of tobacco mosaic virus on its multiplication. *Biochim. biophys. Acta*, **13**, 148.

JEENER, R. (1957). Biological effects of the incorporation of thiouracil into the ribonucleic acid of tobacco mosaic virus. *Biochim. biophys. Acta*, **23**, 351.

JEENER, R. & ROSSEELS, J. (1953). Incorporation of 2-thiouracil-^{35}S in the ribose nucleic acid of tobacco mosaic virus. *Biochim. biophys. Acta*, **11**, 438.

KALCKAR, H. M. (1953). The role of phosphoglycosyl compounds in the biosynthesis of nucleosides and nucleotides. *Biochim. biophys. Acta*, **12**, 250.

LASNITZKI, I., MATTHEWS, R. E. F. & SMITH, J. D. (1954). Incorporation of 8-azaguanine into nucleic acids. *Nature, Lond.* **173**, 346.

LUKENS, L. N. & HERRINGTON, K. A. (1957). Enzymic formation of 6-mercaptopurine ribotide. *Biochim. biophys. Acta*, **24**, 432.

MANDEL, H. G. (1957). Incorporation of 8-azaguanine and growth inhibition in *Bacillus cereus*. *J. biol. Chem.* **225**, 137.

MANDEL, H. G., CARLÓ, P. E. & SMITH, P. K. (1954). The incorporation of 8-azaguanine into nucleic acids of tumor-bearing mice. *J. biol. Chem.* **206**, 181.

MANDEL, H. G. & MARKHAM, R. (1958). The effects of 8-azaguanine during nucleic acid synthesis in *Bacillus cereus*. *Biochem. J.* (in the Press).

MANDEL, H. G., MARKHAM, R. & MATTHEWS, R. E. F. (1957). The distribution of thiouracil in nucleic acid of tobacco mosaic virus. *Biochim. biophys. Acta*, **24**, 205.

MATTHEWS, R. E. F. (1953). Chemotherapy and plant viruses. *J. gen. Microbiol.* **8**, 277.

MATTHEWS, R. E. F. (1954). Effects of some purine analogues on tobacco mosaic virus. *J. gen. Microbiol.* **10**, 521.

MATTHEWS, R. E. F. (1955). Infectivity of turnip yellow mosaic virus containing 8-azaguanine. *Virology*, **1**, 165.

MATTHEWS, R. E. F. (1956). Thiouracil in tobacco mosaic virus. *Biochim. biophys. Acta*, **19**, 559.

MATTHEWS, R. E. F. & SMITH, J. D. (1955). The chemotherapy of viruses. *Advanc. Virus Res.* **3**, 49.

MATTHEWS, R. E. F. & SMITH, J. D. (1956). Distribution of 8-azaguanine in the nucleic acids of *Bacillus cereus*. *Nature, Lond.* **177**, 271.

MUNIER, R. & COHEN, G. N. (1956). Incorporation d'analogues structuraux d'aminoacides dans les protéines bactériennes. *Biochim. biophys. Acta*, **21**, 592.

PETERS, R. A. (1952). Lethal synthesis. *Proc. roy. Soc.* B, **139**, 143.

SMITH, J. D. & MATTHEWS, R. E. F. (1957). The metabolism of 8-azapurines. *Biochem. J.* **66**, 323.

STROMINGER, D. B. & FRIEDKIN, M. (1954). Enzymatic synthesis of thiouracil riboside and thiouracil desoxyriboside. *J. biol. Chem.* **208**, 663.

UMBREIT, W. W. & WADDELL, J. G. (1949). Mode of action of desoxypyridoxine. *Proc. Soc. exp. Biol., N.Y.* **70**, 293.

WACKER, A., TREBST, A., JACHERTS, D. & WEYGAND, F. (1954). Über den Einbau von 5-Bromouracil-[2-^{14}C] in die Desoxyribonucleinsaüre verschiedener Bakterien. *Z. Naturf.* **9**b, 616.

WEYGAND, F., WACKER, A. & DELLWEG, H. (1952). Stoffwechseluntersuchungen bei Mikroorganismen mit Hilfe radioaktiver Isotope. II. Kompetitive und nicht-kompetitive Enthemmung von 5-^{82}Br-Uracil. *Z. Naturf.* **7**b, 19.

ZAMENHOF, S. & GRIBOFF, G. (1954). *E. coli* containing 5-bromouracil in its deoxyribonucleic acid. *Nature, Lond.* **174**, 307.

ZATMAN, L. J., KAPLAN, N. O., COLOWICK, S. P. & CIOTTI, M. M. (1953). Formation of isonicotinic acid hydrazide analog of DPN. *J. Amer. chem. Soc.* **75**, 3293.

SELECTIVE INHIBITION OF
VIRUS MULTIPLICATION

I. TAMM

The Rockefeller Institute for Medical Research, New York

The decisive failure of antimicrobial agents to cause selective inhibition of virus multiplication contributes greatly to the growing evidence that the mechanism is radically different from multiplication of chlamydozoa, rickettsias or bacteria. Viruses appear to lack energy-yielding enzyme systems, and their multiplication is in many ways closely dependent on the metabolism of host cells. Recently certain electron microscopic, biochemical, and immunological observations have suggested that one important feature separating viruses from other micro-organisms may be a lack of virus membranes surrounding loci of virus nucleoprotein synthesis inside host cells. If this is generally true, it follows that a multiplying virus cannot reasonably be considered as something separate from the host cell; rather, it would appear to be very much part of the host cell.

In consequence, emphasis will be placed in this paper on the effects of virus inhibitory compounds on host cell metabolism, and the discussion will deal primarily with problems of selective inhibition of virus multiplication on the cellular level. The general subject of chemotherapy of virus diseases has recently been reviewed in detail and the broad problems have been adequately stated (Horsfall, 1955a, b; Matthews & Smith, 1955; Hurst & Hull, 1956; Tamm, 1956b; Horsfall & Tamm, 1957).

MECHANISM OF VIRUS MULTIPLICATION

A discussion of the mechanism of animal virus multiplication is seriously limited by the incompleteness and fragmentary nature of our knowledge in this field. To present any kind of scheme of the events which occur in the process it is necessary to collate observations made with different viruses in different hosts.

Extracellular non-multiplying virus. Virus particles in the extracellular state are of variable size, composition, and immunological specificity depending on the viral species. As an example, vaccinia virus possesses a double limiting membrane and some internal structure in the form of a nucleoid body (Morgan, Ellison, Rose & Moore, 1954b). In addition to nucleic acid and protein, this virus contains lipid and carbohydrate (Smadel & Hoagland, 1942). Poliomyelitis virus is composed entirely of nucleic acid and protein (Schwerdt & Schaffer, 1955); it is not only much smaller than vaccinia virus but its structure may well be simpler. The nucleic acid in vaccinia virus is of the deoxyribonucleic (DNA) type (Hoagland, Lavin, Smadel & Rivers, 1940) and it is located in the central nucleoid body (Peters & Stoeckenius, 1954). The precise location of the ribonucleic acid (RNA) of poliomyelitis virus is not known. The RNA in influenza virus (Frisch-Niggemeyer & Hoyle, 1956) and also in fowl-plague virus (Schäfer & Zillig, 1954) is associated with a nucleoprotein component which possesses type-specific but not strain-specific complement-fixing activity. It has not been possible to inactivate intact virus particles with either deoxyribonuclease or ribonuclease. The available evidence indicates that the nucleic acid is located in the interior of virus particles.

Certain enzymatic activities have been found associated with extracellular non-multiplying virus particles: the viruses of influenza, Newcastle disease, mumps, and fowl-plague possess a mucoproteinase (Hirst, 1942; Burnet, 1951; Tamm, Bugher & Horsfall, 1955; Klenk, Faillard & Lempfrid, 1955; Gottschalk, 1956; Schäfer & Zillig, 1954), and the virus of avian erythromyeloblastic leukosis shows adenosine triphosphatase activity (Beard, Sharp & Eckert, 1955). In addition, non-multiplying virus particles are capable of exerting many other types of biological activity extracellularly or intracellularly: they may induce antibody production, induce the state of viral interference, agglutinate red blood cells, cause pneumonia in the mouse (Ginsberg, 1951), reduce the rate of glycolysis in leucocytes (Fisher & Ginsberg, 1956) or increase xanthine oxidase activity in the mouse brain as was shown with PR8 virus by Bauer & Bradley (1956).

The infective property of mumps, and influenza A and B virus particles is highly unstable; the respective half-lives in allantoic fluid are 1·4, 1·4, and 2·4 hr. (Horsfall, 1957). The infective property of swine influenza, Newcastle disease, poliomyelitis, and vaccinia virus particles is much more stable.

Intracellular multiplying virus. Little is known about the structure of virus elements during reproduction. Evidence derived from studies with ^{32}P-labelled virus and fluorescein-labelled antibody indicates that upon infecting a susceptible cell influenza A virus particles are broken down to smaller units and the virus nucleic acid may enter into a close relation with nuclear material of the cell (Hoyle & Frisch-Niggemeyer, 1955; Liu, 1955). It is not known how many such units are liberated from a single particle, or whether, if more than one, they are all alike. Although it seems likely that nucleic acids constitute the primary carriers of hereditary properties, proteins may also be of importance.

The structures seen by the electron microscope in infected cells suggest (Morgan, Ellison, Rose & Moore, 1954*a*, *b*) that in the development of herpes, vaccinia and fowl-pox viruses a membrane progressively encloses a preformed component of virus structure. Admittedly it is hazardous to interpret structures as representing steps in a developmental sequence unless their sequential emergence has been followed as a function of time.

Early phases of virus multiplication, concerned with biosynthesis, may occur either in the nucleus or the cytoplasm of the susceptible cell. The earliest indications of soluble complement-fixing antigen by the fluorescent antibody technique in influenza virus-infected cells have been found in the cell nucleus (Liu, 1955), and the nuclear localization of processes associated with the multiplication of herpes simplex virus has been established by three independent methods (Morgan *et al.* 1954*a*; Gray & Scott, 1954; Lebrun, 1956). On the other hand, structures which may be developmental forms of vaccinia virus are localized in the cytoplasm of infected cells where Feulgen-positive material can also be found before the appearance of infective particles (Ryden & Randall, 1957).

If the nucleoprotein of virus particles carries their hereditary properties, then the chemical basis of the biological specificity shown by viruses must be sought in the structure of virus nucleoproteins, and biosynthesis of virus nucleoproteins becomes the central problem in the process of virus multiplication. Unfortunately, the chemical basis of specificity of nucleic acids or proteins has not been elucidated, and our understanding of the mechanism of biosynthesis of these substances is extremely limited. Furthermore, the basic mechanisms which determine the rate of synthesis and the amount synthesized have not been adequately defined. Evidence is accumulating that enzymes play a role not only in the synthesis of small molecular precursors of nucleic acids and proteins but also in the synthesis of the large molecular end products (Ochoa, 1957; Kornberg, 1957; Hoagland, Keller & Zamecnik, 1956). The bulk of the energy required is provided by the mechanisms of oxidative and glycolytic phosphorylation involving a very large number of enzyme reactions (Spiegelman & Sussman, 1952; Potter, 1955). At present there is not any evidence that viruses possess enzymes which might be of importance in the synthesis of virus materials or that they are endowed with energy-yielding mechanisms of their own.

When the ratio of infecting influenza virus particles to susceptible allantoic cells is high the production of new virus is inefficient; the rate of reproduction, the final yield, and the proportion of infective particles are all reduced (Horsfall, 1954, 1955c). That influenza virus particles possess intrinsic toxicity and can damage cells even when they do not reproduce was shown earlier (Henle, G. & Henle, W., 1946; Henle, W. & Henle, G., 1946). Horsfall (1955c) has proposed the hypothesis that damage to cells of the allantoic membrane occurs when about three particles per cell are adsorbed, and that the damage is reflected in a decrease in the efficiency and completeness of virus reproduction.

METABOLISM OF VIRUS-INFECTED CELLS

Although the mechanism of synthesis of virus materials and their assembly into virus particles is not known, some information is available about the metabolic changes which occur in virus-infected cells. The metabolic changes may be caused by the infecting particles or by components liberated from them; they may be related to the process of synthesis of new virus materials, or caused by products of synthesis. The effects of viruses on host cells are variable and factors such as stimulation, depletion, encroachment, or toxicity may be discerned. Primary effects may lead to multiple secondary alterations in host cell metabolism. It should be emphasized that the nature of the effects probably changes in relation to the sequential stages in the reproductive cycle of a virus.

Cytopathology and cytochemistry. Rivers (1928) pointed out that the primary pathological changes in all virus diseases are hyperplasia alone, hyperplasia followed by necrosis, and necrosis alone. Necrosis is attended or followed by a secondary inflammation. The cytopathic manifestations due to viruses have recently been the subject of several review articles (Enders, 1954; Bang, 1955). As yet we do not know anything of the effect of virus infection on intracellular structures such as the endoplasmic reticulum of Porter (1953) or ribonucleoprotein particles of Palade (Palade, 1955; Palade & Siekevitz, 1956).

Tyrrell (1955) observed that although WS (influenza A) and Lee (influenza B) viruses did not cause cell destruction in chick embryo lung cultures, they interfered with cell proliferation.

Infection with a variety of viruses causes an early increase in cytoplasmic RNA and enlargement of the nucleolus (Hydén, 1947; Rake & Blank, 1950; Caspersson & Thorsson, 1953).

Respiration and glycolysis; enzymes. The metabolism of the virus-infected chorio-allantoic membrane has been studied by several workers. Myxoma virus caused increased glycolysis (Kun & Smith, 1950); vaccinia virus caused an early stimulation of oxygen uptake (Caspersson & Thorsson, 1953; Overman & Tamm, 1957) followed by a depression (Overman & Tamm, 1957); and influenza A or B virus did not affect oxygen uptake (Ackermann, 1951 b; Tamm, 1956 a).

Infection of the mouse brain with each of forty-seven neurotropic viruses increased the xanthine oxidase activity (Bauer, 1952; Bauer & Bradley, 1956). Herpes simplex virus infection increased the weights of the liver and heart of the chicken embryo (Ackermann & Francis, 1950); The succinoxidase activity per unit wet weight of liver remained unchanged whereas α-ketoglutaric oxidase activity decreased; both activities were decreased per unit wet weight of heart. Kovacs (1956) reported decreased activity of a number of enzymes due to infection of monkey kidney cells with poliomyelitis virus. Infection of the chorio-allantoic membrane with myxoma, fibroma, herpes simplex, vaccinia, Rous sarcoma, influenza, or Newcastle disease virus brought about an increase in anaerobic hexose diphosphate breakdown (Smith & Kun, 1954).

Chemistry and isotope incorporation. Herpes simplex virus infection of the chicken embryo increased the amount of DNA and RNA per unit of dry liver tissue (Ackermann & Francis, 1950) as well as increasing the total weight of the liver. The DNA and RNA content per cell and the intracellular distribution were unaltered (Johnson & Ackermann, 1954). Infection of Ehrlich's mouse ascites tumour cells with influenza A virus did not alter the cellular content of DNA and RNA (Johnson & Ackermann, 1954).

Multiplication of influenza A virus caused a decrease in the phospholipid concentration of the chorio-allantoic membrane and an increase in incorporation of ^{32}P into the phospholipid fraction (Cohn, 1952). The DNA and RNA concentration or uptake of ^{32}P into nucleic acids was not markedly altered (Cohn, 1952; Womack & Kass, 1953).

Infection of HeLa cells with poliomyelitis type I virus was associated with an enhanced rate of incorporation of ^{32}P into each nucleic acid fraction from 0–2 hr. after infection. The rate of incorporation into DNA declined with time while that into cytoplasmic RNA increased (Loh, Maassab & Ackermann, 1957).

The extensive investigations on the alterations in metabolic activities of mouse brain tissue infected with GD VII encephalomyelitis virus have been reviewed by Pearson (1953). The effects of this virus on ^{32}P-uptake (Rafelson, Winzler & Pearson, 1949) are of special interest from the viewpoint of the mechanism of action of certain inhibitory compounds (Rafelson, Pearson & Winzler, 1950, 1951). These will be summarized below along with the results of studies on inhibition of virus multiplication.

It seems premature to attempt a detailed analysis of the results of these studies in terms of the causes and factors outlined in the beginning of this section. Nor does it seem profitable at the present time to propose specific biochemical hypotheses for the pathogenesis of virus diseases. However, a statement of available facts should facilitate progress along these important and interesting lines of investigation.

INHIBITORY ACTION OF VARIOUS COMPOUNDS

If the premise be accepted that the process of virus multiplication is closely linked to the metabolic activity of the host cell, it follows that any study on virus inhibition which does not encompass the effects of inhibitory compounds on host cell metabolism is incomplete and probably incapable of explaining the mechanism of inhibitory compounds. Therefore, papers on virus inhibition have been selected for review on the basis of whether the effects of compounds on the metabolic activities of host cells had been studied. There is not a single report in the literature which contains information on an inhibitory compound along all of the following lines: (1) effect on the process of virus multiplication; (2) effect on structure and metabolic activities of uninfected host cells; (3) effect on structure and metabolic activities of infected host cells. Nor are there any reports which define the biochemical effect in terms of a comprehensive survey of the important metabolic activities of cells; therefore, the questions of whether an observed effect is primary or secondary, or whether it is the only one or one of many, remain unanswered. It is also true that in only a few studies have the effects on virus multiplication and on some aspect of host cell morphology or metabolism been worked out quantitatively and the results presented in terms of a ratio of the concentration causing a defined effect on host cells to the concentration causing a certain reduction in virus yield (Tamm, 1956a, b). Such ratios provide an indication of the degree of selectivity of virus-inhibitory compounds.

However, a considerable amount of information has accumulated which throws light on metabolic aspects of virus multiplication. Results obtained with influenza virus provide an illustrative example. In single cycle experiments with influenza B virus in the chorio-allantoic membrane *in vitro*, it has been established with the aid of 5:6-dichloro-1-β-

D-ribofuranosylbenzimidazole (DRB) that synthesis of virus RNA precedes the emergence of soluble complement-fixing antigen or virus particles (Tamm & Tyrrell, 1954; Tamm, 1957). Results of studies on inhibition of influenza A virus multiplication by methoxinine (Ackermann & Francis, 1954; Ackermann & Maassab, 1954) are compatible with the view that synthesis of proteins also precedes the appearance of new virus particles. However, the available evidence suggests that the processes concerned with virus multiplication which are inhibitable by methoxinine are of longer duration than those inhibitable by DRB.

It has been shown that production of influenza A or B virus in the chorio-allantoic membrane requires oxygen (Ackermann, 1951 b; Tamm, 1956 a). When the oxygen uptake of the membrane is restricted in decrements by controlling the concentration of antimycin A, a very potent inhibitor of endogenous respiration, the yield of virus produced is directly proportional to the oxygen consumed (Ackermann & Francis, 1954). Inhibition of virus multiplication by malonate and fluoro-acetate suggested that the functioning of the Krebs cycle was essential for influenza virus multiplication (Ackermann, 1951 b, c), and finally, dependence on availability of adenosine triphosphate was demonstrated with the aid of dinitrophenol (Eaton, 1952; Ackermann & Johnson, 1953; Ingraham, Roby & Peterson, 1953).

The oxygen requirement is not constant throughout the various phases of influenza virus multiplication. Pentamidine (Eaton, Perry, Levenson & Gocke, 1952) and 2:5-dimethylbenzimidazole (Tamm, Folkers & Horsfall, 1953; Tamm, 1956 a) at concentrations which lower the oxygen uptake of the membrane, reduce the yield of virus when given during the early phases of multiplication but have no effect on yield after rapid increase in new virus has begun. Thus, it appears that oxygen may be required for biosynthetic processes which take place during the latent period but not for later assembly of particles.

GD VII mouse encephalomyelitis virus

Metabolism of virus-infected brain tissue. The investigations of Rafelson *et al.* (1950, 1951) deserve special mention because experiments on the effects of inhibitors on virus multiplication and on the metabolism of uninfected or infected host tissue were preceded by studies of the effects of virus multiplication on certain metabolic activities of host tissue (Pearson & Winzler, 1949; Rafelson *et al.* 1949). Although GD VII virus multiplication has no significant effect on the oxidative or glycolytic metabolism of minced brain tissue from 1 day-old mice incubated *in vitro* (Pearson & Winzler, 1949), it is associated with marked stimulation of the uptake of ^{32}P into the phospholipid and total protein-bound phosphate fractions of host tissue (Rafelson *et al.* 1949). The increased turnover in the total protein-bound phosphate fraction was due primarily to increased turnover of the RNA fraction, whereas the slower turnover of DNA phosphorus was unaffected by virus infection. The amount of RNA in virus-infected tissue as compared to uninfected brain tissue was increased and that of DNA was decreased. Since it was not possible to isolate pure virus material from minced brains and to determine its composition and ^{32}P-content, the question of whether the increased turnover and amount of RNA in virus-infected tissue represented the contribution of the virus itself remains unanswered. Upon prolonged incubation, the relative specific activities of the phospholipid and total protein-bound phosphate fractions fell.

A study of the kinetics of these changes showed that virus increase in the supernatant fluid had not occurred by 12 hr. but at 18 hr. there was a 100-fold increase and by the 24th hr. maximal yield was reached. In virus-infected tissue the uptake of ^{32}P into the phospholipid and total protein-bound phosphate fractions was markedly stimulated at 6, 12 and 24 hr., that is, ^{32}P-uptake was increased before the appearance of new virus. At 36 and 48 hr. the difference between infected and non-infected tissues became less marked, and after 72 and 120 hr. of incubation the difference was reversed in that the relative specific activity of phospholipid and total protein-bound phosphate fractions was higher in the uninfected than in the infected tissue. Rafelson *et al.* (1949) considered that during prolonged incubation newly formed phospholipid and nucleoprotein might be selectively degraded in GD VII virus-infected brain tissue. It seems more probable that the lowered specific activity reflected decreased uptake, due to cytopathic effects of large quantities of virus present at later times.

Inhibition by amino acids and metabolic antagonists. Rafelson *et al.* (1950, 1951) have reported that certain amino acids and metabolic antagonists inhibit the multiplication of GD VII encephalomyelitis virus in minced brain tissue from 1 day-old mice *in vitro*. The concentration of compounds was 1–3 mg./ml. and a 24-hr. period of incubation was employed. At virus-inhibitory concentrations, L-lysine, L-tryptophan, and L-histidine reduced the uptake of ^{32}PO$_4$ into the phospholipid and protein-bound phosphate fractions of the infected or uninfected host tissue. Inhibition of uptake was marked except for the slight effect of L-lysine on the ^{32}PO$_4$ incorporation into the phospholipid. Rafelson *et al.*

(1950) recognized that the fact that large amounts of certain amino acids may interfere with the phosphorus metabolism of isolated brain tissue was not surprising in view of the many examples of the inhibitory effects of amino acid imbalances in microbiological systems. DL-2-Thiophene-alanine had little effect on $^{32}PO_4$-uptake by uninfected tissue at virus-inhibitory concentration. However, in its presence the stimulating effect of infection with GD VII virus on $^{32}PO_4$-uptake into phospholipid or protein-bound phosphate was almost entirely eliminated. This observation suggested that the processes associated with virus multiplication may be more sensitive to DL-2-thiophenealanine than other processes in the brain.

Benzimidazole, at 1 mg./ml., inhibited virus multiplication and uptake of phosphorus into the phospholipids and protein-bound fraction of minced mouse brain. It reduced $^{32}PO_4$-uptake to the same low levels in infected as uninfected tissue; 8-azaguanine was without effect.

Rafelson *et al.* (1950) observed that all agents which inhibited the multiplication of the virus also eliminated the virus stimulation of $^{32}PO_4$-uptake by brain tissue. In fact, with the exception of thiophenealanine, all virus-inhibitory agents depressed the $^{32}PO_4$-uptake below the control level. Conversely, of the compounds studied, none reduced the uptake of phosphate without at the same time reducing the yield of virus. Rafelson *et al.* (1950) concluded that the multiplication of GD VII virus was intimately associated with the turnover of phosphorus in the phospholipid and total protein-bound phosphorus fractions of the brain.

5-Chlorouridine inhibited the multiplication of GD VII virus and depressed the uptake of $^{32}PO_4$ into the RNA phosphate fraction of the infected tissue below that of the uninfected control tissue (Rafelson *et al.* 1951). Remarkably, the stimulating effect of virus on the uptake of $^{32}PO_4$ into the phospholipid fraction was not eliminated by 5-chlorouridine. The compound did not affect uptake of $^{32}PO_4$ into these fractions of the uninfected control tissue. In the presence of 5-chlorouridine the increase in RNA content associated with virus multiplication failed to occur but 5-chlorouridine did not reduce the amount of RNA in infected tissue below that in uninfected control tissue. It had no effect on the amount of RNA in uninfected tissue.

Uridine by itself appeared to be without effect on virus multiplication, on uptake of $^{32}PO_4$, or on distribution of phosphorus in any of the fractions of the control or virus-infected brain tissue. Uridine partially blocked the inhibitory action of 5-chlorouridine on virus multiplication and on the turnover of $^{32}PO_4$ in the RNA fraction of the infected tissue.

Uridine in the presence of 5-chlorouridine partially restored the virus effect on the RNA content. It seems well established that RNA plays an intimate role in the multiplication of Theiler's GD VII virus in the mouse brain, and the evidence suggests that RNA metabolism associated with virus multiplication was more sensitive to 5-chlorouridine than was normal metabolism of RNA (Rafelson *et al.* 1951).

Influenza and mumps viruses

Eaton, Magasanik, Perry & Karibian (1951) found that L-arginine at 5–10 mg./ml. inhibited influenza A and B and mumps virus multiplication; at 10 mg./ml. it retarded the rate of proliferation of cells of chorio-allantoic membrane explants *in vitro*. Treatment of membrane with L-arginine at 10 mg./ml. before explantation did not affect the ability of cells to grow; however, a concentration of 20 mg./ml. was lethal. At 5 mg./ml. this amino acid did not reduce the oxygen uptake of uninfected tissue, or affect the rate of disappearance of glucose in tissue.

Eaton, Cheever & Levenson (1951) have shown that a nitroacridine and a chloroacridine at a concentration of 20 μg./ml. inhibit the multiplication of influenza A and B viruses in suspensions of minced chorio-allantoic and amniotic membrane tissue. In preliminary studies with mumps virus it was found that a concentration of 10 μg./ml. of the chloroacridine was inhibitory. Either compound at 20 μg./ml. prevented outgrowth of fibroblasts from tissue explants. At 10 μg./ml. the inhibitory effects on influenza A and B virus multiplication and on the proliferation of fibroblasts were reduced. Oxygen uptake and glycolysis were unaffected by either the nitro- or the chloroacridine at 20 μg./ml. The studies on cell proliferation and metabolic activities were carried out with uninfected tissues.

Under similar conditions the minimal inhibitory concentrations of pentamidine and stilbamidine for influenza A and B viruses were 5–20 μg./ml. and 20 μg./ml. respectively (Eaton *et al.* 1952). Both compounds inhibited mumps virus multiplication at concentrations in the range of 0·5–5 μg./ml. Pentamidine inhibited the proliferation of fibroblasts and epithelium and reduced oxygen consumption by the tissue at concentrations from 200 μg./ml. down to 5 μg./ml., depending on the number of days the drug was incubated with the tissue. The inhibitory effect on respiration associated with losses of growth potential of the fibroblasts and epithelium suggested that the diamidines might in some way divert energy from the synthetic processes of the host cell and in this way interfere with virus synthesis (Eaton *et al.* 1952).

Ackermann (1951 a, 1952) has reported that DL-methoxinine and α-amino-p-methoxyphenylmethanesulphonic acid inhibit influenza A virus multiplication in the chorio-allantoic membrane *in vitro* at concentrations which are insufficient to reduce the oxygen uptake of uninfected membranes. The effect of these compounds on protein synthesis was not determined.

Dickinson & Thompson (1957) have reported that *threo-β*-phenyl-serine at 0·1–0·2 mg./ml. is inhibitory for influenza A virus multiplication in suspended fragments or tube cultures of chorio-allantoic membrane. This compound was not cytocidal to chorio-allantoic membrane fragments at 10 mg./ml.; at 1·0 mg./ml. *threo-β*-phenylserine permitted growth of cells from explants of chorio-allantoic membrane, and similar results were obtained with chick embryo lung tissue explants and trypsinized lung cells.

Poliomyelitis virus

Gifford, Robertson & Syverton (1954) have shown that DL-ethionine, 2:6-diaminopurine, benzimidazole, and β-2-thienylalanine do not inhibit the multiplication of type I poliomyelitis virus in HeLa cells *in vitro* except at concentrations which are markedly inhibitory to the respiration of the host cells.

Hull & Lavelle (1953) found that pretreatment of monkey testicular cells *in vitro* with a filtrate designated M-8450, from a *Penicillium stoloniferum* culture, prevented the cytopathogenic effect of three immunological types of poliomyelitis virus. It is not clear whether M-8450 inhibited the multiplication of poliomyelitis viruses, prevented infection of cells, or acted wholly by altering the response of host cells to virus cytopathogenicity. This paper is referred to because it is one of the few reports in the literature indicating that protection of cells in culture against a highly cytopathogenic virus may be possible with an agent other than antibody. Hull & Lavelle (1953) stated that the antibiotic was not toxic at the levels studied.

Among amino acid analogues tested p-fluorophenylalanine was found to be the most active inhibitor of growth and adaptation to maltose by yeast cells (Halvorson & Spiegelman, 1952) and of multiplication of GD VII encephalomyelitis virus (Pearson, Lagerborg & Winzler, 1952). It should be emphasized that on a molar or weight basis p-fluorophenyl-alanine is not a highly active compound. Ackermann, Rabson & Kurtz (1954) found in their thorough investigation that p-fluorophenylalanine at 0·1 mg./ml. prevented spread of infection with poliomyelitis type III virus in HeLa cells when small or moderately large virus inocula were

used. At this concentration p-fluorophenylalanine caused some alteration in the appearance of cells. In the presence of the compound the
disintegration of infected cells proceeded at what appeared to be the
ordinary rate in spite of the fact that new virus was not being produced.
Thus, p-fluorophenylalanine inhibited virus multiplication without
preventing the cytopathogenic effect of the virus.

At present there is not any evidence that an inhibitor of a biosynthetic
process may protect the infected cell against the cytopathogenicity of a
virus. It is of course true that there are very few reports in the literature
stating that such an effect was looked for. However, it is likely that if
protection of cells rather than reduction of virus yield had been the
criterion of successful virus inhibition in the numerous studies which
have been published, few if any claims would have been made that virus
inhibition had been achieved. The findings of Ackermann *et al.* (1954)
with subsaturating doses of virus illustrate the important fact that the
spread of infection can be prevented by reducing the yield of virus from
infected cells. Unfortunately, the concentration of compound required
was rather large in terms of both amount and appreciable cytotoxic
effect.

Furthermore, it should be kept in mind that an inhibitor of biosynthesis may be more toxic to infected than uninfected cells. Such is
the case with benzimidazole derivatives in the chorio-allantoic membrane
infected with vaccinia virus (Tamm & Overman, 1957), but not when
infected with influenza B virus (Tamm, 1956*a*). In monkey kidney cells
infected with type II poliomyelitis virus the cytotoxicity of benzimidazole derivatives is closely similar to their cytotoxicity in uninfected
cells (Tamm & Nemes, unpublished experiments).

INHIBITORY ACTION OF BENZIMIDAZOLE DERIVATIVES

Virus-cell relation

Influenza B virus in the chorio-allantoic membrane. The compound
studied most extensively for its effects on host cells at virus-inhibitory
concentration is 5:6-dichloro-1-β-D-ribofuranosylbenzimidazole, designated DRB (Fig. 1). DRB is structurally related to α-ribazole and
adenosine. At a concentration of 0·000038 M, DRB causes 75 % reduction
in yield of influenza B virus in the chorio-allantoic membrane *in vitro*
(Tamm, Folkers, Shunk & Horsfall, 1954). At this concentration the
oxygen uptake and macroscopic appearance of the uninfected membrane
was unaffected by DRB (Tamm, 1956*a*; Tamm *et al.* 1954), but at a
concentration six times greater, 25 % reduction in oxygen uptake and

1 + macroscopic damage (shown by slight unfolding of membranes) was observed (Tamm, 1956*a*). With further increase in concentration the effects on the membrane increased rapidly. Microscopic examination of membranes showed considerable evidence of damage at concentrations of DRB (e.g. 0·00019 M or 5·0 × 75 % virus-inhibitory concentration) which caused only borderline (±) macroscopic changes and a very slight reduction (5–10 %) in oxygen uptake. However, at the 75 % virus-inhibitory concentration (0·000038 M) large areas of the membrane did not show any evidence of damage.

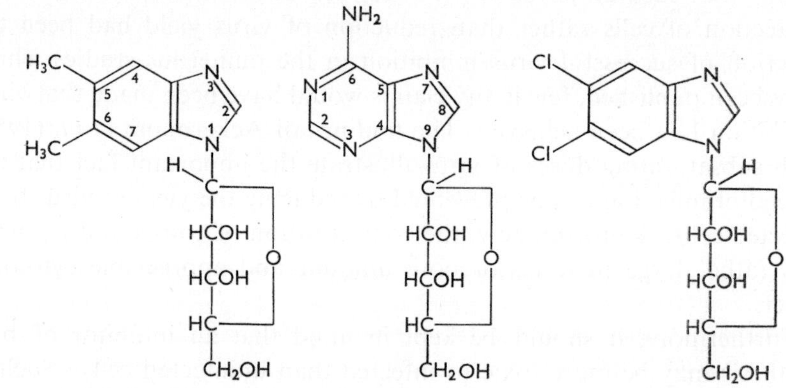

(I) 5:6-Dimethyl-1-α-D-ribofuranosylbenzimidazole or α-ribazole

(II) 9-β-D-Ribofuranosyladenine or adenosine

(III) 5:6-Dichloro-1-β-D-ribofuranosylbenzimidazole (DRB)

Fig. 1. Comparison of the structures of two metabolites (I and II) with the structure of an inhibitor of virus multiplication (III).

Studies on the effect of DRB on cell proliferation showed that at 1·9 × 75 % virus-inhibitory concentration cells of the chorio-allantoic membrane grew out from explants at a reduced rate; on removal of the compound, cells proliferated rapidly and the monolayer of cells surrounding the explant reached the size which had been earlier attained by the control cultures (Tamm *et al.* 1954).

At the 75% virus-inhibitory concentration DRB caused a moderate reduction in the uptake of [8-^{14}C]-adenosine into RNA of the uninfected chorio-allantoic membrane (Tamm, 1957). In these experiments membranes were incubated for 3 hr. in the presence or absence of DRB, after which they were washed and extracted with 2 % perchloric acid in the cold. They were washed again and homogenized, and the suspensions were transferred to planchettes for counting. That the radioactivity was due to incorporation of [8-^{14}C]-adenosine into

RNA was established by treatment of acid-extracted membranes with ribonuclease in appropriate control experiments. Such treatment reduced the count by 75–85 % in membranes incubated in the absence of DRB. The low counts of membranes which had been incubated in the presence of DRB were only slightly affected by ribonuclease treatment. These results indicate that DRB interfered with incorporation of [8-^{14}C]-adenosine into ribonuclease-digestible RNA of the chorio-allantoic membrane.

The effect of DRB on incorporation of [^{14}C]-L-alanine into the protein fraction of the chorio-allantoic membrane was slight in some experiments and nil in others. The protein fraction was isolated by precipitation with 10 % trichloroacetic acid followed by removal of contaminating materials by extraction with hot 10 % trichloroacetic acid, ethanol, and a mixture of ethanol, ether and chloroform. The precipitate was washed with ether and acetone and collected on filter-paper disks for counting.

In single cycle experiments with influenza B virus in the chorio-allantoic membrane *in vitro* (Tamm & Tyrrell, 1954), production of virus particles could be inhibited by DRB only if the compound was given within three hours of virus inoculation. For the production of soluble complement-fixing antigen, processes inhibited by DRB were of even shorter duration. Since processes inhibited by DRB come to completion before soluble complement-fixing antigen or virus particles have been produced in demonstrable amounts in infected tissue, it follows that synthesis of virus RNA is completed before the more complex virus structures are formed.

On the basis of the findings of Allfrey, Mirsky & Osawa (1957) it is likely that inhibition of host RNA synthesis occurs regardless of the time of administration of DRB. The fact that DRB was without effect on virus multiplication when given during the incremental period in single cycle experiments suggests that inhibition of host RNA synthesis during this period is not important to the multiplying virus.

Lack of effect of DRB on protein synthesis in the chorio-allantoic membrane does not necessarily indicate that RNA is of little or no importance for protein synthesis in the membrane; rather, it is likely that the RNA which was playing a role in host protein synthesis during the 3-hr. period of incubation was already present in cells at the beginning of the experiments. If it were possible to study virus protein synthesis separately from host protein synthesis, it is likely that inhibition of virus protein synthesis by DRB given early during the latent period would be demonstrable.

Among the glycosides studied in experiments on inhibition of influenza B virus multiplication, the β-linked ribofuranosides of chlorinated benzimidazoles were the most active and selective derivatives (Tamm, 1954, 1955, 1956 a, b; Tamm, Folkers & Shunk, 1956 a). In contrast, the α-linked D-arabinopyranoside of 5:6-dichlorobenzimidazole (DAB) was not only much less active but it was also considerably less selective as an inhibitor of influenza B virus multiplication (Tamm, 1956 a). In certain reports (Tamm et al. 1954; Tamm, 1954, 1956 a, b; Allfrey et al. 1957) DAB was erroneously identified as the β-linked isomer. To estimate the selectivity of compounds, the concentration required to cause 2 + macroscopic damage to the chorio-allantoic membrane in $vitro$ was determined and the ratio, 2 + damaging to the 75 % virus-inhibitory concentration, found.

Influenza B virus does not cause macroscopic or microscopic changes in the chorio-allantoic membrane in $vitro$ (Tamm, 1956 a); therefore, observations on the possible protective effect of inhibitory compounds against virus cytopathogenicity were not feasible.

$Poliomyelitis$ $type$ II $virus$ in $monkey$ $kidney$ $cells$. On the basis of findings with 5:6-dichloro-1-β-D-ribofuranosylbenzimidazole (DRB) as an inhibitor of influenza B virus multiplication, it was thought that this compound might prove both highly active and moderately selective as an inhibitor of poliomyelitis type II virus since both of these viruses contain RNA (Ada & Perry, 1954; Schwerdt & Schaffer, 1955). However, although DRB was highly active, it was not more selective than unsubstituted benzimidazole as an inhibitor of poliomyelitis virus multiplication in monkey kidney cells (Tamm & Nemes, 1957). An inhibitor of relatively low activity, 5:6-dichloro-1-α-D-arabinopyranosylbenzimidazole (DAB) which was no more selective against influenza B virus than unsubstituted benzimidazole, showed increased selectivity against poliomyelitis virus. To estimate the selectivity of compounds with poliomyelitis virus, the concentration required to cause 3 + microscopic damage to uninfected monkey kidney cells in $vitro$ was determined and the ratio, 3 + damaging to the 75 % virus-inhibitory concentration, found.

In multiple cycle experiments with poliomyelitis type II virus a concentration of 0·00107 M-DAB and a concentration of 0·000095 M-DRB caused 95 % reduction in the yield of virus. In single cycle experiments DAB was as active as in multiple cycle experiments whereas DRB was somewhat less effective and caused 60 % reduction in yield of virus (Nemes & Tamm, unpublished experiments). The effect of these compounds at the stated concentrations on RNA and protein synthesis was determined with uninfected cell suspensions which were incubated and shaken for 3 hr. in the presence of [8-^{14}C]-adenosine or [^{14}C]-L-alanine. Both DRB and DAB inhibited the uptake of [8-^{14}C]-adenosine into RNA. The effect of the β-D-ribofuranoside (DRB) was slightly greater (57 % inhibition) than that of the α-D-arabinopyranoside (DAB) (45 % inhibition). On the other hand, uptake of [^{14}C]-L-alanine into protein was inhibited to a much greater extent by the arabinopyranoside (62 %) than by the ribofuranoside (28 %).

To determine the duration of the inhibitable processes the compounds were introduced at various times after inoculation of virus. As the interval between inoculation of virus and introduction of compound was increased the inhibitory effect of DRB decreased more rapidly than that of DAB. When the interval was 5 hr. the yield of new virus was not reduced by DRB but DAB still caused a moderate reduction in yield. Thus, the biochemical mechanism of action of DRB, that is, inhibition of RNA synthesis, is correlated with the kinetic finding that the greater part of the effect on poliomyelitis virus multiplication takes place early during the latent period. In contrast DAB causes marked inhibition of protein synthesis and its virus inhibitory effect is manifest throughout the whole latent period and even beyond. It should be emphasized that in experiments on cytotoxicity of compounds, in which uninfected cultures were observed for 7 days, DAB caused only slight microscopic changes whereas DRB had a considerable damaging effect on cells. The degree of damage increased with incubation; it became marked after 2–3 days and maximal after 3–5 days. Furthermore, in experiments on protection of cells, DAB caused a slight delay in the development of cytopathic changes due to poliomyelitis virus whereas DRB failed to show such an effect.

In summary, at the concentrations used DAB and DRB caused a similar degree of inhibition of RNA synthesis; the effect of DAB on protein synthesis was marked and that of DRB slight; yet DAB was less cytotoxic than DRB and in single cycle experiments it caused a greater reduction than DRB in the yield of poliomyelitis virus. These findings indicate that a high degree of inhibition of protein synthesis is not necessarily associated with a marked cytotoxic effect, and that cytotoxicity and virus inhibitory activity do not necessarily go hand in hand.

To obtain additional support for these conclusions the inhibitory effects of azaserine and p-fluorophenylalanine were investigated. Azaserine may be considered an inhibitor of purine ribonucleotide synthesis (Buchanan, Levenberg, Melnick & Hartman, 1957; Goldthwait, 1957) and *p*-fluorophenylalanine an inhibitor of protein synthesis (Halvorson & Spiegelman, 1952). It was found that *p*-fluorophenylalanine is considerably more selective than azaserine as an inhibitor of poliomyelitis virus multiplication.

Structure-activity relation

Alkyl derivatives of benzimidazole. In studies on the inhibitory activity of alkyl derivatives of benzimidazole on influenza B virus multiplication it was found (Tamm, Folkers, Shunk, Heyl & Horsfall, 1953) that more extensive substitution in either the benzenoid or the imidazole ring results in marked increase in inhibitory activity on influenza B virus multiplication.

Comparison of these results with those obtained with *Lactobacillus lactis* strain Dorner (Hendlin & Soars, 1951) led to the following observations: (*a*) the activity of benzimidazole and its mono- and dimethyl-derivatives in the influenza B virus system was correlated in most instances with the activity of such compounds against the Dorner strain of *L. lactis*. However, the 2:5-dimethyl derivative failed to inhibit the multiplication of the bacterium although it was inhibitory for influenza virus; (*b*) the activity of 2-alkyl substituted 5:6-dimethyl derivatives against the Dorner strain varied directly with the length of the side chain; each addition produced an increase of moderate degree. With influenza virus the 2-ethyl-5-methyl derivative was considerably more active than the 2:5-dimethyl compound. However, further lengthening of the alkyl side chain at position 2 did not increase activity. These observations suggested that, although alkyl derivatives of benzimidazole may operate in the same biochemical area in the two systems, features specific for each system were present.

Gale & Folkes (1956, 1957) have studied the inhibitory activity of a series of benzimidazole derivatives on glycine incorporation into the protein fraction of disrupted staphylococci. The 5:6-dimethyl derivative was somewhat more active than unsubstituted benzimidazole but the 2-ethyl-5-methyl compound appeared to be of approximately the same low activity as unsubstituted benzimidazole. It should be emphasized that, in contrast, the 2-ethyl-5-methyl compound is nineteen times more active than unsubstituted benzimidazole as an inhibitor of influenza B virus multiplication.

Other non-glycosidic derivatives of benzimidazole. Of fourteen halogen or halogen-alkyl derivatives of benzimidazole (Tamm *et al.* 1954; Tamm *et al.* 1956*a*) only three were sufficiently soluble to permit precise determination of influenza B virus-inhibitory activity, namely, the 5-chloro; 5-chloro-2-methyl; and 5-iodo-4:6-dichloro derivatives. The first two were 2–3 times more active than the corresponding methyl compounds. The last possessed high inhibitory activity but a comparison is not possible since the 4:5:6-trimethyl derivative has not been studied. Results obtained at concentrations at which derivatives were only partially dissolved indicate that compounds with two halogen substituents in the benzenoid ring were more active than those with only one, and that trisubstituted derivatives were more active than the disubstituted ones. Thus, as with alkyl derivatives, activity increases with multiple substitution in the benzenoid ring. The inhibitory activities of 5-chloro, 5:6-dichloro, and 4:5:6-trichloro derivatives on glycine incorporation by disrupted staphylococci relative to that by benzimidazole were approximately 5, 19 and 25 respectively (Gale & Folkes, 1957). The corresponding figures for influenza B virus inhibition are 4·7, 14, and 51 respectively (Tamm *et al.* 1954; 1956*a*).

The activity of 4-nitro-6-chlorobenzimidazole was not significantly different from that of 4:6-dichlorobenzimidazole, and both of these compounds were approximately 3 times more active than the 4:6-dimethyl derivative (Tamm, Folkers & Shunk, 1956*b*). 5:6-Dimethyl-2-aminobenzimidazole was 3·6 times more active than the 2:5:6-trimethyl compound. However, 5-aminobenzimidazole was not inhibitory at a concentration of 0·0035M; at this concentration unsubstituted benzimidazole causes 75 % inhibition, and the 5-methyl compound is 1·8 times and the corresponding chloro compound 4·7 times more active than unsubstituted benzimidazole. Failure of 2-thiolbenzimidazole at a concentration of 0·0025M to inhibit Lee virus multiplication indicates that this compound was not more active than the 2-methyl derivative. These results correspond to those obtained with *Saccharomyces cerevisiae* by Woolley (1944), who also found that substitution of nitro or amino groups in the benzenoid ring did not greatly alter inhibitory activity of benzimidazole derivatives on the multiplication of this microorganism. They differ from the results of Gale and Folkes who found that 5-nitrobenzimidazole was considerably more active than unsubstituted benzimidazole as an inhibitor of glycine incorporation by disrupted staphylococci.

Glycosides of benzimidazoles. In view of the fact that the 5:6-dimethyl-benzimidazole in vitamin B_{12} and also the adenine and guanine moieties in nucleic acids are linked to pentoses (Fig. 1), it appeared fruitful to explore a series of *N*-glycosides of benzimidazoles (Tamm, 1954, 1955, 1956*a*, *b*; Tamm *et al.* 1954; 1956*a*). It seemed likely that ribosides would have a striking effect on virus multiplication but the ribofuranosyl derivative of 2:5- (or 2:6-)dimethylbenzimidazole and the lyxopyranosyl and arabinopyranosyl derivatives of 5:6-dimethylbenzimidazole were not inhibitory at all. On the other hand the β-linked ribofuranosyl derivative of 5:6-dichlorobenzimidazole (DRB, Fig. 1) was 92 times more inhibitory than unsubstituted benzimidazole and approximately 7 times more active than 5:6-dichlorobenzimidazole. The β-D-ribo-furanosides of six halogen derivatives have been synthesized. The type of halogen substituent present in the benzenoid ring is not especially important. In all cases, the β-D-ribofuranoside is more active than the corresponding halogenated benzimidazole without the ribofuranosyl moiety.

The increase in activity on conversion of the simple halogenated benzimidazoles into β-linked ribofuranosides was variable and depended on the number of substituents present in the benzenoid ring; the incre-ment in activity was proportional to the number of halogen atoms as it was increased from 1 to a maximum of 5. For example, 5- (or 6-)-chloro-1-β-D-ribofuranosylbenzimidazole was only 2·7 times more active than 5-chlorobenzimidazole. In contrast, 5- (or 6-)bromo-4:6-(or 5:7-)dichloro-1-β-D-ribofuranosylbenzimidazole was 56 times more active than 5-bromo-4:6-dichlorobenzimidazole. Another way of emphasizing the importance of the presence of multiple halogen substituents in the benzenoid ring is to point out that the β-linked ribo-furanoside of the monobromo-dichloro derivative was 155 times more active than the β-linked ribofuranoside of the monochloro derivative. The β-linked ribofuranoside of 5-(or 6-)bromo-4:6-(or 5:7-)dichloro-benzimidazole at a concentration of $1·8 \times 10^{-6}$ M or 0·72 μg./ml. causes 75 % inhibition of Lee virus multiplication.

The increased activity of β-D-ribofuranosides is not only markedly dependent on the number of halogen atoms present in the benzenoid ring but also on the structure of the carbohydrate moiety. Although conversion of 5:6-dichlorobenzimidazole to the α-D-ribopyranoside failed to increase inhibitory activity, conversion to the arabino-, galacto-, or glucopyranoside caused marked loss in the inhibitory activity. The importance of the structure of the pentose moiety is most pointedly emphasized by the fact that the α-linked ribofuranosides of several halogenated benzimidazoles are all much less active than the corresponding β-linked derivatives. Thus, it has been established that for highest inhibitory activity against the RNA-containing influenza virus the carbohydrate moiety must not only be ribose but that ribo-furanose in the β-linkage is required. The observed structure-activity relations suggest that halogenated β-D-ribofuranosylbenzimidazoles interfere with RNA synthesis directly rather than through vitamin B_{12}.

The special significance of the pentose moiety is also emphasized by the finding that conversion of chlorinated benzimidazoles to corresponding β-D-ribofuranosides does not increase the inhibitory activity against the multiplication of vaccinia virus (Tamm & Overman, 1957) which contains deoxyribonucleic acid (Hoagland *et al.* 1940). In this connexion it is of interest that DRB did not appreciably inhibit DNA synthesis in isolated calf thymus nuclei in concentrations at which synthesis of RNA was markedly reduced (Allfrey, personal communication). In contrast, studies with poliomyelitis virus (Tamm & Nemes, 1957), which, like influenza virus, contains RNA, have shown that the structure-virus inhibitory activity relations for this virus are closely similar to those previously determined for influenza virus. Among the five glycosides studied, the most active derivatives against both viruses were β-linked ribofuranosides of chlorobenzimidazoles. Any departure from the β-D-ribofuranose structure in the carbohydrate moiety of the benzimidazole glycoside resulted in reduced inhibitory activity against both viruses.

It is tempting to conclude that the similarities and differences shown by influenza, vaccinia, and poliomyelitis viruses in susceptibility to inhibition by benzimidazoles reflect the nature of nucleic acid in the virus particle. However, the results of recent comparative studies on selectivity of benzimidazole derivatives as inhibitors of influenza and poliomyelitis virus multiplication, which were described above, indicate that other, as yet unidentified factors, are also of great importance in determining susceptibility to inhibition.

Allfrey *et al.* (1957) have found that DRB has a marked inhibitory effect on incorporation of [6-^{14}C]orotic acid into the pyrimidines of RNA of isolated calf thymus nuclei. The synthesis of RNA could be inhibited at any time by this derivative. DRB also inhibited protein synthesis but only if present at the outset of incubation. The structure-activity relations were not determined for inhibition of RNA synthesis but they were studied for the inhibitory activity of five glycosides of chlorobenzimidazoles on protein synthesis (Allfrey *et al.* 1957). As had been established with influenza and poliomyelitis viruses, the 1-α-D-ribopyranoside and the 1-α-D-arabinopyranoside of 5:6-dichlorobenzimidazole were less active than the 1-β-D-ribofuranoside. Also, the α-linked ribofuranoside of trichlorobenzimidazole was less active than the corresponding β-linked isomer. Thus, the highest inhibitory activity was shown by the β-D-ribofuranosyl derivatives. The activity of the trichloro compound was considerably higher than that of the dichloro derivative.

In contrast, the relations between structure of benzimidazole derivatives and their inhibitory activity on glycine uptake into the protein fraction of disrupted staphylococci are strikingly different (Gale & Folkes, 1957). Substitution of the β-D-ribofuranosyl moiety at position 1 greatly reduced the inhibitory activity of 5:6-dichlorobenzimidazole on glycine incorporation by disrupted staphylococcal cells. With influenza B virus this alteration in structure caused a seven-fold increase in activity. Such a substitution slightly enhanced the inhibitory activity of 4:5:6-trichlorobenzimidazole on glycine incorporation but the enhancement with influenza B virus was fifteen-fold. The action of the α- and β-linked isomers of 4:5:6-(or 5:6:7-)trichloro-1-D-ribofuranosylbenzimidazole were not significantly different in the staphylococcal system. As has been pointed out the β-linked isomer was the more active in inhibiting influenza and poliomyelitis virus multiplication and [1-^{14}C]alanine-uptake by calf thymus nuclei.

The conclusion drawn by Gale & Folkes (1957) that benzimidazole derivatives are affecting different mechanisms in inhibition of glycine incorporation into proteins of disrupted staphylococcal cells and in inhibition of influenza virus multiplication appears warranted. The evidence suggests that in the influenza and poliomyelitis virus systems and in the system of protein synthesis in calf thymus nuclei the β-linked ribofuranosides of chlorobenzimidazoles are acting as highly effective metabolic antagonists of a natural purine riboside, whereas in the system of protein synthesis in disrupted staphylococcal cells a different mechanism is involved.

Modification of chloro-N-glycosylbenzimidazoles. In view of the finding that substitution of an alkyl group at position 2 in the imidazole ring increased inhibitory activity when one or more methyl groups were present in the benzene ring, the inhibitory activity of 5:6-dichloro-2-methyl-1-β-D-ribofuranosylbenzimidazole was compared with that of DRB (Tamm *et al.* 1954). This approach produced a negative result as it was found that substitution of a methyl group at position 2 in DRB caused a 9·5-fold reduction in activity.

Glycitylbenzimidazoles. Since riboflavin contains an *N*-ribityl group, the inhibitory activity of several *N*-glycitylbenzimidazoles was determined (Tamm *et al.* 1954). The ribityl derivative of 5:6-dimethylbenzimidazole, and the arabityl, xylityl, and sorbityl derivatives of 5:6-dichlorobenzimidazole failed to show any inhibitory activity at the concentrations at which they could be tested.

SYNERGISM

Bauer (1955) has reported that the combined protective effect against vaccinia infection in mice of small doses of isatin thiosemicarbazone and 5-(2':4'-dichlorophenoxy)thiouracil given simultaneously is much greater than the effect of either compound given separately. When the molecular ratio of isatin thiosemicarbazone to 5-(2':4'-dichlorophenoxy)-thiouracil was varied it was found that maximum protection was obtained near a ratio of unity. Certain other phenoxypyrimidines also acted synergistically with isatin thiosemicarbazone.

Only a few experiments on the effects of two drugs given simultaneously have been reported in the field of virus inhibition although the number of reports on this subject in the fields of antimicrobial and cancer therapy is fairly large. Such experiments should help to decide whether two compounds act on the same metabolic pathway, whether a greater degree of inhibition can be obtained without increased toxicity, and whether possible development of resistance may be modified.

In experiments with Columbia SK encephalomyelitis virus in the mouse, Shope (1953) found that anti-SK virus immune serum, given 3 or 6 hr. after inoculation of 100–1000 LD_{100} virus subcutaneously, completely protected the mice against the lethal effects of SK virus infection. The anti-SK virus immune serum was obtained from swine recovered from intracerebral infection with SK virus. However, given 48 hr. after virus inoculation it did not have a sparing effect. Helenine, a substance elaborated by *Penicillium funiculosum*, given 3 and 24 hr. after virus inoculation had little effect on the number of mice surviving. However, when helenine was given at 3 and 24 hr. followed by anti-SK serum 48 hr. after inoculation 50 % of the infected mice survived. Shope (1953) concluded that these findings could be best explained on the basis of inhibition of virus multiplication or interference with invasion of the central nervous system for 48 or 72 hr. by helenine and consequent prolongation of the time during which anti-SK virus serum could have a favourable effect through virus neutralization.

Treatment of mice infected with influenza A virus intranasally has been found to be more effective if both L-γ-(o-chlorobenzyl)-δ-oxo-γ-phenylcaproic acid (caprochlorone) and human gamma globulin are used rather than either alone (Liu, Carter, Malsberger, De Sanctis & Hampil, 1957). With combined therapy, mice infected with 3000 MLD_{50} (50 % minimal lethal dose) were protected, whereas caprochlorone alone was capable of protecting mice against death from pneumonia only if the virus inoculum consisted of approximately 3 MLD_{50}, and gamma globulin exerted such an effect only if not more than about 30 MLD_{50} of virus was inoculated. In these experiments, caprochlorone was given by stomach tube three times daily for 5 days and gamma globulin was given subcutaneously once a day for 3 days. In other experiments, treatment was withheld for varying lengths of time. The amount of caprochlorone per dose was 3 or 4 mg. and that of gamma globulin was 0·25 or 0·1 ml. In the groups that received compound alone or gamma globulin alone, there was little effect on the infection unless treatment was started on the day of infection or at most one day later. However, in the groups which received combined therapy beginning as late as 3 days after infection, a significantly lower mortality and marked reduction in pulmonary lesions were observed.

The reports of Shope (1953) and Liu *et al.* (1957) are particularly encouraging in view of the technical progress that has been and is being made in the preparation of human gamma globulin of high antibody content against various viruses.

DIRECT INACTIVATION OF VIRUSES

Although it is not proposed to deal at length with the question of whether direct inactivation of virus particles could provide a useful approach to chemotherapy, a few recent reports will be reviewed to illustrate current thinking and experimentation. Agents which inactivate directly should be considered not only on their own merits but in terms of a possible enhanced effectiveness when combined with compounds which inhibit production of virus.

Various compounds containing a terminal α-ketoaldehyde or α-hydroxyaldehyde grouping have been found capable of protecting embryonated eggs against death when given 15 min. before the inoculation of 50 LD_{50} of influenza A or Newcastle disease virus into the allantoic cavity (McLimans, Underwood, Slater, Davis & Siem, 1957). Two representative compounds, β-ethoxy-α-ketobutyraldehyde hydrate (Kethoxal) and β-diethylaminolactaldehyde hydrochloride were shown to be markedly viricidal against both Newcastle disease and influenza A viruses. At the maximum tolerated dose, Kethoxal protected eggs against 4×10^6 LD_{50} of Newcastle disease virus; 24 μg. was effective against small quantities of virus. The compound showed only slight activity when given 6 hr. after inoculation of Newcastle disease virus and it was inactive when given 5 hr. after inoculation of influenza A virus. Kethoxal was also active against mumps and vaccinia viruses in embryonated eggs.

Protection of monkeys with hyperimmune rabbit antiserum against extensive paralysis and death due to poliomyelitis type I virus has been reported (Liu, Carter & Hampil, 1957). Rhesus monkeys were inoculated with $10–40 \times 50 \%$ tissue culture infective doses ($TCID_{50}$), equivalent to 3–13 monkey paralytic doses, of Mahoney virus intraspinally in the lumbar region. The antiserum was given intravenously; it had a neutralizing titre of 1/50,000 against 100 $TCID_{50}$ of Mahoney virus. Half of the animals received antiserum (20 ml./kg.) intravenously and the remainder served as controls. Virus and antiserum were given simultaneously in some experiments; in others antiserum was administered 24 or 48 hr. after virus inoculation. All monkeys survived in the treated groups whereas the mortality in control groups varied between 75 and 100 %. The incidence of paralysis in the treated groups was 50–100 %; in the control groups paralysis occurred in 75–100 %. However, the degree of paralysis was much less severe in the treated than in the untreated animals and, even when serum was given 48 hr. after virus, paralysis involved only the lower extremities. The control animals became completely paralysed between the 4th and the 8th day. In view of the very high antibody content of the immune serum employed it is likely that the numerous earlier failures were due to a relatively low anti-poliomyelitis antibody content of serum or gamma globulin.

CERTAIN OUTSTANDING PROBLEMS IN SELECTIVE INHIBITION OF VIRUS MULTIPLICATION

In the absence of evidence to the contrary, the following assumptions will be made for the purposes of this discussion: (1) animal viruses do not possess enzymes capable of catalysing either energy-yielding or synthetic reactions; (2) animal viruses do not contain any small molecular components which are not also in host cells.

If these assumptions are correct it follows that the pathways or intermediates in the synthesis of virus and host materials are similar, at least as far as relatively small molecular metabolites are concerned. This would make unlikely the discovery or development of selective inhibitors based on the concept of interference with some metabolic reaction involving specific intermediates for a given virus. Yet, as has been emphasized, viruses possess many specific biological properties, which appear to be linked to large molecular substances. Thus, our ability to consider ways of inhibiting virus synthesis without affecting host cell biosynthetic processes is dependent on a greater understanding of those events which endow nucleic acids or proteins with specific features. It is probable that formation of new molecules involves some kind of interaction between pre-existing nucleic acid or protein molecules and appropriate intermediates which have been suitably activated, and that energy is required in this process. Since at present detailed information is not available about the molecular patterns which are reduplicated or the interactions involved in the process of reduplication, rational approaches to selective inhibition, based on known qualitative differences between virus and host, are not apparent.

This need not mean, however, that an approach to the problem of selective inhibition is impossible today. Although the precise mechanism of action of numerous effective 'broad-spectrum' chemotherapeutic agents against bacteria, rickettsias, and chlamydozoa is not understood as yet, the available evidence is compatible with the view that selective inhibition may be obtained through interference with a metabolic mechanism common to a wide variety of micro-organisms and to host cells. If this be true, then the explanation for selective action must be sought in the circumstances which surround the synthesis and utilization of metabolites by the micro-organism.

Having reached this point in our argument, it is appropriate to recall the emphasis that was placed in the introduction on the likelihood that synthesis of virus materials inside host cells takes place in the absence of a limiting virus membrane. This may, indeed, have a great deal to do with the facts that the multiplication of viruses cannot be selectively inhibited by known chemotherapeutic agents, and that the problem of developing effective agents against viruses is proving difficult. Indeed, the question may be entertained whether it is possible to interfere with the synthesis of virus materials in an infected cell without causing marked inhibition of the synthesis of host materials and consequent serious or irreversible damage to the infected cell or to other cells. At the present time this question cannot be satisfactorily answered, but it seems possible that quantitative differences may exist in the conditions and requirements of virus synthesis which may render this process relatively more susceptible to the effects of potent inhibitors.

Thus far all the chemical compounds used to inhibit virus multiplication have been found, at virus-inhibitory concentrations, to have some effects on host cell metabolism, wherever such effects have been looked for. In spite of this, some of the available inhibitors are sufficiently active and selective to permit demonstration of virus inhibition in animals under restricted experimental conditions (Tamm, 1956b).

Although none of the compounds can be considered as highly selective, the mere fact that marked differences exist among virus inhibitory compounds with respect to selective action, is important.

Metabolic areas of greatest interest

Although biosynthesis of nucleic acids and proteins lies at the core of the problem of multiplication of all viruses, evidence has been presented above suggesting that the most promising approach to selective inhibition of multiplication of one virus is not necessarily the best for another. It would seem highly desirable that studies with representative inhibitors of DNA, RNA, and protein synthesis be undertaken in the same host cell system with different viruses. The results of such studies, if confirmed in several different host cells, should provide indications as to the metabolic area which should be most thoroughly investigated to develop highly effective inhibitors for a given virus.

The simplest and smallest viruses appear to be composed wholly of nucleic acid and protein; however, there are many which also contain lipid and carbohydrate material. Nothing has been said in this paper about approaches to selective inhibition of lipid or carbohydrate synthesis, but these approaches should not be neglected in the total strategy. Nor should the possibility be completely ignored that in the area of transfer of energy utilized in the synthesis of virus materials, there may be possibilities for selective inhibition of virus multiplication.

Nature of compound toxicity

It should be clearly understood that virus-inhibitory activity and cytotoxicity do not appear to be distinct and separable in terms of the varied mechanisms of action of inhibitory compounds at present known. Virus-inhibitory activity and cytotoxicity are operational terms, and it is probable that most compounds used in the past have reduced yield of virus and damaged host cell metabolism through the same basic biochemical mechanism. There may be exceptions to this statement, however, because it is not known whether the effects of the compounds have been chemically specific. In fact, it is likely that some compounds have exerted multiple primary effects on the metabolism of infected cells. There may have been some intracellular metabolic reactions influenced by a compound which were not of importance for virus multiplication, in which case the mechanism of the toxic effects would be distinct from that of its virus-inhibitory action.

It seems important to determine whether the effects on host cells of a compound such as the ribofuranoside of dichlorobenzimidazole (DRB), which has been shown to be an inhibitor of RNA synthesis, are due to interference with a single metabolic event. If it can be established that the effects of DRB on host cells at virus-inhibitory concentration are not wholly due to interference with a step in RNA synthesis but represent in part side effects, a stimulus would be provided for further synthetic work which would have the aim of ridding DRB of its possible side effects. It may also be possible to combat some of the side effects with appropriate metabolites. As an analogy, isoniazid is being supplemented with pyridoxin to reduce its toxicity for nerve tissue without reducing its effectiveness in the treatment of tuberculosis (Biehl & Vilter, 1954).

The question may be asked whether it is possible to inhibit RNA synthesis without immediate inhibition of protein synthesis and vice versa. That the processes of RNA and protein synthesis are interrelated is highly likely, and in certain bacterial systems they appear to be coupled (Pardee & Prestidge, 1956; Yčas & Brawerman, 1957). It is unlikely that these processes are geared to each other as rigidly in mammalian cells, and it will be of crucial importance to determine to what extent and for how long biosynthesis of nucleic acids or protein may be inhibited without serious or irreversible damage to the cell.

It is important to determine whether inhibition of virus multiplication by a chemical compound is wholly due to interference with the synthesis or utilization of a natural metabolite, or whether in some instances an analogue of an intermediate in a metabolic pathway is actually incorporated into the end-product, be it DNA (Dunn & Smith, 1954; Zamenhof & Griboff, 1954), RNA (Matthews, 1954; Matthews & Smith, 1956) or protein (Tarver & Gross, 1955; Brawerman & Yčas, 1957).

Discovery and development of new compounds

Effective chemotherapeutic agents against viruses have not as yet been isolated from biological sources such as mould filtrates, or discovered among the synthetic chemicals empirically tested. However, in view of the rich harvest of compounds from such sources, the discovery of new inhibitors by empirical testing may advance our understanding of the mechanism of virus multiplication and our ability to prevent or treat virus diseases.

It is not proposed to review all the classes of micro-organisms or of synthetic compounds which might provide virus-inhibitory agents; several have already been discussed by other contributors to this Symposium. A few comments on inhibitors of nucleic acid or protein synthesis are pertinent. It is clear already that not all available inhibitors of nucleic acid synthesis are equally effective as inhibitors of influenza B virus multiplication (Tamm, 1956*a*, *b*; Tamm *et al.* 1956*a*, *b*); in fact considerable differences exist with respect both to virus-inhibitory activity and selective action. As far as benzimidazole derivatives are concerned, there appear to exist numerous as yet untapped possibilities for increasing their virus-inhibitory effectiveness through further modifications in structure. Of special interest would be new compounds with a markedly modified pattern of substitutions in the benzenoid ring structure (Tamm, 1955, 1956*b*); a whole new ring might be added to the benzimidazole nucleus. Also of great interest would be N'-β-D-2-deoxyribofuranosides of suitable benzimidazoles since they might possess high activity against DNA-containing viruses (Tamm, 1955, 1956*b*).

During recent years interest in the development of new inhibitors of protein synthesis has been considerably less than that in inhibitors of nucleic acid synthesis; especially in the cancer field the emphasis has been on the latter. In the under-developed field of selective inhibitors of protein synthesis new approaches are called for. As was pointed out above, amino acid analogues are, on a molar or weight basis, relatively inactive (Halvorson & Spiegelman, 1952). Before incorporation into protein, amino acids are activated through a mechanism which involves the formation of enzyme-bound amino acid ~ adenosine monophosphate compounds (Hoagland, 1955; Hoagland, Keller & Zamecnik, 1956). There is evidence that amino acid analogues that inhibit growth either interfere with the activation of amino acids or are themselves activated and incorporated into protein (Sharon & Lipmann, 1957).

Identification of the reactions which occur between activation and incorporation of amino acids may well lead to new approaches to inhibition of protein synthesis. Although the evidence is not good that polypeptides occur as intermediates in protein synthesis (Steinberg, Vaughan & Anfinsen, 1956), it would be of interest to explore the biological effects of synthetic polypeptides composed of natural amino acids and amino-acid analogues. If such compounds proved active as inhibitors of protein synthesis, empirical or rational experiments might lead to the establishment of requirements as to the sequence of component parts necessary for high activity and selectivity.

GENERAL REMARKS

Studies on selective inhibition of virus multiplication are dependent on new knowledge deriving from investigation of nucleic acid and protein biosynthesis. Progress in understanding the mechanisms of nucleic acid and protein biosynthesis is enhanced by the discovery or development of new inhibitors of these processes. Close co-operation between the biologist, biochemist, and organic chemist appears propitious for advance in studies on reduplication of nucleic acids and proteins.

One of the important problems which may be cleared up by studies in this area is the existence of a fundamental self-duplicating ribonucleoprotein particle concerned with biosynthesis of proteins in all living things. There is suggestive evidence that in size and chemical composition this unit of biosynthetic activity may be closely similar to the smallest viruses. It may be postulated that in their overall structural features and energy requirements such fundamental ribonucleoprotein particles are alike regardless of source. However, there are reasons to think that subtle but important differences must exist among such particles from different cell-types as among viruses.

This study was aided by a grant from the National Foundation for Infantile Paralysis.

The benzimidazole derivatives were synthesized by Dr K. Folkers and Dr C. H. Shunk and their associates of Merck Sharp and Dohme Research Laboratories, Rahway, New Jersey.

REFERENCES

ACKERMANN, W. W. (1951a). The role of L-methionine in virus propagation. *J. exp. Med.* **93**, 337.

ACKERMANN, W. W. (1951b). Concerning the relation of the Krebs cycle to virus propagation. *J. biol. Chem.* **189**, 421.

ACKERMANN, W. W. (1951c). The relation of the Krebs cycle to viral synthesis. II. The effect of sodium fluoroacetate on the propagation of influenza virus in mice. *J. exp. Med.* **93**, 635.

ACKERMANN, W. W. (1952). α-Aminosulfonic acids and viral propagation. *Proc. Soc. exp. Biol., N.Y.* **80**, 362.

ACKERMANN, W. W. & FRANCIS, JUN., T. (1950). Some biochemical aspects of herpes infection. *Proc. Soc. exp. Biol., N.Y.* **74**, 123.

ACKERMANN, W. W. & FRANCIS, JUN., T. (1954). Characteristics of viral development in isolated animal tissues. *Advanc. Virus Res.* **2**, 81.

ACKERMANN, W. W. & JOHNSON, R. B. (1953). Some energy relations in a host-virus system. *J. exp. Med.* **97**, 315.

ACKERMANN, W. W. & MAASSAB, H. F. (1954). Growth characteristics of influenza virus. Biochemical differentiation of stages of development. *J. exp. Med.* **100**, 329.

ACKERMANN, W. W., RABSON, A. & KURTZ, H. (1954). Growth characteristics of poliomyelitis virus in HeLa cell cultures: lack of parallelism in cellular injury and virus increase. *J. exp. Med.* **100**, 437.

ADA, G. L. & PERRY, B. T. (1954). The nucleic acid content of influenza virus. *Aust. J. exp. Biol. med. Sci.* **32**, 453.

ALLFREY, V. G., MIRSKY, A. E. & OSAWA, S. (1957). Protein synthesis in isolated cell nuclei. *J. gen. Physiol.* **40**, 451.

BANG, F. B. (1955). Pathology of the cell infected with viruses—morphological and biochemical aspects. *Fed. Proc.* **14**, 619.

BAUER, D. J. (1953). Metabolic aspects of virus multiplication. In *The Nature of Virus Multiplication. Symp. Soc. gen. Microbiol.* **2**, 46.

BAUER, D. J. (1955). The antiviral and synergic actions of isatin thiosemicarbazone and certain phenoxypyrimidines in vaccinia infection in mice. *Brit. J. exp. Path.* **36**, 105.

BAUER, D. J. & BRADLEY, P. L. (1956). The xanthine oxidase groups. A phenomenon associated with the multiplication of neurotropic viruses. *Brit. J. exp. Path.* **37**, 447.

BEARD, J. W., SHARP, D. G. & ECKERT, E. A. (1955). Tumor viruses. *Advanc. Virus Res.* **3**, 149.

BIEHL, J. P. & VILTER, R. W. (1954). Effects of isoniazid on pyridoxine metabolism. *J. Amer. med. Ass.* **156**, 1549.

BRAWERMAN, G. & YČAS, M. (1957). Incorporation of the amino acid analog tryptazan into the protein of *Escherichia coli*. *Arch. Biochem. Biophys.* **68**, 112.

BUCHANAN, J. M., LEVENBERG, B., MELNICK, I. & HARTMAN, S. C. (1957). The specific action of azaserine on enzymes concerned with purine biosynthesis. In *The Leukemias: Etiology, Pathophysiology, and Treatment*, p. 523. Edited by J. W. Rebuck, F. H. Bethell and R. W. Monto. New York: Academic Press, Inc.

BURNET, F. M. (1951). Mucoproteins in relation to virus action. *Physiol. Rev.* **31**, 131.

CASPERSSON, T. & THORSSON, K. G. (1953). Virus und Zellstoffwechsel. *Klin. Wschr.* **31**, 205.

COHN, Z. A. (1952). Quantitative distribution of phosphorus in chorioallantoic membrane as affected by infection with influenza virus. *Proc. Soc. exp. Biol., N.Y.* **79**, 566.

DICKINSON, L. & THOMPSON, M. J. (1957). The antiviral action of *threo-β*-phenylserine. *Brit. J. Pharmacol.* **12**, 66.

DUNN, D. B. & SMITH, J. D. (1954). Incorporation of halogenated pyrimidines into the deoxyribonucleic acids of *Bacterium coli* and its bacteriophages. *Nature, Lond.* **174**, 305.

EATON, M. D. (1952). Observations on growth of virus and the energy-yielding activities of the host cell. *Arch. ges. Virusforsch.* **5**, 53.

EATON, M. D., CHEEVER, F. S. & LEVENSON, C. G. (1951). Further observations of the effect of acridines on the growth of viruses. *J. Immunol.* **66**, 463.

EATON, M. D., MAGASANIK, B., PERRY, M. E. & KARIBIAN, D. (1951). Inhibition of influenza and mumps viruses in tissue culture by basic amino acids. *Proc. Soc. exp. Biol., N.Y.* **77**, 505.

EATON, M. D., PERRY, M. E., LEVENSON, C. G. & GOCKE, I. M. (1952). Studies on the mode of action of aromatic diamidines on influenza and mumps virus in tissue culture. *J. Immunol.* **68**, 321.

ENDERS, J. F. (1954). Cytopathology of virus infections. Particular reference to tissue culture studies. *Annu. Rev. Microbiol.* **8**, 473.

FISHER, T. N. & GINSBERG, H. S. (1956). The reaction of influenza viruses with guinea pig polymorphonuclear leucocytes. II. The reduction of white blood cell glycolysis by influenza viruses and receptor-destroying enzyme (RDE). *Virology*, **2**, 637.

FRISCH-NIGGEMEYER, W. & HOYLE, L. (1956). The nucleic acid and carbohydrate content of influenza A virus and of virus fractions produced by ether disintegration. *J. Hyg., Camb.* **54**, 201.

GALE, E. F. & FOLKES, J. P. (1956). Benzimidazole derivatives and glycine incorporation in disrupted staphylococcal cells. *Biochem. J.* **64**, 4P.

GALE, E. F. & FOLKES, J. P. (1957). The assimilation of amino acids by bacteria. 24. Inhibitors of glycine incorporation in disrupted staphylococcal cells. *Biochem. J.* **67**, 507.

GIFFORD, G. E., ROBERTSON, H. E. & SYVERTON, J. T. (1954). Application of manometric method to testing chemical agents *in vitro* for interference with poliomyelitis virus synthesis. *Proc. Soc. exp. Biol., N.Y.* **86**, 515.

GINSBERG, H. S. (1951). Mechanism of production of pulmonary lesions in mice by Newcastle disease virus (NDV). *J. exp. Med.* **94**, 191.

GOLDTHWAIT, D. A. (1957). Purine nucleotide biosynthesis and neoplasia. In *The Leukemias: Etiology, Pathophysiology, and Treatment.* Edited by J. W. Rebuck, F. H. Bethell & R. W. Monto. New York: Academic Press, Inc.

GOTTSCHALK, A. (1956). Neuraminic acid; the functional group of some biologically active mucoproteins. *Yale J. Biol. Med.* **28**, 525.

GRAY, A. & SCOTT, T. F. McN. (1954). Some observations on the intracellular localization of the virus of herpes simplex in the chick embryo liver. *J. exp. Med.* **100**, 473.

HALVORSON, H. O. & SPIEGELMAN, S. (1952). The inhibition of enzyme formation by amino acid analogues. *J. Bact.* **64**, 207.

HENDLIN, D. & SOARS, M. H. (1951). The effect of 5,6-dimethylbenzimidazole and related compounds on the growth of *Lactobacillus lactis* Dorner. *J. Bact.* **62**, 633.

HENLE, G. & HENLE, W. (1946). Studies on the toxicity of influenza viruses. I. The effect of intracerebral injection of influenza viruses. *J. exp. Med.* **84**, 623.

HENLE, W. & HENLE, G. (1946). Studies on the toxicity of influenza viruses. II. The effect of intra-abdominal and intravenous injection of influenza viruses. *J. exp. Med.* **84**, 639.

HIRST, G. K. (1942). Adsorption of influenza hemagglutinins and virus by red blood cells. *J. exp. Med.* **76**, 195.

HOAGLAND, C. L., LAVIN, G. I., SMADEL, J. E. & RIVERS, T. M. (1940). Constituents of elementary bodies of vaccinia. II. Properties of nucleic acid obtained from vaccine virus. *J. exp. Med.* **72**, 139.

HOAGLAND, M. B. (1955). An enzymatic mechanism for amino acid activation in animal tissues. *Biochim. biophys. Acta,* **16**, 288.

HOAGLAND, M. B., KELLER, E. B. & ZAMECNIK, P. C. (1956). Enzymatic carboxyl activation of amino acids. *J. biol. Chem.* **218**, 345.

HORSFALL, JUN., F. L. (1954). On the reproduction of influenza virus. Quantitative studies with procedures which enumerate infective and hemagglutinating virus particles. *J. exp. Med.* **100**, 135.

HORSFALL, JUN., F. L. (1955a). Approaches to the chemotherapy of viral diseases. *Bull. N.Y. Acad. Med.* **31**, 783.

HORSFALL, JUN., F. L. (1955b). The inhibition of virus reproduction by chemical substances. In *Perspectives and Horizons in Microbiology*, p. 152. Edited by S. A. Waksman. New Brunswick, N.J.: Rutgers University Press.

HORSFALL, JUN., F. L. (1955c). Reproduction of influenza viruses. Quantitative investigations with particle enumeration procedures on the dynamics of influenza A and B virus reproduction. *J. exp. Med.* **102**, 441.

HORSFALL, JUN., F. L. (1957). Viral multiplication. *Proc. IV Internat. Poliomyelitis Conf.*, Geneva. (In the Press.)

HORSFALL, JUN., F. L. & TAMM, I. (1957). Chemotherapy of viral and rickettsial diseases. *Annu. Rev. Microbiol.* **11**, 339.

HOYLE, L. & FRISCH-NIGGEMEYER, W. (1955). The disintegration of influenza virus particles on entry into the host cell. Studies with virus labelled with radiophosphorus. *J. Hyg., Camb.* **53**, 474.

HULL, R. N. & LAVELLE, J. M. (1953). Inhibition of cytopathogenic effect of poliomyelitis viruses in tissue culture by antibiotic M-8450. *Proc. Soc. exp. Biol., N.Y.* **83**, 787.

HURST, E. W. & HULL, R. (1956). The chemotherapy of virus diseases, with brief consideration of the influence of dietary, hormonal and other factors in virus infections. *Pharmacol. Rev.* **8**, 199.

HYDÉN, H. (1947). The nucleoproteins in virus reproduction. In *Nucleic Acids and Nucleoproteins. Cold Spr. Harb. Symp. quant. Biol.* **12**, 104.

INGRAHAM, J. L., ROBY, T. O. & PETERSON, J. H. (1953). Effect of 2,4-dinitrophenol and sodium azide on host cell metabolism and influenza A virus. *Arch. Biochem.* **46**, 215.

JOHNSON, R. B. & ACKERMANN, W. W. (1954). Intracellular pattern of nucleic acid in virus infection. *Proc. Soc. exp. Biol., N.Y.* **86**, 318.

KLENK, E., FAILLARD, H. & LEMPFRID, H. (1955). Über die enzymatische Wirkung von Influenzavirus. *Hoppe-Seyl. Z.* **301**, 235.

KORNBERG, A. (1957). In *Cellular Biology, Nucleic Acids and Viruses. Spec. Pub. N.Y. Acad. Sci.* **5**, 201.

KOVACS, E. (1956). Comparative biochemical studies on normal and poliomyelitis infected tissue cultures. IV. Enzyme-changes in host cells. *Proc. Soc. exp. Biol., N.Y.* **92**, 183.

KUN, E. & SMITH, M. H. D. (1950). Effect of infectious myxoma virus on glycolysis of chorioallantoic membrane of chick embryo. *Proc. Soc. exp. Biol., N.Y.* **73**, 628.

LEBRUN, J. (1956). Cellular localization of herpes simplex virus by means of fluorescent antibody. *Virology*, **2**, 496.

LIU, C. (1955). Studies on influenza infection in ferrets by means of fluorescein-labelled antibody. II. The role of 'soluble antigen' in nuclear fluorescence and cross-reactions. *J. exp. Med.* **101**, 677.

LIU, O. C., CARTER, J. E. & HAMPIL, B. (1957). Serotherapy of poliomyelitis in rhesus monkeys. *Fed. Proc.* **16**, 423.

LIU, O. C., CARTER, J. E., MALSBERGER, R. G., DeSANCTIS, A. N. & HAMPIL, B. (1957). Studies on the chemotherapy of viral infections. II. The effect of caprochlorone on influenza virus infections in mice. *J. Immunol.* **78**, 222.

LOH, P. C., MAASSAB, H. F. & ACKERMANN, W. W. (1957). Phosphorus metabolism of HeLa cells infected with poliovirus. *Bact. Proc. of 57th Gen. meeting Soc. Amer. Bact.* 138.

MATTHEWS, R. E. F. (1954). Effects of some purine analogues on tobacco mosaic virus. *J. gen. Microbiol.* **10**, 521.

MATTHEWS, R. E. F. & SMITH, J. D. (1955). The chemotherapy of viruses. *Advanc. Virus Res.* **3**, 49.

MATTHEWS, R. E. F. & SMITH, J. D. (1956). Distribution of 8-azaguanine in the nucleic acids of *Bacillus cereus*. *Nature, Lond.* **177**, 271.

McLIMANS, W. F., UNDERWOOD, G. E., SLATER, E. A., DAVIS, E. V. & SIEM, R. A. (1957). Antiviral activity of dicarbonyls and related compounds in embryonated eggs. *J. Immunol.* **78**, 104.

MORGAN, C., ELLISON, S. A., ROSE, H. M. & MOORE, D. H. (1954*a*). Structure and development of viruses as observed in the electron microscope. I. Herpes simplex virus. *J. exp. Med.* **100**, 195.

MORGAN, C., ELLISON, S. A., ROSE, H. M. & MOORE, D. H. (1954*b*). Structure and development of viruses observed in the electron microscope. II. Vaccinia and fowl pox viruses. *J. exp. Med.* **100**, 301.

OCHOA, S. (1957). Biosynthesis of ribonucleic acid. In *Cellular Biology, Nucleic Acids and Viruses. Spec. Pub. N.Y. Acad. Sci.* **5**, 191.

OVERMAN, J. R. & TAMM, I. (1957). Multiplication of vaccinia virus in the chorioallantoic membrane *in vitro*. *Virology*, **3**, 173.

PALADE, G. E. (1955). A small particulate component of the cytoplasm. *J. biophys. biochem. Cytol.* **1**, 59.

PALADE, G. E. & SIEKEVITZ, P. (1956). Pancreatic microsomes. An integrated morphological and biochemical study. *J. biophys. biochem. Cytol.* **2**, 671.

PARDEE, A. B. & PRESTIDGE, L. S. (1956). The dependence of nucleic acid syntheses on the presence of amino acids in *Escherichia coli. J. Bact.* **71**, 677.

PEARSON, H. E. (1953). Biochemical aspects of viral growth. *Annu. Rev. Microbiol.* **7**, 179.

PEARSON, H. E., LAGERBORG, D. L. & WINZLER, R. J. (1952). Effects of certain amino acids and related compounds on propagation of mouse encephalomyelitis virus. *Proc. Soc. exp. Biol., N.Y.* **79**, 409.

PEARSON, H. E. & WINZLER, R. J. (1949). Oxidative and glycolytic metabolism of minced day-old mouse brain in relation to propagation of Theiler's GD VII virus. *J. biol. Chem.* **181**, 577.

PETERS, D. & STOECKENIUS, W. (1954). Untersuchungen am Virus der Variola-Vaccine. III. Mitt.: Enzymatischer Abbau des Innenkörpers. *Z. Naturf.* **9** b, 524.

PORTER, K. R. (1953). Observations on a submicroscopic basophilic component of cytoplasm. *J. exp. Med.* **97**, 727.

POTTER, V. R. (1955). Studies on the alternative pathways of glucose metabolism in relation to the design of sequential block chemotherapy. Edited by R. W. Begg, *Canadian Cancer Conference*, **1**, 290. New York: Academic Press, Inc.

RAFELSON, JUN., M. E., PEARSON, H. E. & WINZLER, R. J. (1950). The effects of certain amino acids and metabolic antagonists on propagation of Theiler's GD VII virus and P^{32} uptake by minced one-day-old mouse brain. *Arch. Biochem.* **29**, 69.

RAFELSON, JUN., M. E., PEARSON, H. E. & WINZLER, R. J. (1951). *In vitro* inhibition of radiophosphate uptake and growth of a neurotropic virus by 5-chlorouridine. *Proc. Soc. exp. Biol., N.Y.* **76**, 689.

RAFELSON, JUN., M. E., WINZLER, R. J. & PEARSON, H. E. (1949). The effects of Theiler's GD VII virus on P^{32} uptake by minced one-day-old mouse brain. *J. biol. Chem.* **181**, 583.

RAKE, G. & BLANK, H. (1950). The relationship of host and virus in molluscum contagiosum. *J. invest. Dermatol.* **15**, 81.

RIVERS, T. M. (1928). Some general aspects of pathological conditions caused by filterable viruses. *Amer. J. Path.* **4**, 91.

RYDEN, F. W. & RANDALL, C. C. (1957). A study of three strains of vaccinia virus in stable cell strains L, LLC-M_1, and HeLa. *Amer. J. Path.* **33**, 293.

SCHÄFER, W. & ZILLIG, W. (1954). Über den Aufbau des Virus-Elementarteilchens der klassischen Geflügelpest. I. Mitt.: Gewinnung, physikalisch-chemische und biologische Eigenschaften einiger Spaltprodukte. *Z. Naturf.* **9** b, 779.

SCHWERDT, C. E. & SCHAFFER, F. L. (1955). Some physical and chemical properties of purified poliomyelitis virus preparations. *Ann. N.Y. Acad. Sci.* **61**, 740.

SHARON, N. & LIPMANN, F. (1957). Reactivity of analogs with pancreatic tryptophan-activating enzymes. *Arch. Biochem. Biophys.* **69**, 219.

SHOPE, R. E. (1953). An antiviral substance from *Penicillium funiculosum*. I. Effect upon infection in mice with swine influenza virus and Columbia SK encephalomyelitis virus. *J. exp. Med.* **97**, 601.

SMADEL, J. E. & HOAGLAND, C. L. (1942). Elementary bodies of vaccinia. *Bact. Rev.* **6**, 79.

SMITH, M. H. D. & KUN, E. (1954). Morphological and biochemical studies on the chorio-allantois of the chick embryo following infection with certain viruses. *Brit. J. exp. Path.* **35**, 1.

SPIEGELMAN, S. & SUSSMAN, M. (1952). Energy metabolism of biosynthesis at the cellular level. *Annu. Rev. Physiol.* **14**, 97.

STEINBERG, D., VAUGHAN, M. & ANFINSEN, C. B. (1956). Kinetic aspects of assembly and degradation of proteins. *Science*, **124**, 389.

TAMM, I. (1954). Inhibition of influenza and mumps virus multiplication by 4,5,6-(or 5,6,7-)trichloro-1-β-D-ribofuranosylbenzimidazole. *Science*, **120**, 847.

TAMM, I. (1955). Selective inhibition of virus multiplication by synthetic chemicals. *Bull. N.Y. Acad. Med.* **31**, 537.

TAMM, I. (1956a). Selective chemical inhibition of influenza B virus multiplication. *J. Bact.* **72**, 42.

TAMM, I. (1956b). Antiviral chemotherapy. *Yale J. Biol. Med.* **29**, 33.

TAMM, I. (1957). Ribonucleic acid synthesis and influenza virus multiplication. *Science*, **126**, 1235.

TAMM, I., BUGHER, J. C. & HORSFALL, JUN., F. L. (1955). Ultracentrifugation studies of a urinary mucoprotein which reacts with various viruses. *J. biol. Chem.* **212**, 125.

TAMM, I., FOLKERS, K. & HORSFALL, JUN., F. L. (1953). Inhibition of influenza virus multiplication by alkyl derivatives of benzimidazole. 1. Kinetic aspects of inhibition by 2,5-dimethylbenzimidazole as measured by infectivity titrations. *J. exp. Med.* **98**, 219.

TAMM, I., FOLKERS, K. & SHUNK, C. H. (1956a). High inhibitory activity of certain halogenated ribofuranosylbenzimidazoles on influenza B virus multiplication. *J. Bact.* **72**, 54.

TAMM, I., FOLKERS, K. & SHUNK, C. H. (1956b). Certain benzimidazoles, benzenes, and ribofuranosylpurines as inhibitors of influenza B virus multiplication. *J. Bact.* **72**, 59.

TAMM, I., FOLKERS, K., SHUNK, C. H., HEYL, D. & HORSFALL, JUN., F. L. (1953). Inhibition of influenza virus multiplication by alkyl derivatives of benzimidazole. III. Relationship between inhibitory activity and chemical structure. *J. exp. Med.* **98**, 245.

TAMM, I., FOLKERS, K., SHUNK, C. H. & HORSFALL, JUN., F. L. (1954). Inhibition of influenza virus multiplication by N-glycosides of benzimidazoles. *J. exp. Med.* **99**, 227.

TAMM, I. & NEMES, M. M. (1957). Glycosides of chlorobenzimidazoles as inhibitors of poliovirus multiplication. *Virology*, **4**, 483.

TAMM, I. & OVERMAN, J. R. (1957). Relationship between structure of benzimidazole derivatives and inhibitory activity on vaccinia virus multiplication. *Virology*, **3**, 185.

TAMM, I. & TYRRELL, D. A. J. (1954). Influenza virus multiplication in the chorioallantoic membrane *in vitro*: kinetic aspects of inhibition by 5,6-dichloro-1-β-D-ribofuranosylbenzimidazole. *J. exp. Med.* **100**, 541.

TARVER, H. & GROSS, D. (1955). Incorporation of ethionine into the proteins of Tetrahymena. *Fed. Proc.* **14**, 291.

TYRRELL, D. A. J. (1955). New tissue culture systems for influenza, Newcastle disease and vaccinia viruses. *J. Immunol.* **74**, 293.

YČAS, M. & BRAWERMAN, G. (1957). Interrelations between nucleic acid and protein biosynthesis in microorganisms. *Arch. Biochem. Biophys.* **68**, 118.

WOMACK, C. R. & KASS, E. H. (1953). Influenza virus in allantoic sac tissue culture. Quantitative studies on nucleic acid content during growth and in the presence of cortisone. *J. Immunol.* **71**, 152.

WOOLLEY, D. W. (1944). Some biological effects produced by benzimidazole and their reversal by purines. *J. biol. Chem.* **152**, 225.

ZAMENHOF, S. & GRIBOFF, G. (1954). Incorporation of halogenated pyrimidines into the deoxyribonucleic acids of *Bacterium coli* and its bacteriophages. *Nature, Lond.* **174**, 305.

SPECIFIC INHIBITORS OF
PROTEIN SYNTHESIS

E. F. GALE

Medical Research Council Unit for Chemical Microbiology,
Department of Biochemistry, University of Cambridge

Protein synthesis is a process so fundamental to the growth and existence of all living organisms that it would not, at first sight, offer any promise as a basis for the sort of selective inhibition underlying chemotherapy. Nevertheless, research of the last ten years has shown that some of the more effective chemotherapeutic drugs act by inhibiting protein synthesis or by interfering in some way with the relations between proteins and nucleic acids with the result that protein formation ceases. The biochemistry of protein synthesis has not yet been elucidated and the study of drugs of this nature acquires added interest in that it may help with the unravelling of the underlying reactions. Since these reactions are not understood, it is almost impossible to indicate future rational development of inhibitors for them, so that suggestions for future action come into the realm of wild guesses rather than speculations. However, the success of substances such as chloramphenicol and the tetracyclines means that we must give inhibitors of this group our most serious consideration as full realization of their potentialities may well be a key to the strategy of chemotherapy.

Proteins and nucleic acids are highly complex end products of biosynthesis and it may not be incorrect to regard much of the metabolic and morphological organization of the cell as being necessary for, and specifically designed for, the production of specific proteins and nucleic acids. This means that cessation of protein or nucleic acid synthesis may result from many sorts of interference with metabolic or structural systems. The action of every growth inhibitor discussed in this Symposium will ultimately result in cessation of protein synthesis but in this contribution we shall be concerned with those substances whose action lies in the ultimate stages of protein synthesis *per se* and not in any of the ancillary reactions that lead to those final stages. A note of mysticism in description is inevitable here since we cannot yet give any chemical definition to those 'final stages'. If we consider a bacterial cell growing in a simple medium, then formation of protein within the cell will depend upon (1) mobilization of energy by an exergonic reaction such as oxidation or fermentation of glucose, (2) 'coupling' of such exergonic reactions to endergonic synthetic processes, (3) transport of ions, nutrients, amino acids and other essential metabolites across the surface structures of the cell, (4) synthesis of amino acids, purines, pyrimidines, ribose and other components involved in the protein-nucleic acid relationship, (5) activation of amino acids, (6) the 'final stages' in which the relation between nucleic acids, nucleic acid precursors, amino acids and, possibly, proteins functions with a resultant net synthesis of protein and, probably, further nucleic acids. Each of these processes can be studied apart from the others and specific inhibitors are known for each. In this contribution we are concerned with substances which inhibit (6) but are without significant action on (1)–(5). Process (6) is undoubtedly a most complex one and it is necessary to outline what is known—and what is surmised—about this process before proceeding to discuss the actions of inhibitors on it.

MECHANISM OF PROTEIN SYNTHESIS

All proteins are built up from some twenty different L-amino acids. In microbiological discussions we have to qualify this statement since cell walls of some bacteria contain polypeptide-like complexes which include D-isomers of some amino acids and also 'new' amino acids such as diaminopimelic acid (Salton, 1956; Park & Strominger, 1957; Work, 1957); it is doubtful whether these complexes should be considered as proteins but they may be formed by a mechanism allied to that involved in protein synthesis and, as such, are relevant to our later discussions. Proteins consist of amino acids linked through peptide bonds to form polypeptide chains; they differ in the length of the chain, in the nature of its folding, and in the sequence of amino acids in the chain. The number of possible permutations, combinations and stereochemical variations of amino acid residues in chains and folded chains is astronomical and easily able to accommodate the 620-odd enzymes so far described in the literature (Dixon & Webb, 1958). Although our knowledge of amino acid sequences in proteins is meagre, it seems probable that the sequence in any one protein is specific and invariable. The problems before us therefore include the following:

(1) What determines the amino acid sequence in a specific protein?

(2) How is that sequence imposed upon the coming together of amino acids when that specific protein is synthesized?

(3) What determines which particular proteins shall be made in a particular cell?

The synthesis of any specific protein must involve at least three operations: (*a*) arranging of amino acids in a specific (predetermined) sequence, (*b*) forging of peptide bonds between adjacent residues, and (*c*) folding and cross-linking of the polypeptide chain to yield the specific protein macromolecule. Operations (*a*) and (*c*) are new to biochemists and none of their studies on the biosynthesis of other metabolites throws any light on the *modus operandi*. It may even be, as Burnet (1956) suggests, that they involve as yet undiscovered laws of physics and chemistry.

Peptide bond formation

Operation (*b*), the forging of a peptide bond between two amino acids, can be studied in simple systems such as those synthesizing glutathione (Johnston & Block, 1951; Samuels, 1953) or hippuric acid (Chantrenne, 1951). Polypeptide synthesis can be achieved under somewhat unphysiological conditions by reversal of proteolytic enzymes to give plasteins, or by transpeptidation mechanisms (Hanes, Hird & Isherwood, 1950, 1952; Fruton, Johnston & Fried, 1951). Doubt is thrown on the relevance of such studies to protein biosynthesis by the insensitivity of the reactions to antibiotics, such as chloramphenicol, which are highly effective inhibitors of protein formation in living cells (Samuels, 1953; Gale, 1953). Peptide bond formation as such cannot explain the setting up of specific sequences (or 'patternization') unless every bond is forged by an enzyme displaying specificity towards the residues on either side of the bond; the mind reels before the thought of the enzymes so needed for the synthesis of hundreds of different peptides and, in any case, the problem is merely moved one step further as the enzymes would themselves have to act in controlled order. If patternization precedes peptide bond formation, then the latter could be accomplished by a single non-specific enzyme.

Most speculations on this subject during recent years have involved the use of a template for operation (*a*). The simplest template hypothesis supposes that patternization of amino acids takes place on the surface of a template equipped with groups attracting amino acids into specific positions, and that peptide bonds are then formed between adjacent residues with resultant peeling away of the polypeptide from the template surface—a sort of zipper mechanism (Burnet, 1956). The next question concerns the nature of the template. This must have certain properties: it must have a macromolecular shape similar to that of the polypeptide chain it is to produce; it must have reactive sites at intervals appropriate for placing amino acid residues in specific sequences and distances, and it must possess a number of different reactive sites at least equal to the number of different amino acids it is to organize. Clearly a protein can be a template for self duplication, amino acids 'crystallizing' on to corresponding residues (Haurowitz, 1950), although the initial protein would presumably have to exist, or be held, in open chain formation before it could act in this manner. During the last fifteen years, emphasis has shifted to the nucleic acids as possible templates (Borsook, 1956; Gale, 1957b) or, at least, as the surfaces on which protein chains may be held in the open formation (Haurowitz, 1950).

Nucleic acids and protein synthesis

The evidence that nucleic acid is concerned in protein synthesis has been summarized on a number of occasions (Brachet, 1955; Hotchkiss, 1955; Spiegelman, Halvorson & Ben-Ishai, 1955; Burnet, 1956; Gale, 1957a, b). Briefly: from studies with chromosomes, transforming principles, bacteriophage transduction, and virus genetics it would appear that deoxyribonucleic acid (DNA) determines the types of protein synthesized by a cell, that this role can sometimes be taken over by ribonucleic acid (RNA), and that actual synthesis of protein involves participation of RNA. A pneumococcus unable to utilize mannitol can be transformed to one able to utilize mannitol by growth in the presence of DNA extracted from a mannitol-utilizing strain. The transformation bestows upon the acceptor cell the *ability* to utilize mannitol; actual development of the enzymes concerned requires growth in the presence of the substrate. The ability to form the enzymes can be imposed by DNA from either induced or non-induced donor cells (Marmur & Hotchkiss, 1955). Likewise the ability to produce β-galactosidase is imposed on the disrupted staphylococcal cell by DNA from either induced or non-induced cells but the actual formation of the enzyme depends further on the presence of substrate and the synthesis of RNA (Gale & Folkes, 1955b). In the presence of competent DNA, protein synthesis requires RNA or the synthesis of RNA and many investigations have established that the rate of protein synthesis can be correlated with the amount of RNA in the cells concerned (Caspersson, 1947; Gale, 1953). Studies of the formation of inducible enzymes indicate that concomitant synthesis of RNA is essential for enzyme synthesis (Spiegelman et al. 1955) but investigations with constitutive and inducible enzymes in intact and disrupted staphylococci suggest that this requirement may be peculiar to the synthesis of inducible enzymes (Creaser, 1956; Gale, 1956). Creaser (1956) has proposed that enzyme synthesis is dependent upon RNA but that the RNA component varies in functional stability, the least stable components being found in inducible enzyme formation where continuous synthesis of the component then becomes necessary.

In various mammalian systems it has been shown that the administration of a labelled amino acid is rapidly followed by its incorporation into ribonucleoprotein, appearance in soluble protein occurring at a later stage (Littlefield, Keller, Gross & Zamecnik, 1955; Rabinowitz & Olson, 1956; Littlefield & Keller, 1957). One of the current hypotheses put forward to explain these various findings is that DNA is the primary template which carries the information necessary to control the synthesis of specific proteins and is the genic material conveying information from a cell to its progeny. It seems probable that there is in each cell only one DNA molecule, or one part of a DNA macromolecule, corresponding to each protein made by that cell. If every protein had to be formed at one place only, the rate of formation might be severely restricted and we know that the relative amounts of different proteins in a cell vary widely (McIlwain, 1946). Consequently the suggestion has been made that the information is conveyed to RNA in the first place, the RNA then acting as the actual catalyst of protein synthesis, translating the information into amino acid sequences. Each protein would therefore correspond to a specific RNA carrying the information necessary for its formation. That RNA can act in such a way is shown by the plant and animal viruses which are ribonucleoprotein in nature and in which the RNA moiety appears to possess the ability to organize the synthesis of its specific protein (Burnet, 1956).

If the theory were true, it would follow that RNA synthesis takes place in contact with DNA (i.e. in the nucleus) and, once formed, RNA should be capable of protein synthesis in the absence of DNA. This possibility has been investigated by Goldstein & Plaut (1955) who have shown that RNA synthesis in amoebae does in fact take place in the nucleus and that the RNA then passes out of the nucleus into the cytoplasm. Enucleate amoebae retain the ability to incorporate labelled amino acids into their protein and some evidence of protein synthesis itself has been obtained in such damaged cells (Mazia, 1956). The theory can be summarized diagrammatically:

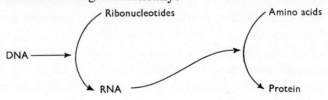

Watson & Crick (1953) have suggested that the DNA macromolecule forms a double helix and have indicated how such a structure could be capable of self-replication. There would seem to be experimental support for this in the recent work of Kornberg, Lehman, Bessman & Sims (1956) who have obtained polydeoxyribonucleotide synthesis in a cell-free enzyme system incubated with the triphosphates of the relevant nucleosides, and find that the extent of the synthesis is dependent upon the presence and amount of DNA primer. However, just as in the case of polyribonucleotide synthesis by polynucleotide phosphorylase (Grunberg-Manago, Ortiz & Ochoa, 1956) the question arises whether the *in vitro* synthesis reproduces the *in vivo* event or is only a part of the biosynthetic mechanism. The *in vitro* synthesis of polyribonucleotides takes place in the absence of amino acids or proteins other than the enzyme and presumably gives rise to random sequences of nucleotides in the product; cellular synthesis of RNA requires the presence of amino acids, is linked with protein in some way, and is believed to give rise to specific sequences of nucleotides in the macromolecule. Likewise DNA synthesis *in vivo* may involve more factors than those required to produce a polydeoxyribonucleotide *in vitro*. Thus Newton (1957) has found that ethidium bromide inhibits the synthesis of DNA in *Strigomonas oncopelti* while allowing synthesis of RNA and protein to continue; the inhibition of DNA synthesis is, however, reversible until RNA synthesis has proceeded to an extent of about 50 % increase, after which the inhibition of DNA synthesis is irreversible. Whatever the future may show concerning the relations between nucleic acids and proteins, there can be little doubt that their biosyntheses are interconnected and that measures designed to inhibit the one may well have repercussions on the other.

Amino acid incorporation

Nucleoprotein complexes possess the property of incorporating amino acids (Gale & Folkes, 1955a; Littlefield *et al.* 1955; Rabinowitz & Olson, 1956; Allfrey, Mirsky & Osawa, 1957; Littlefield & Keller, 1957) although there is some dispute whether this involves protein synthesis or a part of the mechanism thereof. Gale (1957b) has shown that the rate of incorporation of a single amino acid in staphylococcal preparations does not bear any relation to the rate of net synthesis of protein under a variety of conditions. There seems little doubt, however, that amino acid incorporation is brought about as a result of the function of a part or parts of the protein synthesizing mechanism and that inhibitors of incorporation also inhibit protein synthesis to some extent. Certainly experiments involving the measurement of amino acid incorporation are easier to perform, more consistently reproducible and more accurately estimated than those involving measurement of net protein synthesis or development of enzymic activities. Consequently studies of the inhibition of incorporation are most pertinent to the present discussion.

Incorporation of amino acids in the various preparations so far investigated appears to depend upon the presence of nucleic acid. Investigations of the role of the nucleic acid fall into two main groups: those with bacterial fragments and those with microsome preparations from animal tissues. Gale (1957b) has shown that the ability of disrupted staphylococcal cells to incorporate amino acids can be markedly decreased if nucleic acid is removed from the preparation. The incorporation can be restored by putting back staphylococcal nucleic acids, DNA being more effective on an optical density basis than RNA. If RNA is digested with ribonuclease the digest proves as effective as the whole nucleic acid in restoring incorporation but the activity is now dialysable. Fractionation of the digest shows that the activity lies in trace components which can be separated from recognized nucleotides, polynucleotides and nucleosides. These 'incorporation factors' possess stabilities, electrophoretic properties, solubilities and ultraviolet spectra indicating that they are not identical with any known nucleotide or nucleoside derivative and they have not, at the time of writing, been identified. They clearly play an important role in incorporation processes, especially in the activity of the nucleic acid component, and may well present a site for the action of inhibitors of protein synthesis.

The incorporation of amino acids into ribonucleoprotein of the microsomal fraction of liver and ascites tumour cells has been studied in considerable detail by Littlefield et al. (1955), Hoagland, Keller & Zamecnik (1956), and Hoagland, Zamecnik & Stephenson (1957). In these systems the amino acid first becomes activated in the presence of adenosine triphosphate (ATP) (Hoagland, 1955) in a reaction represented as:

Amino acid (α) + ATP + enzyme →

$$\text{amino acyl-AMP-enzyme} + \text{pyrophosphate.} \quad (1)$$

The amino acyl-AMP (adenosine monophosphate) product has not been isolated and is thought to exist at the enzyme surface only. Incorporation of the amino acid into the microsomal ribonucleoprotein also requires the presence of guanosinetriphosphate (GTP). The activating enzyme preparation contains ribonucleic acid and, if the preparation is incubated with [^{14}C]leucine and ATP, the leucyl residue becomes attached to, or combined with, the ribonucleic acid part of the preparation. In the presence of GTP the leucyl residue becomes incorporated in the insoluble ribonucleoprotein of the microsomes. There are thus two sorts of ribonucleic acid concerned in the complete process. The ribonucleic acid ('rna') of the activating enzyme preparation is of low molecular weight and exists in a soluble form in the cytoplasm; the ribonucleic acid (RNA) of the microsome is sedimented with the microsomal fraction and is of high molecular weight. Hoagland *et al.* (1957) interpret their findings as follows: the 'activated' amino acid residue (α) is transferred from the surface of the activating enzyme to the soluble 'rna' to give an amino acyl-rna complex

$$\alpha\text{-AMP-enzyme} + \text{rna} \rightarrow \alpha\text{-rna} + \text{enzyme} + \text{AMP}. \tag{2}$$

The amino acid residue can then be transferred to the ribonucleoprotein of the microsome in the presence of GTP

$$\overset{\text{GTP}}{\alpha\text{-rna} + \text{RNA} - - - - \rightarrow \alpha\text{-RNA} + \text{rna}.} \tag{3}$$

Incorporation of α into the microsomal ribonucleoprotein involves insertion of the amino acid into peptide bonds and it is not known whether this requires the simultaneous presence of other amino acids for synthesis of a polypeptide structure or whether the incorporation can occur by some addition or exchange reaction. Reaction (3) is almost certainly complex and remains to be elucidated. It is improbable that α is transferred directly from one ribonucleic acid to another so that we can add a further step:

$$\alpha\text{-rna-X} \rightarrow \alpha\text{-X} + \text{rna}, \tag{4}$$

$$\alpha\text{-X} + \text{RNA} \rightarrow \alpha\text{-RNA} + \text{X}, \tag{5}$$

where X may be a nucleotide residue or this may be the place where the incorporation factors of Gale (1957*b*) come into the picture. Holley (1957) has shown that a conversion of AMP $\rightarrow$ ATP will take place in rat liver homogenates and that this conversion is dependent upon the presence of alanine and is abolished by ribonuclease. He suggests that nucleotides other than AMP may be involved in the later stages of the incorporation process.

The dependence of ribonucleic acid synthesis on the presence of amino acids is relevant at this point. Gale & Folkes (1953*a*) showed that RNA synthesis in *Staphylococcus aureus* occurs to a significant extent only in the presence of all those amino acids necessary for protein synthesis. The general conclusion has been confirmed by demonstrations with a number of organisms that amino acid-less mutants are unable to synthesize RNA in the absence of the required amino acids (Gros & Gros, 1956; Pardee & Prestidge, 1956; Yčas & Brawerman, 1957). Quantitative considerations preclude simultaneous polymerization of amino acid-nucleotide complexes to yield protein and RNA together, and Yčas & Brawerman (1957) conclude that the most probable explanation is that both protein and RNA arise from the same precursors. The amino

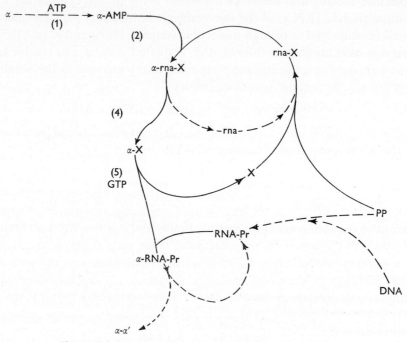

Fig. 1. Scheme summarizing present position concerning the
possible pathways for the incorporation of amino acids

α = amino acid	rna = soluble ribonucleic acid fraction
α-α′ = peptide chain	X = carrier component
ATP = adenosinetriphosphate	RNA = microsomal ribonucleic acid fraction
AMP = adenosinemonophosphate	RNA-Pr = ribonucleoprotein
GTP = guanosinetriphosphate	DNA = deoxyribonucleic acid
PP = purine/pyrimidine ribosides	

acyl-adenylate complex of Hoagland (1955) could form one such precursor although similar derivatives of the other RNA bases would be necessary for RNA formation. Yčas & Brawerman (1957) suggest that a pool of such precursors could give rise to protein in the presence of an adequate supply of amino acids, the nucleotides then acting as carriers; alternatively the pool could give rise to RNA in the presence of catalytic amounts of amino acids even if protein synthesis were blocked as in the case of chloramphenicol inhibition (Gale & Folkes, 1953b).

Where so much is unknown it is doubtful whether one can attempt synthesis of facts obtained with biological systems so different as microsomes and bacteria. The activating enzymes have been described in a wide variety of cells but little is known as yet of the heterogeneity of ribonucleic acid in general. As shown below, Pardee, Paigen & Prestidge (1957) have produced evidence that the RNA of *Escherichia coli* can be separated into major and minor components of high and low molecular weight respectively and it may be that these correspond to the 'microsomal' and 'soluble' ribonucleic acid fractions described above.

For the purposes of our discussions in this Symposium it is desirable that we should have some mental picture of the mechanism of protein synthesis in the light of knowledge so far available. Consequently we put forward a diagrammatic synthesis strictly for speculative purposes only and in the full knowledge that it will be incomplete if not altogether wrong by the time of the Symposium (Fig. 1).

INHIBITION OF PROTEIN SYNTHESIS

From this point we can proceed in two ways. First, we can deduce the sort of substance which might be expected to inhibit protein synthesis taking place along the lines indicated in the previous section. Second, we can take substances which have been discovered empirically and later found to act as inhibitors of protein synthesis, try to see how they act and then deduce improvements, if possible. The first, or rational, approach is restricted in the present instance by the limitations of our knowledge of the process to be inhibited and, although it has led to the invention of inhibitors of the process *per se*, few of these have proved to possess selective toxicity. Inhibitors of chemotherapeutic use have come from the second type of approach and the study of their mode of action may well enable us to make the rational attack more subtle and effective in the future.

The rational approach: inhibition by metabolite analogues

When a biochemist wishes to design a specific inhibitor of a known reaction, his first approach is to modify the structure of one or more of the reactants in the hope that he will produce a substance sufficiently similar to the reactant to be able to combine with the enzyme concerned or to enter otherwise into the reaction, and sufficiently dissimilar either to inactivate that enzyme or to give rise to an inactive (or even toxic) product. The principles involved have been discussed by Woolley (1952a, 1958). The scheme set out in Fig. 1 indicates the nature of the reactants concerned in protein synthesis which could be investigated in this way.

Analogues of amino acids. The synthesis of proteins involves the supply and activation of some twenty-odd amino acids. In the environment in which chemotherapeutic agents are to work, it would not be feasible to deprive the organism of amino acids but this might be achieved in-directly by supplying an analogue of a specific amino acid with the intention of inhibiting the corresponding activating enzyme or otherwise competing with the natural substrate in the course of incorporation. The first attempts to exploit such a possibility were made by McIlwain (1941) with the use of amino-sulphonic acid analogues of natural amino acids; today substances such as *p*-fluorophenylalanine, azatryptophan and tryptazan are commonly used as inhibitors of enzyme synthesis (Halvorson, Spiegelman & Hinman, 1955; Spiegelman *et al.* 1955). In some cases such analogues inhibit the corresponding activating enzyme but in others the analogues undergo activation and become incorporated into protein in the place of the natural substrate (Munier & Cohen, 1956; Davie, Koningsberger & Lipmann, 1956; Brawerman & Yčas, 1957). Analogues such as *p*-fluorophenylalanine or tryptazan which enter into the structure of proteins result in inhibition of enzyme formation as the unnatural proteins formed are enzymically inactive but they do not prevent the formation of 'protein' in the chemical sense of the term.

Woolley (1950) has suggested that chloramphenicol can be regarded as an analogue of phenylalanine, differing from that amino acid in four positions:

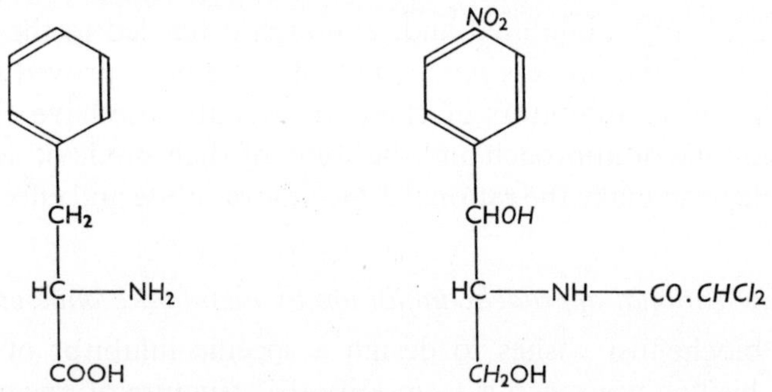

He found that the growth inhibitory action of chloramphenicol could be partially antagonized by phenylalanine. It might follow from this that chloramphenicol would inhibit the incorporation of phenylalanine into protein; it is shown below (Fig. 6) that phenylalanine incorporation is indeed inhibited by the antibiotic but that the incorporation of other amino acids is affected to the same or greater extent and that the action is not specific towards phenylalanine. Other reports have indicated some antagonism of chloramphenicol by tyrosine, tryptophan, glycine and indole (Mentzer, Meunier & Molho-Lacroix, 1950; Truhaut, Lambin & Boyer, 1951; Molho & Molho-Lacroix, 1952; Bergmann & Sicher, 1952). DeMoss & Novelli (1955) did not find any inhibition of amino acid activating systems in bacterial extracts by chloramphenicol.

Analogues of purines and pyrimidines. Protein synthesis can be markedly accelerated by supplying mixtures of purines and pyrimidines or their ribosides (Gale, 1953) and it seems probable that some form of turnover of the 'rna' may be involved. It might therefore be possible to interrupt protein synthesis by supplying analogues of purine or pyrimidine bases. Thus Spiegelman *et al.* (1955) prevented the synthesis of β-galactosidase in *Escherichia coli* by the presence of 5-hydroxy-uridine and Creaser (1956) inhibited β-galactosidase formation in *Staphylococcus aureus* by supplying 8-azaguanine to the organism during synthesis. This type of approach has been particularly successful in the design of inhibitors of virus growth and, as such, is dealt with elsewhere in this Symposium (Markham, 1958; Tamm, 1958). Gillespie, Engelman & Graff (1954, 1956) have synthesized a wide variety of benzimidazole derivatives in which the 4 and 6 positions have been substituted by methoxy-, ethoxy- or nitro-groups; many of these substances have proved toxic to the growth of bacteria, protozoa and embryos while some, such as 6-hydroxy-4-nitrobenzimidazole, proved to be mutagenic. These substances may act as analogues of guanine and Smith & Matthews (1957) have found that the 8-azapurines which are effective inhibitors of growth are converted into, and incorporated as, 8-aza-guanine. If guanine plays some role different from that of the other purines and pyrimidines, this may be connected with the functions of GTP in the incorporation of amino acids (see p. 219). We do not yet know whether triphosphates of the other nucleosides have specific roles, while ATP is involved in so many reactions in the cell that any ATP antagonist would interfere in many processes other than protein synthesis. Woolley (1944) found that the inhibitory action of benzimi-dazole itself on the growth of yeast could be antagonized by purines, guanine being more effective than adenine. The activities of substituted benzimidazoles, as shown below, appear to be more complex than can be explained on a basis of antagonism of purine metabolism only.

Analogues of peptides. Most hypotheses of protein synthesis involve an arrangement of amino acids on a template surface and the formation of peptide bonds between residues so arranged. It would seem possible that a peptide structure could combine irreversibly with the template surface and so block its synthetic function. It may be relevant in this connexion that many bacterial antibiotics are polypeptide in nature and frequently contain D-isomers of amino acids. Antibiotics such as poly-myxin and tyrocidin act by virtue of their surface activity (Newton, 1958) but bacitracin is not surface-active, does not give rise to alterations in the permeability of bacterial membranes and inhibits the incorpora-tion of certain amino acids into the protein fraction of sensitive organ-isms so it may act as such a template poison (Gale, 1953).

Penicillin can be written as an analogue of glutathione:

Penicillin   Glutathione

and it might be thought to act by blocking glutathione metabolism. Hanes et al. (1950) found that penicillin inhibits the formation of γ-glutamyl peptides when glutathione is incubated with γ-glutamyl transferase and an acceptor amino acid. However, it was later found that glutathione is not a specific substrate for this enzyme (Hanes et al. 1952) and that the transfer of γ-glutamyl groups from γ-glutamyl-glutamic acid is inhibited by penicillin in concentrations of the same order as those of the substrate (Talalay, 1954; Samuels, 1955). The synthesis of glutathione by bacterial extracts is not affected by penicillin (Samuels, 1953).

Inhibition of amino acid incorporation: an experimental approach

In an attempt to learn something of the mechanism of incorporation, Gale & Folkes (1957) investigated the nature of substances which inhibit glycine incorporation in disrupted staphylococcal cells. They studied the action of a variety of general metabolic inhibitors, chelating agents and analogues of purines and pyrimidines; their findings can be sum-marized as follows:

(1) Although ethylenediaminetetra-acetic acid and $\alpha\alpha$-dipyridyl were without action, 8-hydroxyquinoline (oxine) proved to be a potent inhibitor of incorporation. The effect of concentration (Fig. 2) was unusual in that 10^{-5}M-oxine was markedly more toxic than 10^{-3}M. This result is reminiscent of that obtained by Albert, Gibson & Rubbo (1953) for the antibacterial action of oxine. These authors found that oxine is non-toxic in the absence of heavy metal ions and suggested that the

toxic substance is the chelate complex formed by metal and oxine present in equimolar amounts; in the presence of excess oxine the metal becomes completely chelated and consequently unable to combine with reactive sites in the biological system (see Fig. 3). That a similar explanation holds in the case of incorporation is made probable by the finding that removal of heavy metal ions from the incubation medium results in a marked decrease in the inhibitory action of added oxine.

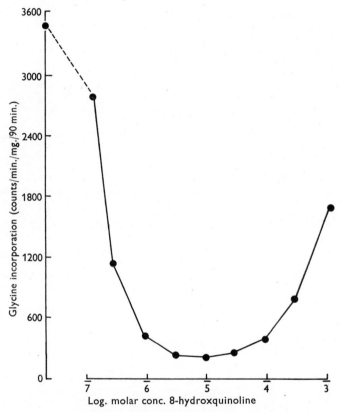

Fig. 2. Effect of 8-hydroxyquinoline on the incorporation of glycine
by disrupted staphylococcal cell preparations.

(2) A wide variety of purine and pyrimidine analogues had little or no action on glycine incorporation under the conditions tested. Certain derivatives of benzimidazole were efficient inhibitors.

(3) Substitution with Cl, CH_3, CH_3O, C_2H_5O, NO_2, in positions 4, 5 and 6 markedly increased the inhibitory action of benzimidazole. 5:6-Dimethylbenzimidazole, or the corresponding 5:6-dichloro derivative, was a good inhibitor; substitution of α- or β-D-ribofuranosyl

15   MS VIII

groups in position 1 largely abolished the toxic action of these derivatives. In this and other respects, the results differ from those of Tamm
(1958) on the inhibition of virus growth by benzimidazole compounds
and indicate that the basis of the inhibition is probably different in the
two systems. 1-Allyl-5:6-dimethylbenzimidazole was the best inhibitor
of incorporation in this group.

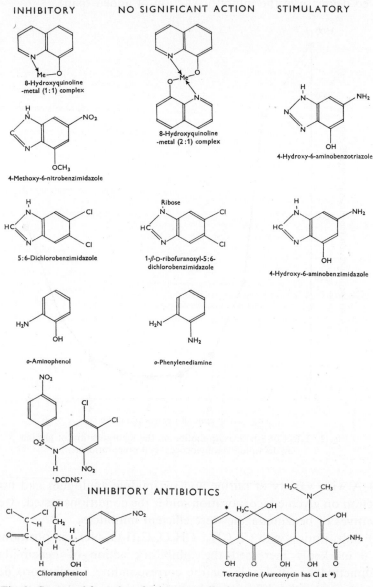

Fig. 3. Structural formulae of substances affecting amino acid incorporation.

(4) Fig. 4 shows the inhibitory action of substances derived in the first place by opening the imidazole ring of 5:6-dichlorobenzimidazole. 1:2-Dichloro-4:5-diaminobenzene has an inhibitory action of the same degree as 5:6-dichlorobenzimidazole. This result led to investigation of the action of analogues of 1:2-dimethyl-4:5-diaminobenzene, since Woolley (1951) had shown that such substances act as inhibitors of the growth of *Staphylococcus aureus* and suggested that they act by inhibiting the metabolism of dimethyldiaminobenzene which is a precursor of benzimidazole compounds such as vitamin B_{12} and riboflavin. The most effective inhibitor of this series, described by Woolley (1952b) and

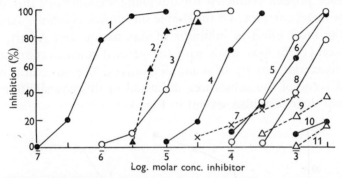

Fig. 4. Inhibition of glycine incorporation in disrupted staphylococcal cells by derivatives and analogues of benzimidazole.

1   1:2-Dichloro-4-(*p*-nitrobenzenesulphonylamido)-5-nitrobenzene (DCDNS)
2   1:2-Dichloro-4-bromophenol
3   1:2-Dichloro-4-(*p*-nitrobenzenesulphonylamido)-benzene
4   1:2-Dichloro-4-aminophenol
5   1:2-Dichloro-4:5-diaminobenzene
6   5:6-Dichlorobenzimidazole
7   1:2-Dimethyl-4-(*p*-nitrobenzenesulphonylamido)-benzene
8   5-Chlorobenzimidazole
9   1-β-D-Ribofuranosyl-5:6-dichlorobenzimidazole
10 Benzimidazole
11 1-β-D-Ribofuranosyl-5:6-dimethylbenzimidazole

found to be effective against the growth of mammary cancers in mice (Woolley & Schaffner, 1954), was 1:2-dichloro-4-(*p*-nitrobenzene-sulphonylamido)-5-nitrobenzene (DCDNS).

Fig. 4 shows that removal of the nitro-group in position 5 reduces the inhibitory action of DCDNS while the further substitution of the chloro-groups with methyl-groups markedly decreases its activity. *p*-Nitro-benzenesulphonamide itself is devoid of inhibitory action.

(5) 4-Hydroxy-6-aminobenzimidazole or 4-hydroxy-6-aminobenzo-triazole activates glycine incorporation and antagonizes the inhibition due to 8-hydroxyquinoline, benzimidazole derivatives and certain amino-

phenols but is without antagonistic action for DCDNS (see Fig. 3). From these results the conclusion is drawn that the structure below, or an analogue thereof, forms an active centre in the incorporation mechanism. Such structures form complexes with polyvalent metals and it may be that the active component is a metal complex. In this case the inhibition due to oxine-metal complexes would be due to a structural resemblance to, and consequent competition with, the natural active component. If this hypothesis is correct, it should be possible to inhibit incorporation—and thence protein synthesis—by designing analogues of this structure or of the metal complex. Of the simple substances available, oxine seems to be the most effective inhibitor of this nature and Albert, Rees & Tomlinson (1956) have dealt with the general considerations affecting the antibacterial activity of oxine derivatives. The structural relationships of some of the substances discussed in this contribution can be seen from their formulae set out in Fig. 3.

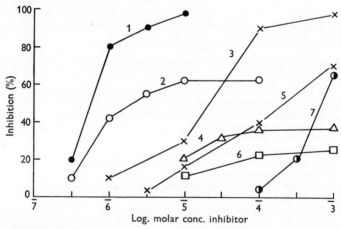

Fig. 5. Inhibition of glycine incorporation in disrupted staphylococcal cells by antibiotics.

1	'DCDNS'	5	Terramycin
2	Penicillin	6	Puromycin
3	Aureomycin	7	5:6-Dimethylbenzimidazole
4	Chloramphenicol		

Antibiotics. Fig. 5 shows the inhibition of glycine incorporation by some of the substances mentioned above and by certain antibiotics. Penicillin and chloramphenicol show a marked difference from many other inhibitors in that their action reaches a plateau value so that even high concentrations do not stop incorporation completely. The degree of inhibition at which the plateau is reached varies with the amino acid whose incorporation is being studied (Gale, 1953). Streptomycin, suramin and isoniazid are without significant action.

Specific inhibitors of protein synthesis: the empirical approach

Chloramphenicol. Chloramphenicol is an excellent example of a chemo-therapeutic agent that was discovered as an inhibitor of bacterial growth and whose mode of action has been narrowed down by a series of elimi-nating investigations to lie in the inhibition of protein synthesis. Its action has been investigated in considerable detail on *Staphylococcus aureus* (Gale & Folkes, 1953*b*, 1955*a, b*; Gale, 1953), on *Escherichia coli* (Hahn & Wisseman, 1951; Wisseman, Smadel, Hahn & Hopps, 1954; Hahn, Wisseman & Hopps, 1955; Cohen & Rickenberg, 1956), on *Bacillus subtilis* (Hahn, Wisseman & Hopps, 1954) and on various enzyme systems (Smith, Worrel & Swanson, 1949; Samuels, 1953; Smith, 1953). At bacteriostatic concentrations it is without significant effect on glucose fermentation, glucose oxidation, glutathione synthesis, simple peptide synthesis, phosphorylation, bioluminescence (*Achromo-bacter fischeri*), motility, passage of amino acids across bacterial cell membranes or concentration within the cell by permease action. DeMoss & Novelli (1955) did not find any inhibition of amino acid activation. At bacteriostatic concentrations chloramphenicol inhibits inducible enzyme formation (Hahn & Wisseman, 1951) and general protein synthesis (Gale & Folkes, 1953*b*) but not RNA or DNA synthesis. Hahn *et al.* (1954) made the interesting observation that chloramphenicol inhibits the growth of *Bacillus subtilis* but does not interfere with the formation of D-glutamyl polypeptide by the organism, whereas the L(+) *erythro*-stereoisomer of the antibiotic (chloramphenicol being the D(−) *threo*-stereoisomer) inhibits D-glutamyl polypeptide formation but does not affect the growth of the organism. They sug-gested that the mechanism of formation of D-glutamyl polypeptide is analogous to that of the formation of L-amino acid polypeptides in protein synthesis and that the L(+) *erythro*- and the D(−) *threo*-stereoisomers act as antimetabolites of unknown but related functional units in the synthetic processes concerned.

In *Staphylococcus aureus* Gale & Folkes (1953*b*) found that concen-trations of chloramphenicol which brought about complete inhibition of protein synthesis stimulated the synthesis of RNA by as much as 50 %. Wisseman *et al.* (1954) did not find any stimulation of RNA synthesis by *Escherichia coli* under the conditions used by them but Harrington (1955) working under the same conditions showed that purine-like materials accumulate in the medium when this organism is incubated in the presence of limiting concentrations of chloramphenicol. Addition of an inhibitor to a biosynthetic process frequently leads to accumulation of precursors normally forming substrates of the blocked reaction. The accumulation of RNA in the presence of chloramphenicol might arise as a result of a block in a reaction involving 'rna' such as reaction (3) on p. 219.

Hoagland *et al.* (1957) distinguish the intermediate 'rna' from the ribonucleic acid of the microsome by solubility and molecular weight. Pardee *et al.* (1957) have examined the ribonucleic acid of *Escherichia coli* and find that it separates on electrophoresis into two fractions. The major fraction is of high molecular weight (upper limit 4×10^5) and firmly bound to protein; the minor fraction, amounting to 10–20 % of the total, has a higher electrophoretic mobility and a molecular weight of less than 5000. The minor fraction appears to be heterogeneous as judged by fractionation procedures and has a base composition different from that of the major fraction. It is also found in conjunction with protein but is bound much less firmly than the major portion as it is liberated from protein in the course of sonic disintegration of the organisms. When cells are incubated in concentrations of chloramphenicol which limit the synthesis of protein, there is an increase in ribonucleic acid in the cells and the 'new' material is similar in mobility and firmness of binding to protein to the minor 'normal' component. It appears to differ from the normal minor component in size as judged by fractionation procedures, and its base composition is similar to that of the normal major component. If radioactive phosphate is present during the incubation, the new component becomes labelled. The new nucleic acid is bound to protein although protein synthesis cannot be detected; presumably it is bound by pre-existing protein. Neidhardt & Gros (1957) have found that the new ribonucleic acid (rna[c]) which accumulates in the presence of chloramphenicol is unstable and breaks down in the course of subsequent incubation in the absence of antibiotic. If chloramphenicol is added to the incubation mixture during the course of such subsequent incubation, rna[c] is resynthesized but this resynthesis needs the presence of a source of energy in addition to chloramphenicol. Neidhardt & Gros (1957) followed the liberation of adenine, ribose and phosphate during the breakdown of rna[c]; on addition of chloramphenicol, resynthesis of rna[c] took place during which adenine and ribose but not phosphate were taken up again. The resynthesis was also unusual in that it did not show a dependence upon amino acids whereas ribonucleic acid synthesis under normal conditions requires the presence of amino acids.

Chloramphenicol inhibits the incorporation of amino acids into the protein of *Staphylococcus aureus* but the effect varies with the particular

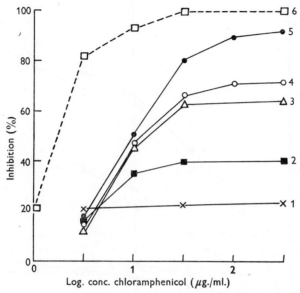

Fig. 6. Inhibition of the incorporation of amino acids in disrupted staphylococcal cells by chloramphenicol.

1	Alanine	4	Glutamic acid
2	Glycine	5	Leucine
3	Phenylalanine		

Curves 1–5 represent inhibition of incorporation when disrupted cells are incubated with a source of energy and the named amino acid only. Curve 6 represents inhibition of total protein synthesis when disrupted cells are incubated with a complete mixture of amino acids.

amino acid studied (Gale & Folkes, 1955*a*). It can be seen from Fig. 6 that the various incorporation processes all display the same sensitivity to 3 μg. chloramphenicol/ml. but that the inhibition at higher concentrations reaches a plateau value characteristic of each amino acid. The figure also shows the effect of the antibiotic on total protein or specific enzyme synthesis, and it can be seen that this is markedly more sensitive than the incorporation of any one amino acid although it is conceivable that the effect on total protein synthesis represents the summation of the effects on individual amino acids.

The action of chloramphenicol on protein synthesis is reversible; if organisms that have been incubated in the presence of amino acids and antibiotic are washed free from inhibitor and resuspended in the presence of amino acids and an energy source, they resume protein synthesis immediately (Gale & Folkes, 1953*a*, *b*); RNA synthesis takes place at the same time. However, we have recently found that the inhibition of glutamic acid incorporation in disrupted staphylococcal cells is not so

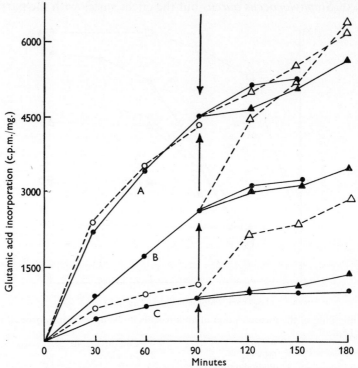

Fig. 7. Effect of chloramphenicol on glutamic acid incorporation in disrupted staphylococcal cells.

Incubation 0–90 min. takes place in the presence of ^{14}C-labelled glutamic acid, ATP and HDP (A) without addition, (B) with 10 μg. chloramphenicol/ml., (C) with 100 μg. chloramphenicol/ml. Dotted lines O – – – O show effect of adding 0·4 mg. staphylococcal ribonucleic acid to the system at time 0. At time 90 min. (at arrows) cell preparations are centrifuged and washed free from antibiotic, etc. They are then resuspended under the same conditions in the absence of antibiotic. ●—●, continuation of first incubation without washing; ▲—▲, washed preparation put up in glutamic acid, ATP, HDP; △– – –△, washed preparation put up in glutamic acid, ATP, HDP with addition 0·4 mg. staphylococcal ribonucleic acid.

readily reversed. Fig. 7 shows the course of glutamic acid incorporation in the presence of 10 or 100 μg. chloramphenicol/ml.; after 90 min. the preparation is washed free from antibiotic but there is little or no reversal of the inhibition of incorporation. However, the addition of RNA markedly stimulates the recovery from inhibition; the residual inhibition left after the removal of 10 μg. chloramphenicol/ml. is completely and rapidly abolished by the presence of RNA. The effect of

RNA can again be reproduced by an equivalent amount of the corresponding 'incorporation factor' preparation. RNA has little effect if added to the incubation mixture before incorporation begins or after incubation in the absence of chloramphenicol. It seemed possible that incorporation of glutamic acid in the presence of chloramphenicol inactivated the corresponding RNA or incorporation factors; however it has been found that maximum residual inhibition (i.e. inhibition remaining after the disrupted cells have been washed free from antibiotic) is obtained by incubation of the preparation with chloramphenicol in the presence of ATP and hexose diphosphate (HDP), the presence of glutamic acid having little or no effect. Little residual inhibition is obtained if the preparation is incubated with chloramphenicol and phosphate buffer in the absence of a source of energy.

From these various findings it would appear that chloramphenicol alters, or in some way interferes with the function of, the ribonucleic acid component concerned in amino acid incorporation. If the minor component of the ribonucleic acid of *Escherichia coli* is related to the 'rna' of the scheme on p. 220 then it seems that chloramphenicol may prevent the function of this component as a carrier of amino acid residues. If it simply blocked the transfer of the residue α from α-rna to the next component X, then the chloramphenicol-resistant portion of incorporation (Fig. 6) would correspond to the accumulation of α-rna. The work of Hoagland *et al.* (1957) would indicate that the nature of the bond holding α to 'rna' differs from the peptide bonds retaining residues incorporated in the normal way. We have been unable to show any differences between glutamic acid incorporated in the presence of chloramphenicol (supposedly α-rna) and glutamic acid incorporated in the absence of antibiotic (supposedly α-RNP); tests included release of label by ribonuclease, lipase, or hot trichloroacetic acid, and degree of exchange on subsequent incubation with [^{12}C]glutamic acid, ATP and HDP. It seems improbable therefore that there is any difference in the nature of the incorporation taking place in the presence or absence of chloramphenicol. A hypothesis in accordance with the facts known at present would be that chloramphenicol undergoes activation in the presence of ATP and then combines with 'rna' to form an inactive rna^c complex which may be an analogue of α-rna. This would explain the requirement for an energy source noted by Neidhardt & Gros (1957) for the formation of rna^c and the independence of the process on amino acids; the requirement for additional ribonucleic acid to release residual inhibition of glutamic acid incorporation; the accumulation of a 'new' ribonucleic acid during incubation with chloramphenicol in a full

234 E. F. GALE

medium, while the various plateaux shown by the inhibition curves in Fig. 6 would be explained by differing affinities for 'rna' of the various activated amino acids and chloramphenicol and the relative stabilities of the complexes formed. An elaboration of this hypothesis is suggested by the finding that the release of residual inhibition (Fig. 7) is accomplished by the 'incorporation factor' preparation; if this constitutes the X of the scheme on p. 220 then activated chloramphenicol may replace X to lead to the formation of rna^c devoid of incorporating function— this suggestion would then be in accord with that put forward by Hahn *et al.* (1954). These various ideas can be tested if and when labelled chloramphenicol becomes available.

Smith *et al.* (1949) tested some forty-nine enzyme systems for sensitivity to chloramphenicol; of these only esterase was inhibited by growth-limiting concentrations. Liver esterase and the enzyme from *Escherichia coli* were both sensitive; in the case of *E. coli* 50 % inhibition of esterase activity was obtained with that concentration of chloramphenicol producing approximately 50 % inhibition of growth rate. It is interesting to speculate whether esterase plays any part in protein synthesis. Dr D. Raacke has pointed out that, for example, the combination of an amino acid with 'rna' may involve an ester bond between the carboxyl of the amino acid and the 2-hydroxyl of ribose. An esterase might therefore be concerned with opening this bond or transferring the amino acyl residue to the next carrier, and chloramphenicol might, in turn, inhibit this activity. This would give rise to the situation described above where there would be a difference in the nature of the bond holding residues incorporated in the presence of chloramphenicol and that holding residues incorporated in the absence of inhibitor; evidence of such a difference has not been obtained. Furthermore, we have recently found that the addition of liver esterase or pancreatic lipase markedly enhances, rather than releases, the inhibitory action of chloramphenicol on glutamic acid incorporation by disrupted staphylococcal cells.

Tetracyclines. Gale & Folkes (1953*b*) found that aureomycin and terramycin, at bactericidal concentrations, effect a specific inhibition of protein synthesis in *Staphylococcus aureus*. The tetracyclines differ from chloramphenicol in that they bring about complete inhibition of glycine incorporation (see Fig. 5). Aureomycin displays other inhibitory effects at high concentrations; Loomis (1950) found that 100–300 μg./ml. uncouple oxidative phosphorylation in mitochondrial preparations and suggested that such effects may be partly responsible for the toxicity of this antibiotic.

Saz and his co-workers (Saz & Marmur, 1953; Saz & Slie, 1954a, b; Saz & Martinez, 1956) have shown that aureomycin at growth-limiting concentrations inhibits the enzyme which reduces organic nitro-compounds (including chloramphenicol, which can be used as substrate). The organic nitro-reductase has been isolated in a purified state and shown to be a metallo-flavoprotein; the apo-enzyme can be activated by flavine-adenine-dinucleotide and Mn^{2+}. Aureomycin is a chelating agent and, since its action on the enzyme can be reversed by Mn^{2+}, it is suggested that it inhibits the enzyme by combining with the essential metal ion. Enzymes have been isolated from aureomycin-sensitive and resistant organisms and have been found to differ in the firmness with which the metal is bound to the protein; sensitivity is correlated with ease of dissociation (and, presumably, removal) of the metal component. It is improbable that organo-nitro-reductase is itself concerned in protein synthesis but the system may well provide a model for the anti-biotic action of aureomycin by indicating the importance of its metal chelating properties. The possibility that a metal component is concerned in amino acid incorporation has been discussed above.

Penicillin as an inhibitor of protein synthesis

Investigations concerning the action of penicillin have followed two main lines: studies of the consequences of growth of susceptible cells in the presence of the antibiotic, and studies of the effect of the antibiotic on non-growing cells. As Hotchkiss (1950) pointed out, the primary effect of penicillin should be demonstrable in non-growing cells since events which take place during growth arise as a consequence of such a primary action. The only effect so far demonstrated of penicillin *at growth-limiting concentrations* on non-growing cells is the inhibition of the incorporation of certain amino acids into the protein of staphylococci (Gale & Folkes, 1953b; 1955a). The experimental conditions are: washed intact or disrupted staphylococcal cells are incubated with a source of energy (glucose or a mixture of ATP and HDP) and a single labelled amino acid; after incubation the labelled amino acid is found to have become incorporated into the protein fraction of the cells and in certain cases this incorporation is inhibited by the presence of penicillin during incubation. Fig. 8 shows the effect of penicillin concentration on the incorporation of [^{14}C]glutamic acid and it can be seen that growth inhibitory concentrations effect *c.* 50 % inhibition; increasing the concentration of antibiotic does not markedly increase the degree of inhibition, which reaches a plateau value at about 50%. Fig. 8 also shows that total protein synthesis is not inhibited until the penicillin concentration is many times the growth inhibitory level. The results with chloramphenicol have prepared us for the finding that inhibition of incorporation may vary with the amino acid studied and the values given in Table 2 are those obtained on the inhibition plateau in each case. Penicillin differs from chloramphenicol in that the incorporation of a number of amino acids is not affected at all. The incorporation

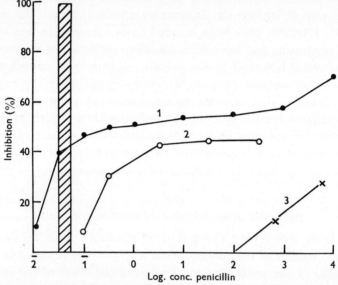

Fig. 8. Effect of penicillin on incorporation of glutamic acid and on total protein synthesis. Curve 1, inhibition by penicillin of incorporation of glutamic acid in intact *Staphylococcus aureus* incubated with source of energy and glutamic acid only; curve 2, as for 1 but experiment carried out with disrupted cell preparation; curve 3, inhibition by penicillin of net protein synthesis in intact *S. aureus* incubated with glucose and complete mixture of amino acids. Cross-hatched area shows concentration of penicillin preventing growth of organism used.

processes for glycine, glutamic acid, lysine, aspartic acid and alanine are sensitive although in no case is inhibition complete. Very similar results are obtained with bacitracin (Gale, 1953).

From what has been set out above, it would be expected that inhibition of amino acid incorporation would be reflected in inhibition of protein synthesis. Fig. 8 shows however that total protein synthesis is not sensitive to penicillin (in marked contrast to chloramphenicol where protein synthesis is more sensitive than individual incorporation reactions). Gale & Folkes (1955*b*) and Creaser (1955) have shown that the formation of *β*-galactosidase in *Staphylococcus aureus* is inhibited by penicillin; in disrupted cell preparations *β*-galactosidase formation is inhibited but not catalase development. Table 1 shows that there is no general differentiation between the development of inducible and constitutive enzymes as far as penicillin inhibition is concerned. Inhibition of enzyme development again shows a plateau which may correspond to a small inhibition as shown in Table 1; the plateau value is also found to be somewhat variable for any one enzyme from time to time. From these observations it would seem that penicillin is an inhibitor of protein synthesis but that the specificity and partial nature of its action would put it in a different class from chloramphenicol and the tetracyclines.

Table 1. *Effect of penicillin on the development of enzymic activities in* Staphylococcus aureus

Washed cells are incubated for 90 min. at 37° in phosphate, glucose and a mixture of eighteen amino acids together with the natural purines and pyrimidines and, in the case of inducible enzymes, substrate. Parallel experiments are set up with and without 6μg. penicillin/ml. Enzymic activities are estimated before and after incubation: column (*a*) shows the % increase in activity during incubation; column (*b*) shows the % inhibition of this increase by penicillin.

	% increase (*a*)	% inhibition (*b*)
Constitutive enzyme systems		
Invertase	120	0
Pyrophosphatase	114	3
Catalase	54	3
Glucose oxidation	62	5
Glucose fermentation	205	9
Arginine dihydrolase	210	32
Glutamic acid permease	125	100
Inducible enzyme systems		
β-Galactosidase	1500	76
Galactozymase	870	37
Nitratase	375	0
Maltase	272	4

Amongst the effects that have been described of growth of *Staphylococcus aureus* in penicillin have been cessation of the ability of the cells to accumulate free glutamic acid (Gale & Taylor, 1947), cessation of the ability to oxidize nucleosides (Gros, Beljanski & Macheboeuf, 1951), accumulation of uridine pyrophosphate hexosamine-amino acid complexes—the 'Park compounds' (Park, 1952), inhibition of RNA synthesis (Mitchell & Moyle, 1951; Strominger, 1957), inhibition of 'XP' synthesis (Mitchell & Moyle, 1951), and cessation of cell-wall synthesis (Lederberg, 1956, 1957). Park & Strominger (1957) have shown that the same hexosamine-amino acid complex is found both in the cell wall of staphylococcus and in the 'Park compounds' so that one of the actions of penicillin may be to prevent the polymerization of the 'Park compounds' to cell-wall material. This is the subject of another contribution to the Symposium (Park, 1958) and is brought forward here in order that its relevance to the other actions of penicillin might be assessed. One of the questions that now arise is whether these various effects are consequences of some primary inhibition of protein synthesis, or whether the effects on amino acid incorporation and protein formation are secondary to a disturbance of function of wall or membrane.

The ability to accumulate and concentrate free amino acids within the cell is dependent upon an active transport mechanism in the cell membrane. The recent studies of Cohen & Rickenberg (1956) have suggested that such mechanisms involve the presence of a specific protein in the membrane; Monod has suggested the name 'permease' for such proteins acting specifically and catalytically to bring about transfer of substances across membranes. In the case of galactoside transfer Rickenberg, Cohen, Buttin & Monod (1956) have shown the presence of a specific inducible permease in *Escherichia coli* whereas the permeases involved in the transport of amino acids appear to be of limited but not strict specificity (Cohen & Rickenberg, 1956). When *Staphylococcus aureus* cells are incubated in a medium containing glucose and a complete mixture of amino acids, the ability to concentrate [^{14}C]glutamic acid increases and this may be attributed to an increase in glutamic acid permease; in the presence of penicillin at growth-limiting concentration this increase in permease is completely prevented. If penicillin can be regarded as an inhibitor of the synthesis of specific proteins, then glutamic acid permease is one of the proteins whose synthesis is most sensitive to inhibition and is completely inhibited as opposed to the partial inhibitions shown in Table 1. Amino acid permeases are concerned with the passage of amino acids into the cell; it is possible, as Work (1957) has pointed out, that permeases are likewise required for the passage of substances out of the cell so that inhibition of cell-wall synthesis might be attributable to inhibition of the permease needed to transport precursors such as 'Park compounds' through the membrane to the external site of polymerization.

The cell wall material contains peptides and the 'Park compound' precursors contain D-glutamic acid, DL-alanine and L-lysine. The question arises whether any part of the incorporation of amino acids as studied by Gale & Folkes (1955a) concerns cell-wall residues rather than cellular protein. The disrupted cell preparation used by Gale & Folkes includes cell-wall material and this necessarily forms part of the trichloroacetic acid precipitate in which incorporation is measured. An attractive explanation of the plateau shown for penicillin inhibition of glutamic acid incorporation would be that penicillin blocks that part of the incorporation which relates to the cell-wall peptide. L-Amino acids are used in these studies whereas the cell-wall glutamic acid is in the D-form but racemization might occur during the course of the incubation. The discovery by Ghuysen (1957) of a lysopeptidase which digests staphylococcal wall substance makes it possible to test this suggestion. The disrupted staphylococcal preparation has now been incubated with a number of different amino acids, the preparation divided into two parts after incorporation has taken place and, in each case, one part digested with Ghuysen's enzyme until the wall has been removed. The

Table 2. *Inhibition by penicillin of amino acid incorporation in disrupted staphylococcal cells*

Disrupted cell preparation was incubated with a single [^{14}C]labelled amino acid (as below) in the presence of ATP and HDP with and without 30 μg. penicillin/ml. After 90 min. at 37° the preparation was centrifuged, washed, divided into two fractions (a) and (b). Fraction (b) was incubated for 3 hr. with 10 μg. lysopeptidase/mg. dry-weight preparation. Both fractions were then precipitated with trichloroacetic acid, final concentration 5%, washed and prepared for counting as described by Gale & Folkes (1955a). Column (a) shows the % inhibition of incorporation measured in fraction (a); column (b) the % inhibition measured in fraction (b) where the cell wall has been removed. Column (c) shows the % recovery in (b) of the radioactivity incorporated in (a).

| | % inhibition by penicillin | | % recovery after removal of cell wall |
| | Wall material present | Wall material absent | |
Amino acid	(a)	(b)	(c)
Glycine	69	70	91
DL-Alanine	35	33	92
L-Glutamic acid	53	61	101
L-Aspartic acid	23	25	96
L-Lysine	32	36	91
L-Phenylalanine	5	0	93
L-Arginine	8	10	82
L-Leucine	0	5	100

two parts have then been precipitated with trichloroacetic acid as usual and the incorporation in the protein fraction compared with that in the protein + wall fraction. The experiments have also been carried out in the presence of penicillin and the results are shown in Table 2. It can be seen that the loss of radioactivity on removing wall material from the preparation is within the experimental error so that any incorporation into wall peptides that occurs is insignificant and certainly not comparable with the decrease in incorporation produced by penicillin. In confirmation it can be seen that the inhibitory effect of penicillin is the same whether wall material is included in the estimations or not. Clearly, the incorporation processes affected by penicillin do not involve the cell-wall peptides. Although cessation of cell-wall synthesis is an important result of the presence of penicillin and leads to lysis, the effects of penicillin on amino acid incorporation and permease formation suggest that the primary seat of its action lies in some form of protein synthesizing mechanism—although it may well be that the sensitive mechanism resides in the cell membrane.

The passage of wall precursors to their site of polymerization may depend upon the presence of penicillin-sensitive permease-like agents in the membrane. On the other hand, the 'Park compounds' contain uridine residues which disappear during cell-wall synthesis and there is an apparent similarity between this polymerization process and the formation of protein from amino acyl-nucleotides which suggests that there may be a common mechanism. Penicillin resembles chloramphenicol in that its inhibition of incorporation processes reaches a plateau value; the effects of penicillin and chloramphenicol at plateau concentrations are additive, if not synergic, so they presumably affect different sites of action. Gale & Folkes (1955b) found that the incorporation of [^{14}C]uracil into RNA which accompanies β-galactosidase synthesis is inhibited by penicillin, while Strominger (1957) found a similar inhibition during synthesis of protein by intact *Staphylococcus aureus* and showed that it was accompanied by accumulation of 'Park compounds'. He suggested that the inhibition of RNA synthesis was due to the side-tracking and trapping of uridine by the 'Park compounds'. On this view, inhibition of wall-precursor polymerization results in immobilization of uracil with consequent impairment of RNA synthesis and its accompanying protein synthesis. It might also explain why the amino acids whose incorporation is partially inhibited by penicillin correspond, in the main, with those found in cell-wall material, since the accumulation of the 'Park compounds' might likewise side-track, or inhibit, some component of their incorporation mechanism. No role of uracil has yet been demonstrated in amino acid incorporation (other than its presence in ribonucleic acid) but there are plenty of gaps in our knowledge at present and it would seem probable that roles for all the bases will eventually be discovered.

We can thus put forward, very tentatively, suggestions that the three types of 'specific inhibitors of protein synthesis' that we have discussed bring about their effects by inactivating or immobilizing specific components of the mechanism which transfers an active amino acid from the surface of the activating enzyme to its position in or on the ribonucleoprotein template: chloramphenicol may inactivate the soluble 'rna' component, penicillin may directly or indirectly immobilize uracil, and aureomycin may inactivate a metal component or compete with a specific metal complex. To speculate further on these premises would indeed be building a house on sand.

SELECTIVE ACTION

So little is known of the intimate mechanism of protein synthesis that it is not possible to say whether the mechanism is common to all tissues or not. The general picture as far as dependence on activating enzymes and nucleic acids is concerned is similar in all cells so far investigated. The intracellular organization of protein- and nucleic acid-containing components differs in different cells: thus mammalian cells contain mitochondria, microsomes and cytoplasmic reticular structures, whereas the bacterial cell displays a different order of internal organization (Bradfield, 1956). The cytoplasmic membrane, or protoplast membrane, appears at the moment to play a more important role in microbial metabolism—especially the permease systems—than in mammalian metabolism. Where microbial cells possess specific structures such as wall components or permeases, their synthesis offers an obvious site of selective inhibition; the unexcelled selective action of penicillin appears to be based upon such a mechanism. On the other hand, chloramphenicol appears to act upon some general mechanism of protein synthesis. It prevents the synthesis of all bacterial proteins, as far as we can tell at present, and, although comparatively few investigations have been reported for mammalian tissues, Straub & Ullman (1957) find that chloramphenicol inhibits the synthesis of amylase by pancreatic tissue. Allfrey et al. (1957) report little effect of chloramphenicol on alanine incorporation in thymus nuclei but such a result need not necessarily mean that chloramphenicol is without action on protein synthesis *per se* since a similar result is obtained for the incorporation of alanine by *Staphylococcus aureus* (see Fig. 6). Chloramphenicol is a broad spectrum antibiotic as far as bacteria are concerned but is without effect on most yeasts and protozoa while its use as a chemotherapeutic agent indicates that it cannot have any significant effect on protein synthesis in the mammal. It is possible that species specificities exist in the nature of the 'rna' components of cells and that the selective action of chloramphenicol lies in its ability or otherwise to combine with these components; it is also possible that an enzyme is required for the activation of chloramphenicol and that this enzyme is not of universal distribution. The most probable explanation of its differential action lies in differing permeabilities towards the antibiotic

242   E. F. GALE

of the membranes enclosing synthetic sites in different cells. These are merely a few of the many matters which remain to be investigated in this field.

REFERENCES

ALBERT, A., GIBSON, M. I. & RUBBO, S. D. (1953). The influence of chemical constitution on antibacterial activity. Part VI. The bactericidal action of 8-hydroxyquinoline (oxine). *Brit. J. exp. Path.* **34**, 119.

ALBERT, A., REES, C. W. & TOMLINSON, A. J. H. (1956). The influence of chemical constitution on antibacterial activity. Part VIII. 2-Mercaptopyridine-*N*-oxide and some general observations on metal binding agents. *Brit. J. exp. Path.* **37**, 500.

ALLFREY, V. G., MIRSKY, A. E. & OSAWA, S. (1957). Protein synthesis in isolated cell nuclei. *J. gen. Physiol.* **40**, 451.

BERGMANN, E. D. & SICHER, S. (1952). Mode of action of chloramphenicol. *Nature, Lond.* **170**, 931.

BORSOOK, H. (1956). The biosynthesis of peptides and proteins. *Proc. 3rd Int. Congr. Biochem., Brussels* 1955, p. 92. New York: Academic Press.

BRACHET, J. (1955). The biological role of the pentose nucleic acids. In *The Nucleic Acids* II, p. 475. New York: Academic Press.

BRADFIELD, J. R. G. (1956). Organization of bacterial cytoplasm. In *Bacterial Anatomy. Symp. Soc. gen. Microbiol.* **6**, 296.

BRAWERMAN, G. & YČAS, M. (1957). Incorporation of the amino acid analog tryptazan into the protein of *Escherichia coli*. *Arch. Biochem. Biophys.* **68**, 112.

BURNET, F. M. (1956). *Enzyme, Antigen and Virus*. Cambridge: University Press.

CASPERSSON, T. (1947). The relations between nucleic acid and protein synthesis. In *Nucleic Acid. Symp. Soc. exp. Biol.* **1**, 127.

CHANTRENNE, H. (1951). The requirement for coenzyme A in the enzymatic synthesis of hippuric acid. *J. biol. Chem.* **189**, 227.

COHEN, G. N. & RICKENBERG, H. V. (1956). Concentration spécifique réversible des amino acides chez *Escherichia coli*. *Ann. Inst. Pasteur*, **91**, 693.

CREASER, E. H. (1955). The induced (adaptive) biosynthesis of β-galactosidase in *Staphylococcus aureus*. *J. gen. Microbiol.* **12**, 288.

CREASER, E. H. (1956). The assimilation of amino acids by bacteria. 22. The effect of 8-azaguanine upon enzyme formation in *Staphylococcus aureus*. *Biochem. J.* **64**, 539.

DAVIE, E. W., KONINGSBERGER, V. V. & LIPMANN, F. (1956). The isolation of a tryptophan-activating enzyme from pancreas. *Arch. Biochem. Biophys.* **65**, 21.

DEMOSS, J. A. & NOVELLI, G. D. (1955). An amino acid dependent exchange between inorganic pyrophosphate and ATP in microbial extracts. *Biochim. biophys. Acta* **18**, 592.

DIXON, M. D. & WEBB, E. (1958). *Enzymes*. London: Longmans, Green & Co.

FRUTON, J. S., JOHNSTON, R. B. & FRIED, M. (1951). Elongation of peptide chains in enzyme-catalysed transamidation reactions. *J. biol. Chem.* **190**, 39.

GALE, E. F. (1953). Assimilation of amino acids by Gram-positive bacteria and some actions of antibiotics thereon. *Advanc. Protein Chem.* **8**, 285.

GALE, E. F. (1956). Nucleic acids and enzyme synthesis. In *Enzymes, Units of Biological Structure and Function. Ford Hosp. Symp.* **4**, 49.

GALE, E. F. (1957*a*). The biochemical organization of the bacterial cell. *Proc. roy. Soc.* B, **146**, 166.

GALE, E. F. (1957*b*). Nucleic acids and protein synthesis. *Harvey Lect.* **51**, 25.

GALE, E. F. & FOLKES, J. P. (1953*a*). The assimilation of amino acids by bacteria. 14. Nucleic acid and protein synthesis in *Staphylococcus aureus*. *Biochem. J.* **53**, 483.

GALE, E. F. & FOLKES, J. P. (1953*b*). The assimilation of amino acids by bacteria. 15. Actions of antibiotics on nucleic acid and protein synthesis in *Staphylococcus aureus*. *Biochem. J.* **53**, 493.

GALE, E. F. & FOLKES, J. P. (1955*a*). The assimilation of amino acids by bacteria. 20. The incorporation of labelled amino acids by disrupted staphylococcal cells. *Biochem. J.* **59**, 661.

GALE, E. F. & FOLKES, J. P. (1955*b*). The assimilation of amino acids by bacteria. 21. The effects of nucleic acids on the development of certain enzymic activities in disrupted staphylococcal cells. *Biochem. J.* **59**, 675.

GALE, E. F. & FOLKES, J. P. (1957). The assimilation of amino acids by bacteria. 24. Inhibitors of glycine incorporation in disrupted staphylococcal cells. *Biochem. J.* **67**, 507.

GALE, E. F. & TAYLOR, E. S. (1947). The assimilation of amino acids by bacteria. 5. The action of penicillin in preventing the assimilation of glutamic acid by *Staphylococcus aureus*. *J. gen. Microbiol.* **1**, 314.

GHUYSEN, J. M. (1957). Activités bactériolytiques de l'actinomycétine de *Streptomyces albus* G. *Arch. Intern. Physiol. Biochim.* **65**, 173.

GILLESPIE, H. B., ENGELMAN, M. & GRAFF, S. (1954). Benzimidazoles and benzotriazoles as growth antagonists. *J. Amer. chem. Soc.* **76**, 3531.

GILLESPIE, H. B., ENGELMAN, M. & GRAFF, S. (1956). Some new benzimidazoles and quinoxalines. *J. Amer. chem. Soc.* **78**, 2445.

GOLDSTEIN, L. & PLAUT, W. (1955). Direct evidence for nuclear synthesis of cytoplasmic ribose nucleic acid. *Proc. nat. Acad. Sci., Wash.* **41**, 874.

GROS, F., BELJANSKI, M. & MACHEBOEUF, M. (1951). Action de la pénicilline sur le métabolisme de l'acide ribonucléique chez *Staphylococcus aureus*. *Bull. Soc. Chim. biol., Paris*, **33**, 1696.

GROS, F. & GROS, F. (1956). Rôle des aminoacides dans la synthèse des acides nucléiques chez *Escherichia coli*. *Biochim. biophys. Acta*, **22**, 200.

GRUNBERG-MANAGO, M., ORTIZ, P. J. & OCHOA, S. (1956). Enzymic synthesis of polynucleotides. I. Polynucleotide phosphorylase of *Azotobacter vinelandii*. *Biochim. biophys. Acta*, **20**, 269.

HAHN, F. E. & WISSEMAN, JUN., C. L. (1951). Inhibition of adaptive enzyme formation by antimicrobial agents. *Proc. Soc. exp. Biol., N.Y.* **76**, 533.

HAHN, F. E., WISSEMAN, JUN., C. L. & HOPPS, H. E. (1954). Mode of action of chloramphenicol. II. Inhibition of bacterial D-polypeptide formation by an L-stereoisomer of chloramphenicol. *J. Bact.* **67**, 674.

HAHN, F. E., WISSEMAN, JUN., C. L. & HOPPS, H. E. (1955). Mode of action of chloramphenicol. III. Action of chloramphenicol on bacterial energy metabolism. *J. Bact.* **69**, 215.

HALVORSON, H., SPIEGELMAN, S. & HINMAN, R. L. (1955). The effect of tryptophan analogs on the induced synthesis of maltase and protein synthesis in yeast. *Arch. Biochem. Biophys.* **55**, 512.

HANES, C. S., HIRD, F. J. R. & ISHERWOOD, F. A. (1950). Synthesis of peptides in enzymic reactions involving glutathione. *Nature, Lond.* **166**, 288.

HANES, C. S., HIRD, F. J. R. & ISHERWOOD, F. A. (1952). Enzymic transpeptidation reactions involving γ-glutamylpeptides and α-amino-acyl peptides. *Biochem. J.* **51**, 25.

HARRINGTON, M. (1955). The action of antibiotics on *Bacterium coli*. Thesis, National University of Ireland, University College, Cork.

HAUROWITZ, F. (1950). *Chemistry and Biology of Proteins*, p. 326. New York: Academic Press.

HOAGLAND, M. B. (1955). An enzymic mechanism for amino acid activation in animal tissues. *Biochim. biophys. Acta*, **16**, 288.

HOAGLAND, M. B., KELLER, E. B. & ZAMECNIK, P. C. (1956). Enzymatic carboxyl activation of amino acids. *J. biol. Chem.* **218**, 345.

HOAGLAND, M. B., ZAMECNIK, P. C. & STEPHENSON, M. L. (1957). Intermediate reactions in protein biosynthesis. *Biochim. biophys. Acta*, **24**, 215.

HOLLEY, R. W. (1957). An alanine-dependent ribonuclease-inhibited conversion of AMP to ATP and its possible relationship to protein synthesis. *J. Amer. chem. Soc.* **79**, 658.

HOTCHKISS, R. D. (1950). The abnormal course of bacterial protein synthesis in the presence of penicillin. *J. exp. Med.* **91**, 351.

HOTCHKISS, R. D. (1955). The biological role of the deoxypentose nucleic acids. In *The Nucleic Acids* II, p. 435. New York: Academic Press.

JOHNSTON, R. B. & BLOCK, K. (1951). Enzymatic synthesis of glutathione. *J. biol. Chem.* **188**, 221.

KORNBERG, A., LEHMAN, I. R., BESSMAN, M. J. & SIMS, E. S. (1956). Enzymic synthesis of deoxyribonucleic acid. *Biochim. biophys. Acta*, **21**, 197.

LEDERBERG, J. (1956). Bacterial protoplasts induced by penicillin. *Proc. nat. Acad. Sci., Wash.* **42**, 574.

LEDERBERG, J. (1957). Mechanism of action of penicillin. *J. Bact.* **73**, 144.

LITTLEFIELD, J. W. & KELLER, E. B. (1957). Incorporation of C¹⁴ amino acids into ribonucleoprotein particles from the Ehrlich mouse ascites tumour. *J. biol. Chem.* **224**, 13.

LITTLEFIELD, J. W., KELLER, E. B., GROSS, J. & ZAMECNIK, P. C. (1955). Studies on cytoplasmic ribonucleoprotein particles from the liver of the rat. *J. biol. Chem.* **217**, 111.

LOOMIS, W. F. (1950). On the mechanism of action of aureomycin. *Science*, **111**, 474.

MCILWAIN, H. (1941). Bacterial inhibition by aminosulphonic analogues of some natural aminocarboxylic acids. *Brit. J. exp. Path.* **22**, 148.

MCILWAIN, H. (1946). The magnitude of microbial reactions involving vitamin-like compounds. *Nature, Lond.* **158**, 898.

MARKHAM, R. (1958). Contribution to this Symposium.

MARMUR, J. & HOTCHKISS, R. D. (1955). Mannitol metabolism, a transferable property of pneumococcus. *J. biol. Chem.* **214**, 383.

MAZIA, D. (1956). Nuclear products and nuclear reproduction. In *Enzymes: Units of Biological Structure and Function. Ford Hosp. Symp.* **4**, 261.

MENTZER, C., MEUNIER, P. & MOLHO-LACROIX, L. (1950). Faits de synergie et d'antagonisme entre la chloromycetine et divers amino-acides vis-à-vis de cultures d'*E. coli. C.R. Acad. Sci., Paris*, **230**, 241.

MITCHELL, P. D. & MOYLE, J. (1951). Relationships between cell growth, surface properties and nucleic acid production in normal and penicillin-treated *Microccus pyogenes. J. gen. Microbiol.* **5**, 421.

MOLHO, D. & MOLHO-LACROIX, L. (1952). Étude comparée de l'antagonisme entre quelques derivés de la phénylalanine et la chloromycetine, la β₂-thiénylalanine, et la β-phénylsérine. *Bull. Soc. Chim. biol., Paris*, **34**, 99.

MUNIER, R. & COHEN, G. N. (1956). Incorporation d'analogues structuraux d'aminoacides dans les protéins bactériennes. *Biochim. biophys. Acta*, **21**, 592.

NEIDHARDT, F. C. & GROS, F. (1957). Metabolic instability of the RNA synthesized by *Escherichia coli* in the presence of chloromycetin. *Biochim. biophys. Acta*, **25**, 513.

NEWTON, B. A. (1957). The mode of action of phenanthridines: the effect of ethidium bromide on cell division and nucleic acid synthesis. *J. gen. Microbiol.* **17**, 718.

NEWTON, B. A. (1958). Contribution to this Symposium.

PARDEE, A. B., PAIGEN, K. & PRESTIDGE, L. S. (1957). A study of the ribonucleic acid of normal and chloromycetin-inhibited bacteria by zone electrophoresis. *Biochim. biophys. Acta*, **23**, 162.

PARDEE, A. B. & PRESTIDGE, L. S. (1956). The dependence of nucleic acid syntheses on the presence of amino acids in *Escherichia coli*. *J. Bact.* **71**, 677.

PARK, J. T. (1952). Uridine-5′-pyrophosphate derivatives. 1. Isolation from *Staphylococcus aureus*. 2. A structure common to three derivatives. 3. Amino acid containing derivatives. *J. biol. Chem.* **194**, 877, 885, 897.

PARK, J. T. (1958). Contribution to this Symposium.

PARK, J. T. & STROMINGER, J. L. (1957). Mode of action of penicillin. Biochemical basis for the mechanism of action of penicillin and for its selective toxicity. *Science*, **125**, 99.

RABINOWITZ, M. & OLSON, M. E. (1956). Evidence for a ribonucleoprotein intermediate in the synthesis of globin by reticulocytes. *Exp. Cell Res.* **10**, 747.

RICKENBERG, H. V., COHEN, G. N., BUTTIN, G. & MONOD, J. (1956). La galactoside-perméase d'*Escherichia coli*. *Ann. Inst. Pasteur*, **91**, 829.

SALTON, M. R. J. (1956). Bacterial cell walls. In *Bacterial Anatomy*. *Symp. Soc. gen. Microbiol.* **6**, 81.

SAMUELS, P. J. (1953). The assimilation of amino acids by bacteria. 17. Synthesis of glutathione by extracts of *Escherichia coli*. *Biochem. J.* **55**, 441.

SAMUELS, P. J. (1955). Bacterial metabolism of peptides. *Thesis*, Cambridge University Library.

SAZ, A. K. & MARMUR, J. (1953). The inhibition of organic nitro-reductase by aureomycin in cell-free extracts. *Proc. Soc. exp. Biol., N.Y.* **82**, 783.

SAZ, A. K. & MARTINEZ, L. M. (1956). Enzymatic basis of resistance to aureomycin. 1. Differences between flavoprotein nitro reductases of sensitive and resistant *Escherichia coli*. *J. biol. Chem.* **223**, 285.

SAZ, A. K. & SLIE, R. B. (1954*a*). The inhibition of organic nitro reductase by aureomycin in cell-free extracts. 2. Cofactor requirements for the nitro reductase enzyme complex. *Arch. Biochem. Biophys.* **51**, 5.

SAZ, A. K. & SLIE, R. B. (1954*b*). Reversal of aureomycin inhibition of bacterial cell-free nitro reductase by manganese. *J. biol. Chem.* **210**, 407.

SMITH, G. N. (1953). The possible modes of action of chloromycetin. *Bact. Rev.* **17**, 19.

SMITH, G. N., WORREL, C. S. & SWANSON, A. L. (1949). Inhibition of bacterial esterases by chloramphenicol (chloromycetin). *J. Bact.* **58**, 803.

SMITH, J. D. & MATTHEWS, R. E. F. (1957). The metabolism of 8-azapurines. *Biochem. J.* **66**, 323.

SPIEGELMAN, S., HALVORSON, H. O. & BEN-ISHAI, R. (1955). Free amino acids and the enzyme forming mechanism. In *Amino Acid Metabolism*, p. 124. Edited by W. D. McElroy & B. Glass. Baltimore: Johns Hopkins Press.

STRAUB, F. B. & ULLMAN, A. (1957). On the mechanism of amylase synthesis. *Biochim. biophys. Acta*, **23**, 665.

STROMINGER, J. L. (1957). Microbial uridine-5′-pyrophosphate *N*-acetyl-amino sugar compounds. 2. Incorporation of uracil-2-C^{14} into nucleotide and nucleic acid. *J. biol. Chem.* **224**, 525.

TALALAY, P. S. (1954). Glutathione breakdown and transpeptidation reactions in *Proteus vulgaris*. *Nature, Lond.* **174**, 516.

TAMM, I. (1958). Contribution to this Symposium.

TRUHAUT, R., LAMBIN, S. & BOYER, M. (1951). Contribution à l'étude du mécanisme d'action de la chloromycétine vis-à-vis d'*Eberthella typhi*. Rôle du tryptophane. *Bull. Soc. Chim. biol.* **33**, 387.

WATSON, J. D. & CRICK, F. H. C. (1953). Molecular structure of nucleic acids. A structure for deoxyribonucleic acid. *Nature, Lond.* **171**, 737.

WISSEMAN, JUN., C. L., SMADEL, J. E., HAHN, F. E. & HOPPS, H. E. (1954). Mode of action of chloramphenicol. 1. Action of chloramphenicol on assimilation of ammonia and on synthesis of proteins and nucleic acids in *Escherichia coli. J. Bact.* **67**, 662.

WOOLLEY, D. W. (1944). Some biological effects produced by benzimidazole and their reversal by purines. *J. biol. Chem.* **152**, 225.

WOOLLEY, D. W. (1950). A study of non-competitive antagonism with chloromycetin and related analogues of phenylalanine. *J. biol. Chem.* **185**, 293.

WOOLLEY, D. W. (1951). Selective toxicity of 1,2-dichloro-4,5-diamino-benzene: its relation to requirements for riboflavin and vitamin B_{12}. *J. exp. Med.* **93**, 13.

WOOLLEY, D. W. (1952a). *A study of antimetabolites.* New York: John Wiley & Sons, Inc.

WOOLLEY, D. W. (1952b). Some aggregate analogs of p-aminobenzoic acid and dimethyldiaminobenzene possessing unusual biological properties. *J. Amer. chem. Soc.* **74**, 5450.

WOOLLEY, D. W. (1958). Contribution to this Symposium.

WOOLLEY, D. W. & SCHAFFNER, D. W. (1954). Effect of analogs of dimethyldiaminobenzene on various strains of transplanted mammary cancers of mice. *Cancer Res.* **14**, 802.

WORK, E. (1957). Biochemistry of the bacterial cell wall. *Nature, Lond.* **179**, 841.

YČAS, M. & BRAWERMAN, G. (1957). Interrelations between nucleic acid and protein biosynthesis in micro-organisms. *Arch. Biochem. Biophys.* **68**, 118.

MECHANISMS OF
CHEMOTHERAPEUTIC SYNERGY

B. W. LACEY

Westminster Medical School, London

In spite of the enormous increase in armamentarium since Ehrlich's day, and the development in real warfare of 'bewitched balls which fly in search of the enemy', Ehrlich's ideal: the 'therapia sterilisans magna' (Ehrlich, 1913), is still as elusive as ever. With few exceptions, instead of eradicating all microbes with one or two doses of one drug, only a fraction of the invading population can be killed at once, or none can be killed directly, or therapy must be prolonged, perhaps for life, or two or more drugs or agents must be used.

THE MEANING OF SYNERGY

Probably all agree that synergy implies working together towards some objective, but the objective is seldom explicitly stated. To the clinician any combination is synergic which, in comparison with a single drug, helps him to reach his immediate objective, whether this be eradication of the infecting agent, cure or suppression of the disease, abolition of infectivity, or prevention of reinfection. The laboratory worker, however, must decide first whether to restrict the meaning of synergy to effects which appear more than additive, and secondly the nature of the end effect to be observed. The first decision only applies to combinations of two agents which are separately active, for an increased effect from the addition of an inactive agent is clearly synergic. The second is precisely that facing anyone testing prospective chemotherapeutic agents singly: should one use an *in vitro* effect such as diminished rate of growth, stasis, rate of killing, or completeness of killing? Or should one choose an *in vivo* effect on an experimental infection such as suppression of disease, delay or prevention of death, or eradication of infection?

In an excellent review, Jawetz & Gunnison (1953), defined synergy in terms of a large increase in the rate of killing during the first 12 hr. Their reasons were (*a*) that a more than additive growth-inhibitory effect might be due to increased killing, increased stasis, action on different members of a population, or a delayed appearance of mutants, whereas a more than additive rapid bactericidal effect almost certainly reflected a direct toxic action on bacterial cells, and (*b*) that *in vitro* results then most closely conformed with clinical results. In this paper, however, synergy will be used in a broader sense of a more than additive effect, whatever effect is observed and whether or not each component is separately active *in vivo* or *in vitro* or even a substance.

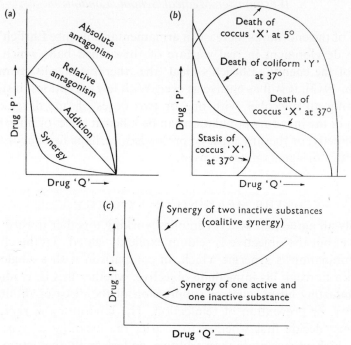

Fig. 1. Lines of equal effect (isobols) of two drugs in combination.

Although the most informative way of representing the interaction of two drugs is probably as a family of dose-effect curves (see Loewe, 1953), the most useful way appears to be in the form of isobols (lines of equal biological effect) on isobolograms as developed by Loewe (Käer & Loewe, 1926; Loewe, 1953) and illustrated in Fig. 1. Fig. 1 (*a*) shows the isobols conventionally interpreted as representing synergy, addition and antagonism. Fig. 1 (*b*) shows how two drugs which are synergic for one effect, or at one temperature, or for one organism, may be antagonistic, additive or show an undulating relation for another. Synergic combinations between one active and one inactive and between two inactive drugs (coalitive synergy) are represented in Fig. 1 (*c*). The action of some antibacterial combinations *in vitro* (e.g. Zipf & Halbeisen, 1954; Elion, Singer & Hitchings, 1954) and the results of a few chemotherapeutic studies (e.g. Miller & Verwey, 1954; Rollo, 1955) have been recorded in this form. Yet up to the present the interaction of two anti-microbial drugs appears not to have been analysed sufficiently in any case for a comprehensive series of isobols to be constructed.

Tactical aspects of combined therapy have been fully discussed in several recent reviews (see Garrod, 1953; Hobby, 1954; Bickel, 1955; Elek, 1956; Dowling, 1957). But because these are addressed to the practising clinician they logically emphasize the immediately available and useful, and avoid the untried and speculative. Here our object is different although complementary: to review the theoretical and distant possibilities of combined therapy however impractical and unexplored they may be at present. For this purpose it is convenient to divide the whole field of antimicrobial synergy into two broad classes: of cytotoxic and non-cytotoxic synergy, and consider the existing practice and possibilities in each class when both, one or neither component is separately toxic to the microbe *in vitro*. The two broad classes are defined as follows:

Cytotoxic synergy: leading by direct toxic action to death or stasis of the microbe and hence demonstrable *in vitro* on a homogeneous population of microbes in the absence of host cells.

Non-cytotoxic synergy: not demonstrable *in vitro* on a homogeneous population and hence demonstrable only *in vivo*, or *in vitro* only in the presence of phenotypically resistant organisms, resistant mutants, other organisms or host cells.

Combinations showing cytotoxic synergy may, of course, also be synergic *in vivo*. The therapeutic result of any combination can therefore be visualized as the resultant of two components. Ideally both cyto-toxic and non-cytotoxic components will be synergies. A therapeutic synergy, however, can still result from a combination whose synergy in one way overcomes an antagonism in another.

CYTOTOXIC SYNERGY

Synergy of two toxic drugs

Some six classes of synergic or additive combination may be distin-guished in this group by their combined action *in vitro*, inhibitability and type of cross resistance. Table 1 and Fig. 2 summarize their pro-perties and presumptive modes of action. The first class (see A + B, Fig. 2) includes most close relatives such as two sulphonamides, two tetracyclines or two streptomycins. Combinations in this class may show a small therapeutic synergy through a reduced host toxicity but

Table 1. *Combinations of two toxic drugs* (see also Fig. 2)

Site[a], route[b] and sequence[c]	Class no.	Can both drugs be antagonized separately by the same agent?	Which of the two drugs can be antagonized by an agent not antagonizing the other?	Pattern of cross-resistance	Action *in vitro* on a homogeneous population	Combination in Fig. 2
Same site of action						
Same route	1	Yes	Neither	Reciprocal[d]	Additive[f]	A+B
Different route	2	Yes	Both	Nil or reciprocal	Additive	A+C
Different sites of action						
Same sequence	3	Yes	One	One-sided[e]	Synergic[f]	A+D
Convergent sequences	4	Yes	Both	One-sided	Synergic	A+E
Different sequences						
Overlapping routes	5	Sometimes	Both	One-sided	Variable[g]	E+F
Different routes	6	No	Both	Nil	Variable	A+F or A+G

(a) Presumptive site of action.
(b) Presumptive route by which drug reaches site.
(c) Presumptive chemical sequence blocked.
(d) Resistance to one is accompanied by resistance to the other and vice versa.
(e) Resistance to one is accompanied by resistance to the other but not vice versa.
(f) See Fig. 1(a).
(g) See Fig. 1(b).

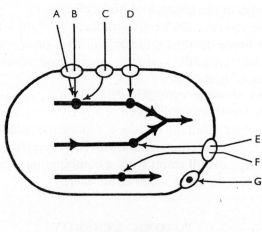

A, B, etc.   Inhibitory drugs

——▶   Biochemical sequence

●   Site of action

—→   Route of drug to site

◯   Transport system

Fig. 2. Hypothetical modes of antimicrobial action. (See also Table 1.)

are otherwise of no special interest. The second class $(A + C)$ is exemplified by p-arsenophenyl butyric acid and melarsen with a trypanosome. Both drugs are phenylarsenoxides and presumably act on the same —SH groups because each is antagonizable by glutathione. Each, however, presumably reaches the site by a different route because each is specifically antagonizable, one by p-aminobenzoic acid and the other by surfen C (see Work & Work, 1948; Albert, 1951).

Class 3 $(A + D)$ includes all combinations showing sequential blocking. The idea of sequential inhibition was first put forward by Beerstecker & Shive (1947) following their discovery that *Escherichia coli*, in a glucose + salts medium, could be inhibited by either tyrosine or β-hydroxyphenylalanine, and that the two inhibitors together were synergic. Since, moreover, phenylalanine would non-competitively antagonize tyrosine and competitively antagonize β-hydroxyphenylalanine, they proposed that both inhibitors acted on the same sequence, tyrosine inhibiting the synthesis, and β-hydroxyphenylalanine the utilization, of phenylalanine. The expression 'sequential blocking' was coined by Potter (1951) for the interaction of malonate and fluoroacetate on citric acid formation by rat tissues, and Pittillo & Foster (1954) suggested that a synergic effect could be expected when each member of a combination could be antagonized separately by the same metabolite. Sequential blocking almost certainly underlies the markedly synergic inhibition *in vitro* of *Streptococcus faecalis* by antifolics and antithymines, of *Lactobacillus casei* by antifolics and antipurines (Elion *et al.* 1954) and of *Proteus vulgaris* by sulphonamides, antifolics and antipurines (Hitchings, Elion & Singer, 1955). It also accounts for the therapeutic synergy of sulphonamides and antimalarials on *Plasmodium gallinaceum* in chicks (Greenberg & Richeson, 1950; Rollo, 1955), *Eimeria tenella* in chicks (see Kendall, 1956) and toxoplasmosis in the mouse (Eyles & Coleman, 1953). There is, however, still no explanation for the mere additive effect of antifolics and antipurines on *Streptococcus faecalis* (Elion *et al.* 1954). Class 4 $(A + E$ in Fig. 2) is represented by the action of antipurines and antithymines on *S. faecalis* (Elion *et al.* 1954), i.e. by the simultaneous interference with two precursors needed for the same product. Elion and his colleagues suggest the term 'concurrent blocking' for this. Experimentally, concurrent is distinguishable from sequential blocking in that the action of each drug in concurrent blocking is separately and selectively antagonizable. Classes 3 and 4 are of special interest because they offer not only a rational approach to synergic chemotherapy of new growths as well as bacteria, but also a high probability of obtaining an effective level of inhibition with either relatively small doses of toxic agents or inhibitors of negligible effect alone. As Beerstecker & Shive (1947) and Albert (1956) have pointed out, the advantages of sequential blocking result from the relatively small dosage required to effect, say, an 80–90 % inhibition of an enzyme and hence, with two such inhibitions in sequence a 96–99 % inhibition of the whole synthesis. To achieve the same overall effect with one drug would require a very large, perhaps physically impossible or toxic amount of one drug. The arithmetic of concurrent blocking is probably similar.

The presence of one-sided cross-resistance distinguishes combinations of class 5 (E+F in Fig. 2) from those of class 6. For example, in *Escherichia coli*, the development of resistance to neomycin is usually accompanied by the appearance of resistance to streptomycin, whereas development of resistance to streptomycin occurs without change in neomycin sensitivity. Polymyxin resistance similarly tends to be accompanied by neomycin and streptomycin resistance, but not the reverse (see Finland, 1955). Pairs of drugs in this class often have a similar or related chemical structure and for this reason may use a common transport system.

All the combinations normally used in chemotherapy belong to class 6 (A+F, etc.). On the basis of their restricted definition of synergy, Jawetz & Gunnison (1953) divided antibiotics into two groups. Group I included penicillin, streptomycin, bacitracin and neomycin. These were often synergic or additive but never antagonistic to each other. Group II included chloramphenicol, the tetracyclines and, at times, the sulphonamides. These were additive with each other. Combinations of antibiotics of group I with those of group II might be synergic, additive or antagonistic according to the organism, concentrations of drugs and length of exposure. Polymyxin appeared unique in often being synergic with members of both groups but never antagonized by any of group II. Coleman, Gunnison & Jawetz (1953) subsequently added erythromycin to group II; recently, Gunnison, Kunishige, Coleman & Jawetz (1955) failed to find any synergy (of their kind) at 4° or in the absence of nutrients, and showed that combinations synergic in broth may be antagonistic in water (see Fig. 1 (*b*)).

Although cross-resistance is not found in class 6, an increased sensitivity to one drug may accompany increased resistance to the other. Szybalski & Bryson (1952) called this 'collateral sensitivity' and both they and Welsch (1955) have discussed its possible causes. It has been noted with many combinations, e.g. to suramin with resistance to trypaflavine (Jancsó & Jancsó, 1935), to sulphadiazine with proguanil

(Greenberg, 1949), to polymyxin with chloramphenicol (Szybalski & Bryson, 1952), or penicillin (Briggs, Crawford, Abraham & Gladstone, 1957), and to phenazines with isoniazid (Barry *et al.* 1957) (see also Finland, 1955). Similarly, mouse leukaemia L 1210 cells resistant to 6-mercapto-purine may be more susceptible to A-methopterin; and Law, Taormina & Boyle (1954) have obtained some promising results in treatment with the two drugs in combination. The possibility of exploiting a collateral sensitivity, although mooted by Szybalski & Bryson (1952), seems not to have been realized in microbial disease. But Welch (1956), in reviewing interference with nucleic acid metabolism, concludes that

at the present time the greatest hope for the attainment of 'cures' probably is to be found in the use of various logical combinations of antagonists through which potentiation of inherent activity may be obtained, or through the deliberate development of resistance to one agent in order possibly to obtain predictable changes in metabolic pathways and thus heightened susceptibility to another compound or combinations of compounds.

This approach, however, must wait on a more intimate knowledge of microbial metabolism. Meanwhile the effects of any particular combination in any environment on any organism remain logically unpredictable.

Synergy of one toxic drug and one non-toxic drug or factor

The effect of any drug on any cell almost always depends on the immediate environment of the cell and often also on the past history of the cell. Many non-inhibitory drugs or factors may thus enhance *in vitro* the toxic action of an antimicrobial substance. They are conveniently divided into six groups according to their presumptive modes of action.

1. *Promoting growth*

The dependence of the killing action of penicillin on growth, first shown by Hobby, Meyer & Chaffee (1942), has been amply confirmed since with bacteriostasis by sulphonamides (Hobby & Dawson, 1944; Chain & Duthie, 1945), oxytetracycline (Gunnison *et al.* 1955), reduced temperature (Bigger, 1944; Gunnison *et al.* 1955), reduced nutrients (Bigger, 1944; Miller & Foster, 1944), old inflammatory exudate (Wood & Smith, 1956) and a high concentration of penicillin itself (Eagle, 1951).

The killing action of isoniazid has similarly been shown to be abolished, or markedly reduced, when growth is inhibited or restricted by oxytetracycline (Mackaness & Smith, 1953), streptomycin (Szybalski & Bryson, 1953; Koch-Weser, 1956), a temperature of 4° (Koch-Weser,

1956), absence of carbon source (Schaefer, 1954), anaerobiosis (Mitchison & Selkon, 1956) or exhaustion of the medium (Koch-Weser, 1956).

Conditions allowing growth appear to be necessary for activity, or
maximal activity, of many other substances. Thus erythromycin fails to
kill group A streptococci at 4°, or when the cocci are in a static phase,
but rapidly kills multiplying organisms (Haight & Finland, 1952);
6-azathymidine is taken up by *Streptococcus faecalis* in any phase of
growth yet leads to rapid death of only multiplying cells (Welch, Prusoff
& Lajtha, 1955); limitation of any one of several essential metabolites, or
of their utilization by analogues, markedly reduces the action of 8-aza-
guanine on *Tetrahymena gelei* W (Kidder, Dewey & Parks, 1952); a
small amount of uracil increases the effect of 6-azauracil on non-
multiplying cells of *S. faecalis* but decreases it on multiplying cells
(Handschumacher & Welch, 1956); oxytetracycline may have a rapid
killing action on viridans streptococci during rapid growth in the
presence of a heat-, acid- and alkali-stable factor in Difco proteose
peptone (Klein, 1953). Growth, however, is certainly not essential, or
even advantageous, for all inhibitors. With some organisms at least,
streptomycin, neomycin and polymyxin may be as rapidly lethal at 4°
as at 37°, and more effective at 37° in distilled water than in broth
(Gunnison *et al.* 1955).

In view of Park & Strominger's (1957) recent findings it is now possible
to compare the action of penicillin on sensitive bacteria with that of
acridines on yeast (Slonimski, 1953). In both instances, multiplication
is necessary to manifest the inhibition of an unessential synthesis: of cell
wall substance by lysis or protoplast formation, or of cytochrome
oxidase by 'petite colonie' mutation. By analogy it is tempting to
imagine that isoniazid has a comparable action on the tubercle bacillus
so that, with the right environment, a large proportion of a population
might be converted to isoniazid-resistant protoplasts.

2. *Increasing physiological sensitivity by some means other than growth promotion*

In the words of Jawetz, Gunnison, Bruff & Coleman (1952), 'it is
not logical to search for synergistic effects only among drugs which in
low concentrations inhibit the micro-organisms in the test-tube. It
seems true, however, that those drugs which are ineffective even in very
high concentration against a given organism probably will not enter into
synergistic combinations against that organism'. Nevertheless, in a
deliberate search for synergy of this kind, Lettré (1954) found that either
bulbocapnine or phlorizin, with no antimitotic power alone, would

markedly enhance the antimitotic activity of colchicine. Although no comparable study in microbiology appears to have been made, several synergies of this kind have been discovered and are still unexplained. Thus, for example, nicotinamide may potentiate penicillin against staphylococci (Frieden, 1945) and Lemco sulphonamides against *Escherichia coli* (Bigger & Ware, 1950). Gillissen (1954) has also observed that isoniazid (without inhibitory action alone) can greatly reduce the minimal inhibitory concentration of Elkosin (Ciba) (6-sulphonamido-2:4-dimethylpyrimidine) for *Salmonella paratyphi-B* or *Proteus* species. It might be argued that this last adjuvant action is secondary to a growth promotion resulting from chelation by the isoniazid of toxic metals, for isoniazid, like all antimycobacterial agents, is a chelator and known to suppress the toxicity of nickel, copper, etc., for species of *Bacillus* and *Pseudomonas* (Weinberg, 1957). This seems unlikely, however, because sulphanilamide affects cells in a late phase of growth more rapidly than those in a logarithmic phase (Youmans, 1947) and is not reputedly more active under conditions of growth.

From experiments with a variety of bacteria, Van Eseltine & Rahn (1949) distinguish two types of toxic agent: those like sulphanilamide, phenol, mercuric chloride and cetylpyridinium chloride with a minimal toxicity at or near 30°, and those like gentian violet, sodium azide and duponol whose toxicity decreases continuously with rise in temperature from 15 to 40°. Probably most substances are of the first type for, over limited ranges of temperature and with some organisms, increase in toxicity with rise in temperature has been reported with the following: bismuth compounds and arsenicals (Eagle, 1939), sulphanilamide (White, 1939), penicillin (Eagle & Musselman, 1944), quinine (Johnson & Lewin, 1946), polymyxin (Bliss, Chandler & Schoenbach, 1949), streptomycin and *p*-aminosalicylic acid (Marks, 1951), isoniazid (Knox, King & Woodroffe, 1952), potassium (Haynes, Kuehne & Rhodes, 1955), chloramphenicol and terramycin (Knothe & Butenberg, 1955) and 8-azaguanine and flavotin (Sterbenz & Lilly, 1956). With *Bacillus cereus*, Knox & Collard (1952) found that a hundredfold increase in sensitivity to penicillin between 37 and 42° was accompanied by, and might be explained by, an absence of adaptive penicillinase formation at 42°. Overall, however, too little is known of drug-parasite-temperature interaction to make any generalization.

As a rule, the influence of pH on drug-sensitivity can be correlated with an influence on the ionization of either drug or microbial receptors (see Albert, 1951). But, since change in pH may induce a profound change in carbohydrate metabolism (Mickelson & Werkman, 1938;

Watt & Werkman, 1951), it seems reasonable to suppose that pH may also at times directly affect the physiological sensitivity. The peculiar interaction of pH, pyrazinamide and tubercle bacilli probably involves a mechanism of this kind because it clearly cannot be attributed to an effect of pH on ionization of the drug. Pyrazinamide is usefully anti tuberculous *in vivo* yet within a 'physiological' pH range has no action on tubercle bacilli *in vitro*. Nevertheless it is bactericidal *in vitro* between pH 4·5 and 5·5 (McDermott, Tompsett & Stern, 1954; Wasz-Höckert, McCune, Lee, McDermott & Tompsett, 1956) and, presumably because monocytes may have a pH near 5·0 (Sprick, 1956), it also exerts a slow lethal effect on human bacilli in rabbit monocytes (Mackaness, 1956).

Change in E_H, like change in pH, may lead to gross changes in carbohydrate metabolism (Englesberg, Gibor & Levy, 1954; Englesberg, Levy & Gibor, 1954) and hence conceivably to change in drug sensitivity. Oxine fails to inhibit staphylococci at oxidation-reduction potentials below 0·06 v (at pH 7·0) (Rubbo, Albert & Gibson, 1950), and malonate has no action on *Escherichia coli* under anaerobic conditions (Quastel, 1956). Williamson & White (1956) found dihydro-streptomycin similarly more active against facultative anaerobes under aerobic conditions, whereas all other compounds tested, including penicillin, chloramphenicol, erythromycin and the tetracyclines, were more inhibitory under anaerobic conditions. It is of interest here that cobalt not only specifically antagonizes oxine against *Staphylococcus aureus* (Rubbo *et al.* 1950) but also permits growth of *Clostridium tetani* under aerobic conditions (Dedic & Koch, 1956).

3. *Increasing permeability of the organism*

The non-ionic detergent Tween 80 can increase the sensitivity of tubercle bacilli a hundredfold to penicillin (Kirby & Dubos, 1947), a thousandfold to streptomycin (Fisher, 1948) and markedly to preparations of bovine pancreatic deoxyribose nuclease (Fletcher, Epstein & Jewell, 1953). That stimulation of growth, through increased permeability to nutrients, is not responsible for the effect of Tween 80 on deoxyribose nuclease, is suggested by the absence of potentiation with Triton A_{20} in spite of an equivalent growth and dispersion (Fletcher *et al.* 1953). Tween 80 is also synergic with polymyxin D against *Escherichia coli* (Bliss & Worth, 1950), and wetting agents are well known to be synergic with disinfectants such as mercurials (Brewer, 1950).

Although at present it appears reasonable to assume that these effects reflect an increased permeability to the drug, an actual increased entry of drug remains to be shown.

4. *Increasing penetrability of the drug*

According to Höber (1945), neutral molecules penetrate membranes more readily than the corresponding ion. An increased penetrability, resulting from a reduced ionization, is presumably therefore the principal factor underlying the well-known enhancement of activity of some basic substances, such as diamidines, streptomycin or erythromycin, by a rise in pH, or of some acid ones, such as mandelic acid, by a fall in pH. Other factors, of course, are the relative activity of ion and neutral molecule at their site of action (see Albert, 1951) and the effect of pH on the organism, mentioned in section 2 above.

Very often, several metal ions, in greatly subinhibitory concentrations, will increase the activity of chelating agents in normal media. Thus, for example, copper may enhance (*a*) the bacteriostatic (Rubbo *et al.* 1950), bactericidal and fungistatic activity (Albert, Gibson & Rubbo, 1953) (see Horsfall, 1956; Hollingshead, 1956) of 8-hydroxyquinoline; (*b*) the antimycobacterial action of isoniazid (Sorkin, Roth & Erlenmeyer, 1951), 2-aminophenol, antipyrinazobarbituric acid (Hahn, Bäumler, Roth & Erlenmeyer, 1953), 8-hydroxyquinoline (Erlenmeyer, Bäumler & Roth, 1953) and 5-oxyquinoline (Sorkin, Roth & Erlenmeyer, 1953); (see also Weinberg, 1957). In general, the metal chelate complex is more lipophilic than the uncomplexed substance and Albert and his colleagues (1953) attribute the enhancing effect of copper on oxine to an improved penetration of the bacterial cell. Strong support for this view, and also evidence of an optimum fat solubility, is provided by Byrde & Woodcock's (1957) finding that a non-toxic chelating agent, ethylenediamine-tetra-acetic acid (EDTA), can enhance the fungistatic activity of chelating agents which are more toxic in their unchelated state than as their copper or zinc complex, such as 5-amyloxine, 5:7-dichlorooxine or 2-mercapto-benzthiazole. Conversely, EDTA can abolish the fungistatic activity of oxine, an agent more active as the metal complex. In both cases the EDTA can be presumed to sequester metal ions which would otherwise diminish (with 5-amyloxine, etc.) or increase (with oxine, etc.) the lipoid solubility and hence penetrability and hence activity of the toxic chelator.

5. *Inhibiting destruction or antagonism*

Any substance inhibiting either the formation or action of penicillinase should be synergic with penicillin *in vitro* against penicillinase producers, and might be of immense value in treating staphylococcal infections acquired in hospital. Dietz & Bondi (1948) found that

0·02 % sodium azide would increase the toxicity of penicillin for penicillinase-producing staphylococci. Since azide at this concentration only slightly depressed growth and had no demonstrable effect on penicillinase activity, it presumably inhibited production or release of penicillinase. Recently Bondi *et al.* (1955) noted that penicillinase production in a basal medium could be reduced to 50 % of normal by isoleucine and to a less extent by purines and by other amino acids. Tyrosine, cystine, valine, glutamic acid and maltose increased production up to threefold. Although neither of these findings is of immediate practical interest, a further indication that Bondi & Dietz's goal may not be unattainable is given by Pollock's (1955) report that polyhydroquinone sulphonate almost certainly inhibits either synthesis or release of penicillinase by *Bacillus cereus*. Meanwhile the chemotherapeutic use of a penicillinase inhibitor seems imminent. Cephalosporin C is a penicillin-like antibiotic with a low activity. It is insensitive to penicillinase and inhibits it competitively (Abraham & Newton, 1956). It shows a marked synergy with penicillin against penicillinase-producing staphylococci but only an additive effect of negligible value against nonproducers (Crawford & Abraham, 1957). Hence cephalosporin C is to penicillin what neostigmine is to acetylcholine, a competitive inhibitor of enzymic destruction with a low intrinsic activity of its own.

Other penicillin-like compounds with little or no antibacterial activity might also prove of value as inhibitors of penicillinase formation or action. Thus, for example, it would seem worth while to test the nontoxic members of the group examined by Brownlee & Woodbine (1948), the inactive L-isomer of penicillin (see du Vigneaud *et al.* 1946), *N*-phenylacetyl-L-cysteinyl-D-valine, which is slightly synergic with penicillin against *Bacillus megaterium* (Holly, Peel, Luz & Folkers, 1952), and the yellow pigment produced by *Penicillium chrysogenum* Q 176 (see Arnstein & Grant, 1956). The activity of several plant-growth substances is antagonized by their inactive optical isomers (Wain, 1953) and, in general, isomers are probably more often antagonistic than synergic. Smrt *et al.* (1957), however, found the L- and D-isomers of cycloserine to have a synergic static action *in vitro* on *Escherichia coli* strain B. The synergy was most obvious at 40 hr. and therefore may prove to be against growth of resistant mutants rather than a cytotoxic one. None of the three optical isomers of chloramphenicol has so far been found to show more than 2 % of the growth inhibitory power of the active D(−)-*threo* isomer (Maxwell & Nickel, 1954). Nevertheless, two at least are not devoid of biological action since the L(+)-*erythro* isomer inhibits D-polypeptide synthesis by *Bacillus subtilis* (Hahn,

Wisseman & Hopps, 1954) and the L(+)-*threo* isomer inhibits the incorporation of glycine into purines in Ehrlich carcinoma cells (LePage, 1953). It would be of interest to see what action any of the three had in combination with chloramphenicol, or another antimicrobial agent, especially on chloramphenicol-resistant strains which, like *Pseudomonas aeruginosa*, destroy the molecule.

Potent inactivators of isoniazid have been found in culture filtrates and extracts of *Mycobacterium phlei* as well as of virulent (H37Rv) and avirulent (H37Ra) strains of human tubercle bacilli (Youmans & Youmans, 1955; 1956). These are non-dialysable, often heat-labile, inactivate isoniazid rapidly *in vitro* and appear active in the mouse. Their concentration reaches a maximum in 40–50 day-old cultures; but no attempt to inhibit their synthesis has been reported. 'Cord factor' also antagonizes isoniazid in the mouse (Bloch & Noll, 1955), but it is not produced by saprophytes, has no action on isoniazid *in vitro* and therefore cannot be identified with the Youmans' substances.

Pseudomonas aeruginosa produces an interesting antagonist of streptomycin which Cornforth & James (1954) identified as a mixture of 4-hydroxyquinoline-*N*-oxides. The natural mixture will antagonize some 260 times its weight of dihydrostreptomycin, and a tribromo derivative some 1000 times its weight (Lightbown & Jackson, 1956). However, here too, factors influencing its formation, and hence the possibility of rendering *P. aeruginosa* more sensitive to streptomycin, appear not to have been explored.

6. *Inhibiting mutation to resistance*

In theory, a means of reducing the rate of spontaneous mutation to resistance would be of great value with drugs such as isoniazid, streptomycin or erythromycin. Yet, as Bryson & Szybalski (1955) point out, although a faint indication that this might be possible can be read into the depression by certain nucleosides of spontaneous mutations in *Escherichia coli* (Novick & Szilard, 1952), there seems to be no immediate prospect of achieving any useful synergy in this way. It is conceivable, however, that anti-mutagens occur naturally and that the failure to recover phenanthridium-resistant trypanosomes from mice (but not cattle) (Browning, 1949), and the very rare isolation of streptomycin-resistant tubercle bacilli from small animals, even in the presence of caseation and cavitation (Wolinsky & Steenken, 1953), reflect a diminished rate of mutation to resistance in these animals rather than a selective pressure in favour of the sensitive strain.

Synergy of two non-toxic drugs

In pharmacology, the interaction of two ineffective drugs to produce an effect is known as 'coalitive synergy' (see Fig. 1 (c) and Loewe, 1953). It is well exemplified in the production of ejaculation by pernoston and coramine in combination when neither drug alone is effective in any dosage (Loewe, 1938). In microbiology an analogous interaction underlies any need for a balance, for example, of ions for maximal growth (Eisler, 1909) or the appearance of an antigen at the surface (Lacey, 1953). Overall, however, very few have been recorded, presumably because experiments have usually been designed on the unjustifiable assumption that factors do not interact. Perhaps the nearest approach to coalitive antibacterial synergy can be seen in the synergic inhibition by amino acids of histidine uptake in *Neurospora crassa* (see Mathieson & Catcheside, 1955). On a minimal medium containing $1 \cdot 0 \times 10^{-4}$M-histidine, a histidine-requiring mutant (K26) will take up histidine, and hence grow, albeit at a much reduced rate, in the presence of either 16×10^{-4}M-DL-methionine or the same concentration of L-arginine. But histidine uptake, and hence growth, is completely inhibited in the presence of 1×10^{-4}M of both DL-methionine and L-arginine.

A priori one would expect the co-existence of alternative metabolic pathways to be revealed at times by cytotoxic synergies of this kind. The virtual absence of such synergies may therefore reflect a real scarcity of alternative pathways (see Davis, 1952) as much as the experimental difficulties of discovering coalitive synergies.

Coalitive cytotoxic action may be mimicked by two inactive substances which react chemically with each other to produce an active compound. Three examples of this kind, cited by Knox (1956) are: the chelation of iron by oxine to form a bactericidal 1:1 complex (Albert *et al.* 1953); the production of a substance toxic to the tubercle bacillus from spermine by spermine oxidase (see Hirsch, 1955); and the reaction of amygdalin and emulsin to produce hydrogen cyanide.

NON-CYTOTOXIC SYNERGY

Synergy of two toxic drugs

Independently of any cytotoxic synergy against a homogeneous population, two antimicrobial drugs may be synergic *in vivo* by having either different activities on different members of a heterogeneous population or different accessibilities to populations of microbes in different parts of the host. In the first group the heterogeneity may be caused by differences between (i) species, (ii) wild type and mutant, (iii) stages in the multiplication or different forms of one species, or (iv) members of the same species in different physiological states.

1. *Against a mixed flora*

There are several diseases usually or often caused by two or more presumptively synergic organisms, e.g. actinomycosis by *Actinomyces israelii* with an actinobacillus; gas gangrene by a clostridium with a coliform; appendicitis by a *Bacterioides* sp. with a coliform; fistulous withers by *Actinomyces bovis* with *Brucella abortus*; Meleney's infection by an anaerobic streptococcus with *Staphylococcus aureus*. In these, one organism is often an anaerobe or microaerophil (as in the examples above) sensitive to penicillin and resistant to streptomycin, while the other is an aerobe, or facultative anaerobe, resistant to penicillin and sensitive to streptomycin. In such diseases a therapeutic synergy is logically predictable and almost certainly obtainable with a suitable combination of drugs.

A combination of two drugs with different spectra is similarly synergic in the prophylactic removal of the normal caecal and colonic flora before operations on the bowel. In the human mouth, the normal, penicillin-sensitive, Gram-positive flora seems to prevent colonization of the surface by irritant saprophytes. *Escherichia coli* probably performs the same function in the caecum and colon. If either is removed by chemotherapy (most easily by local application), an unpleasant or dangerous stomatitis or enteritis may result. A second drug, toxic to the potential colonizer may then show a useful prophylactic synergy. In the guinea-pig, penicillin-sensitive Gram-positive rods (chiefly lactobacilli and *Bacillus* species) predominate throughout the alimentary tract and it is not surprising, in retrospect, that penicillin in this animal leads to death with profuse growth of Gram-negative rods (De Somer, van de Voorde, Eyssen & van Dijck, 1955). Erythromycin also is toxic to the guinea-pig (Kaipainen & Faine, 1954), probably by the same mechanism.

2. *Against growth of drug-resistant mutants*

In theory, two drugs could delay the outgrowth of resistant mutants in two distinct ways: (*a*) by both drugs inhibiting the wild type, one only fairly frequent single mutants and neither very infrequent double mutants; (*b*) by one drug inhibiting the wild type, the other principally, or exclusively, mutants resistant to the first, i.e. exploiting a collateral sensitivity (see above). Occurrence of the first mechanism has several times been demonstrated with rapidly growing organisms and drugs such as streptomycin (Finland, 1955). Although technical difficulties prevent a similar proof *in vitro* of combined action against tubercle bacilli, the clinical evidence of its occurrence is very strong. Indeed, the well-established superiority of drug combinations over single agents in tuberculosis is commonly held to depend entirely on this mechanism. But streptomycin and isoniazid also show a cytotoxic synergy (Mackaness & Smith, 1953; Singh & Mitchison, 1954; Meadow & Knox, 1956) which presumably contributes to their success *in vivo*. In theory, the best drugs to use in combination for this purpose are those always ideal: (i) showing a cytotoxic synergy leading to rapid death, (ii) not showing cross-resistance, (iii) non-mutagenic, and (iv) of a kind to which the microbe shows a multi-step pattern of resistance (see Bryson & Szybalski, 1955).

3. *Against different forms or stages*

The malaria parasite varies greatly in sensitivity to drugs at different stages of its life-cycle (Covell, Coatney, Field & Singh, 1955). How far the observed differences reflect differences in sensitivity of the parasite's enzymes, permeability of the parasite or host cells, or presence of antagonists is not known. Combinations of complementary drugs, however, may show obvious synergy. Thus a 4-aminoquinoline (such as chloroquine), which is an active schizontocide, and an 8-aminoquinoline (such as primaquine), which is active against gametocytes and exo-erythrocytic forms, will, when given simultaneously or consecutively, effectively terminate the acute attack, abolish infectivity and eradicate the infection (Alving *et al.* 1955). By the same mechanism suramin and hetrazan would probably be synergic in onchocerciasis, for Burch (1949) found suramin more active against adult filaria and hetrazan more active against microfilaria. And by analogy, it seems certain that some combinations of agents which are separately active at different stages of virus development (see Matthews & Smith, 1955, p. 141) will prove synergic.

4. *Against organisms in different physiological states*

According to McCune & Tompsett (1956) pyrazinamide and isoniazid are the only drugs capable in combination of killing tubercle bacilli in the spleen of an infected mouse. Two factors seem to be necessary for sterilization, (i) a period of 8 weeks pyrazinamide therapy, and (ii) concurrent or prior treatment with isoniazid or other drug (McCune, Tompsett & McDermott, 1956). Even oxytetracycline, which is of no value in human disease, will serve as the other drug. The spleen was not sterilized in one trial when isoniazid was given after pyrazinamide. At the changeover from isoniazid to pyrazinamide, the whole residual microbial population is still sensitive to isoniazid (as tested *in vitro*) and evidently therefore physiologically insusceptible to isoniazid; i.e. it is a population of persisters in the sense used by Bigger (1944). McCune and his colleagues conclude that pyrazinamide sterilization requires some prior change in the bacillus in response to the environment. Isoniazid and pyrazinamide are thus complementary to each other, for the first is lethal to multiplying organisms at normal pH, the second slowly lethal to dormant organisms at low pH. Given together, or consecutively in the right sequence, they are synergic.

5. *Against populations in different places*

A substance which penetrates a natural tissue barrier, such as the blood-brain or blood-cerebrospinal fluid barrier, is not necessarily the most active drug available for use on both sides of the barrier. Hence two drugs of different penetrability may be synergic. Thus suramin (Bayer 205) reinforces the action of tryparsamide and the two are usually combined in treatment of trypanosomiasis in the intermediate or late stages. Suramin, although highly trypanocidal, has six sulphonic acid groups which prevent it reaching the brain or cerebrospinal fluid (CSF). Tryparsamide, in contrast, has no activity *in vitro* and only a moderate activity in early (non-neural) trypanosomiasis. It penetrates freely to the brain in the pentavalent state and is there reduced to a trivalent form extremely toxic to trypanosomes. The trivalent form does not penetrate to the CSF when given intramuscularly (see Lourie, 1943).

In amoebiasis, chloroquine and a tetracycline show this type of synergy, for chloroquine is highly active against amoebae in the liver but probably absorbed too quickly to have an effect in the lower bowel. Tetracyclines are also absorbed but are partly excreted again into the bowel (Cole, 1953).

Synergy of one toxic drug and one non-toxic drug or factor

Four principal ways can be distinguished in which a non-toxic substance may show an adjuvant action only demonstrable *in vivo*: (1) increasing the concentration or duration of action of the toxic drug, (2) selectively reducing the toxicity of the drug for the host, (3) reducing virulence of the microbe, and (4) raising host resistance.

1. *Increasing the concentration or duration of action*

Fig. 3 illustrates the hazards which beset the passage of any drug from the mouth to a site of action in the body or microbe. After passing any barrier it is liable to be changed (biotransformed) to an inactive derivative, accumulate in an inactive form adsorbed to, or dissolved in, some tissue such as fat, or be excreted unchanged. In an admirable review of synergy, Veldstra (1956) refers to these three side tracks as 'sites of loss'. Evidently a non-toxic synergist may act by increasing penetration of a barrier or decreasing loss at one or more of the three 'sites'.

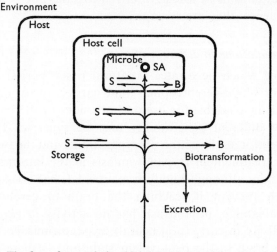

Fig. 3. The fate of an antimicrobial drug *in vivo*. SA = site of action.

(*a*) *By increasing penetration.* Most attempts to increase penetration *in vivo* have aimed to increase permeability of either the blood-brain barrier (i.e. cerebral capillary-brain substance barrier) or the blood-CSF barrier. In view of the reports (Weed & McKibben, 1919; Foley, 1921) that the normal flow of CSF from perivascular spaces to ventricles and subarachnoid space could be reversed by the osmotic pressure exerted by intravenously injected hypertonic sodium chloride, Lourie (1943) suggested using such injections in conjunction with drugs capable of penetrating to the CSF, in advanced sleeping sickness. So far no one appears to have tried this. More recently, Hurst & Davies (1950) tested the effect of various substances on the passage of sulphanilamide and other compounds into the brain of mice. Although glycerol increased, and coal-gas reduced, the passage of sulphanilamide, no pattern emerged from which any useful prediction could be made. Any synergy of this kind is thus likely to be discovered only by accident or trial and error. Nevertheless, a number of enzymes such as hyaluronidase, lecithinase, trypsin and streptokinase, which have been shown to inhibit oedema formation and increase tissue permeability, also increased the permeability of the mouse blood-brain barrier to barbital (Beiler, Brendel & Martin, 1956). Trypsin also doubles or quadruples the CSF penicillin level in dogs (Moss, Beiler & Martin, 1955).

The accessibility of intracellular organisms to drugs varies greatly with drug, host cell and invading organism. Some drugs, e.g. isoniazid and tetracycline, penetrate well that part of the cytoplasm where tubercle bacilli multiply in rabbit macrophages, whereas others, such as p-aminosalicylic acid and streptomycin, do not (Mackaness, 1952; Suter, 1952; Mackaness & Smith, 1952). The ratio of inhibitory concentrations of streptomycin for tubercle bacilli intra- and extracellularly may vary between 50:1 for bacilli in macrophages (Mackaness, 1952) to over 500:1 for bacilli in HeLa cells (Shepard, 1956). For *Brucella suis* in leucocytes the ratio may be 25,000:1, that is 50–500 times greater still (Shaffer, Kucera & Spink, 1953). This suggests that brucellas in some cells are protected by either a second barrier—conceivably the nucleus—or a local antagonist not available to tubercle bacilli. It follows that a means of counteracting this protection might much improve the present chemotherapy of brucellosis.

Many inactive solvents and close relatives of active substances are well known to potentiate the action of insecticides by increasing their penetration of insect cuticle (see Webb, 1949; Veldstra, 1956). No comparable synergy is known in chemotherapy, but a need for it is suggested by the fact that *Trichophyton rubrum* is sensitive to many agents *in vitro* yet remains virtually unkillable when causing disease of nails or skin.

(*b*) *By decreasing storage in tissue depots.* Veldstra (1956) has shown that the plant growth activity of a number of substances can be greatly enhanced by somewhat more lipophilic analogues possessing little or no intrinsic activity. Thus in the pea test, the activity of naphthaleneacetic acid is increased by either of two more lipophilic but inactive substances, decahydronaphthaleneacetic acid or 2:4-dichloronaphthoxyacetic acid. Full activity of, say, 1 g. of the active substance is shown by a mixture of 0·025 g. of the active substance with from 0·5 to 1·0 g. of the inactive one. Veldstra attributes this synergy to a displacement of the active substance from a 'silent site of loss' by a compound with greater affinity for the silent site. In a search for this kind of synergy in chemotherapy, Veldstra found that the inactive but more lipophilic 9-chloro-9-deoxycinchonidine, or the corresponding quinine derivative, would greatly enhance the action of quinine against *Plasmodium gallinaceum* in the chick. Analogous derivatives of quinidine and cinchonine, which belong to a different steric series, were not synergic. No application of this synergy is known but it would now seem of interest to attempt to detach penicillin K (capryl penicillin) from its binding to serum protein (Tompsett, Shultz & McDermott, 1947) by a synthetic penicillin or derivative of a close relative such as cephalosporin C. It is also conceivable that one of the isomers of chloramphenicol, or one of the many inactive or slightly active analogues which have been synthesized, would prove to be usefully synergic in this way with chloramphenicol.

(*c*) *By biotransformation blockade.* In extensive studies, Brodie and his co-workers (Brodie, 1956; Brodie & Hogben, 1957) have established that, in reptiles and higher animals, substances with a high oil to water partition ratio are in general transformed in microsomes of liver cells to polar derivatives more easily excreted. Several substances may inhibit this biotransformation and so prolong the action of many non-polar drugs. The best known, because first discovered, is the diethyl-aminoethyl ester of diphenylpropylacetic acid (SKF 525-A), but 2:4-dichloro-6-phenylphenoxyethyldiethylamine (Lilly 18947) (Fouts & Brodie, 1955) and iproniazid (Fouts & Brodie, 1956) are also effective inhibitors. All three act relatively non-specifically, probably by reducing permeability of the microsomes to lipophilic substances. In rats, the transforming activity of liver microsomes (at least for some substances) is much less in the female and can be increased by administration of testosterones. Conversely, it may be reduced in the male by oestrogens. In rats, therefore, female hormones can be regarded as inhibitors in the same class as SKF 525-A itself. In rabbit liver, reduction of the nitro group of chloramphenicol to an amino group is inhibited by SKF 525-A (Fouts & Brodie, 1957) and presumably by this means the action might be prolonged *in vivo*.

Other biotransformations can be specifically inhibited. In a search for inhibitors of sulphonamide inactivation Johnson (1955*a*) found that isoniazid, and several other amides, inhibited conversion of sulphanil-amide in pigeon liver extracts to the inactive N^4-acetyl derivative. Some amides were also active *in vivo*, and in the rabbit an oral dose of *p*-amino-salicylic acid hydrazide doubled the blood level of free sulphanilamide produced by a single dose (Johnson, 1955*b*). Since chloramphenicol is excreted in the bile in an inactive acetylated form, an inhibitor of its acetylation might be a valuable synergist for the control of chloramphenicol-sensitive organisms in the biliary tract.

The experimental chemotherapy of new growths provides an interesting example of synergy in this class. Both folic acid and its degradation product, 2-amino-4-hydroxy-6-formylpteridine, are devoid of carcinostatic activity but either markedly potentiates the anti-mammary carcinoma action of 8-azaguanine (Shapiro & Gellhorn, 1951; Shapiro, Kream & Dietrich, 1952). The formylpteridine inhibits the conversion *in vivo* of 8-azaguanine to inactive 8-azaxanthine and there seems little doubt that this is the mechanism of its synergic action.

(*d*) *By decreasing excretion.* Factors influencing the excretion of substances by the kidney, and the design of reversible inhibitors of excretion were reviewed by Beyer (1954). In general, ability of a substance to inhibit tubular excretion of penicillin (and hence four-fifths of its total renal excretion) runs parallel with (i) the rate of its own tubular reabsorption, (ii) its power to block reabsorption of uric acid from glomerular filtrate, (iii) its ability to inhibit the coupling of glycine with *p*-aminobenzoic acid, and (iv) its ability to block tubular excretion of phenol red, *p*-aminohippuric acid and *p*-aminosalicylic acid (*p*-AS). Thus penicillin, *p*-AS, uric acid and inhibitors of their transport all compete for the same tubular transport mechanism and whether the mechanism is transporting substances inwards or outwards.

At present probenecid (*p*-(di-*n*-propylsulphamyl)benzoic acid) is the most active inhibitor available for clinical use and with it a three- to sixfold rise in penicillin blood levels may be obtained. It is probably also the most active agent for increasing the excretion of uric acid and of proven therapeutic value in gout. A 4-phenylsulphoxyethyl deriva-tive of phenylbutazone is reported to be even more active (Burns *et al.* 1957). But since maximal inhibition of penicillin excretion (i.e. all the tubular four-fifths) is already attainable with probenecid, it is unlikely to be of special value in chemotherapy.

Inhibitors of tubular excretion are evidently highly specific, and penicillin and *p*-AS are the only drugs whose excretion can be restricted at present. Both cephalosporin C and synnematin B, however, are closely related to penicillin and, since both may be synergic with penicillin (Crawford & Abraham, 1957; Jackson, Rubenis & Mellody, 1957, respectively), it will be of interest to see if their excretion is also reduced by probenecid.

2. *Selectivity antagonizing toxicity for the host*

It would clearly be of much practical value, as well as theoretical interest, if the toxicity of polymyxin, neomycin or bacitracin to the kidney, of pyrazinamide to the liver, and of other antituberculous substances to the nervous system, could be selectively reduced. An account by Bryer (1955) of an interesting failure to antagonize polymyxin toxicity can be paraphrased as follows: polymyxin D is one of the few substances in which D-serine is known to occur; D-serine itself produces renal lesions like those of polymyxin; DL-methionine antagonizes the toxicity to the kidney of D-serine but not of polymyxin D. In contrast, pyridoxine has been shown to reduce the incidence of peripheral neuritis during isoniazid therapy, without evidence of diminished anti-mycobacterial effect, in both men (Oestreicher, Dressler & Middle-brook, 1954) and mice (Wasz-Höckert, McCune & Tompsett, 1956). It thus allows the dosage of isoniazid to be increased up to 16 mg./kg./day, except in fat people, and probably with slight advantage (Middlebrook & Dressler, 1955).

A most successful but so far unexploited example of this synergy is the use by Rutten, Winkler & de Haan (1950) of a high concentration of sulphanilamide with four non-competitive inhibitors of sulphanilamide (methionine, xanthine, thymine and valine) to kill T_2, T_4 and T_6 phages in *Escherichia coli* strain B. Without the inhibitors strain B was killed by the sulphanilamide. By analogy it seems possible that *p*-amino-benzoic acid, or a related compound might diminish the toxicity of di-aminodiphenylsulphone more for man than the leprosy bacillus. Selective antagonism of this kind has been used in obstetrics by combining *N*-allylmorphine with morphine (Woods, 1956). The *N*-allylmorphine antagonizes the respiratory depression but not the analgesia produced by morphine. In a comparable way, a high concentration of magnesium is included in a selective medium for *Bordetella pertussis* (Lacey, 1954) because it antagonizes the action of a diamidine (M & B 938) more against *B. pertussis* than against *Escherichia coli* and other unwanted organisms, and so enhances the overall selectivity for *Bordetella pertussis*. Similarly cobalt selectively antagonizes the action of oxine against Gram-positive organisms (Rubbo *et al.* 1950); and Casamino acids increase the inhibitory concentration of azaserine, etc., more for *Escherichia coli* than for *Bacillus subtilis* (Reilly, 1956). In pharmacology, Woolley, van Winkle & Shaw (1957) have developed a most interesting combination in 5-hydroxytryptophan and 1-benzyl-2:5-dimethylserotonin; the first passes the blood-brain barrier and is converted to serotonin (5-hydroxy-tryptamine), the second cannot pass into the brain but antagonizes the undesirable effects of serotonin outside the brain. The net result is therefore equivalent to an intracerebral injection of serotonin. By analogy it should be possible to prevent some of the unpleasant side effects of tetracycline therapy, resulting from loss of the normal Gram-negative flora of the bowel, by giving the tetracycline parenterally (by injection) and a non-absorbable antagonist, such as a magnesium salt, by mouth.

3. *Reducing virulence of the microbe*

It is clearly not essential in chemotherapy either to kill or inhibit growth directly and, in reviewing the physiological background to microbial inhibition, Knight (1952) recognized the formation of 'specific non-essential metabolic products' as a fourth-class of metabolic processes and a possible target for antimicrobial agents. Although no current therapy depends entirely on this mode of attack, much is probably helped by it. At times, substatic concentrations of established chemo-therapeutic substances may have an obvious effect as, for example, when tetracyclines inhibit pigment formation by *Chromobacterium prodigiosum* (Weil, 1952) or penicillin inhibits germination of spores of *Bacillus macerans* (Sacks, 1955). At others, the effect may be more subtle such as the accumulation of a xanthine precursor induced by sulphanilamide in *Escherichia coli* (Shive *et al.* 1947) or the antigenic transformation by patulin or polymyxin in *Paramecium aurelia* (Austin, Widmayer & Walker, 1956). In either case the virulence may be altered by an accompanying change in toxigenicity, invasiveness or toxicity to the host cell. Thus neo-salvarsan-treated spirochaetes of relapsing fever fail to cause infection even though visually indistinguishable from normal spirochaetes (Ehrlich, 1913); subinhibitory concentrations of suramin appear to sensitize trypanosomes to phagocytosis (Reiner & Leonard, 1932); non-killing concentrations of penicillin almost certainly reduce the virulence of type III pneumococci (Eagle, Fleischman & Musselman, 1950; Esplin & Marcus, 1954) and sensitize *Pseudomonas aeruginosa* to phagocytosis (Lambin & Desvignes, 1952); thiosemicarbazones, at one-fiftieth of the concentration needed to affect growth rate, diminish the virulence of tubercle bacilli (Bloch & Noll, 1953); chlortetracycline reduces the virulence of *Escherichia coli* for rabbits at one-quarter the level needed to inhibit growth (Avezzù, 1953); 6-mercaptopurine leads to a slow loss of viability in mouse sarcoma S-180 without immediate visible change (Clarke, Philips, Sternberg & Stock, 1954); and substatic concentrations of various antibiotics inhibit the production by *Staphy-lococcus aureus* of α-lysin and coagulase (Langlade, 1956).

Many substances or factors with negligible inhibitory or killing activity may likewise affect virulence or the production of enzymes, toxins or surface antigens which are known, or can reasonably be presumed, to contribute to virulence (see Dubos, 1954, pp. 58–64). Thus, for example, change in the growth medium has been found to change invasiveness, or resistance to phagocytosis, in tubercle bacilli (Seibert, Long & Morley, 1933; see also Bloch, 1955), *Bordetella pertussis* (Gray, 1946), *Bacillus anthracis* (Lincoln *et al.* 1946), *Salmonella typhi-murium* (Maaløe, 1948), meningococci (Murray, 1954) and *Rhizoctonia solani* (Butler, 1954). All such changes could be regarded as 'modulations', that is changes induced in the whole population through alterations of microbial metabolism. In contrast, the reduction in virulence of type III pneumococci for mice (Avery & Dubos, 1931), rabbits (Goodner, Dubos & Avery, 1932) and monkeys (Francis, Terrell, Dubos & Avery, 1934) during treatment with a bacterial polysaccharidase (Dubos & Avery, 1931) must be put in a separate class of genuine 'modifications', that is changes directly produced by physico-chemical means without participation of microbial metabolism.

The enormous success already achieved with powerful killing and growth inhibitory agents tends, perhaps, to deflect attention from these drug-induced alterations of virulence. Nevertheless, in virus diseases, and others for which there is still no satisfactory chemotherapy, the modulators and modifiers may well prove finally, either as single agents or as synergists, of greater value than the inhibitors and killers.

4. *Increasing resistance of the host*

With a suitable experimental design, penicillin can be shown to eradicate pus-forming organisms independently of phagocytes or antibodies. This sterilizing power of penicillin has been demonstrated in streptococcal infection of mice rendered leucopenic by X-irradiation (Kaplan, Speck & Jawetz, 1952; Smith & Wood, 1956a), in pneumococcal infection of rabbits rendered leucopenic by benzene (Gowans, 1953a) and on streptococci, protected from phagocytosis by enclosure in agar disks, in the peritoneum of rabbits (Darnell, Pesch & Glaser, 1955). In all these experiments, however, the penicillin was given either before the 12th hour after infection, or in massive dosage, or both.

Apart from these results, the bulk of experimental and clinical evidence leaves no doubt that chemotherapy by itself very seldom eradicates an infecting organism. In general, therefore, host resistance complements chemotherapy, and anything improving host resistance is *a priori* likely to be synergic. Only the potential role of antibodies, phagocytes and temperature change can be considered here. Many other host factors have been discussed in recent reviews by McDermott (1952), Hart (1954), Bickel (1955), Lurie (1955), Wilson & Miles (1955), Jawetz (1956) and Swift (1957).

Antibodies. The relative or absolute need at times of antibodies for successful chemotherapy has been demonstrated in several ways. In mice, a synergistic action of antiserum has been shown with (*a*) sulphonamides against streptococci (Loewenthal, 1939), meningococci (Branham, 1940) and *Clostridium septicum* (Henderson & Gorer, 1940), and (*b*) penicillin against pneumococci (Buck & Schnitzer, 1944) and *C. welchii* (Siebenmann & Plummer, 1945). In mice also, vaccination may potentiate both sulphonamide therapy of pneumococcal infection (MacLean, Rogers & Fleming, 1939) and penicillin therapy of streptococcal infection (Eagle, Fleischman & Levy, 1953). In humans with typhoid fever, Marmion (1952) found that vaccination was associated with a lower relapse rate when chloramphenicol was given intermittently.

Less direct evidence of the value of antibodies is provided by (*a*) the lower relapse rate and higher antibody titres found to follow delay in treatment of humans with typhoid fever (Marmion, 1952; El-Rooby & Gohar, 1956), or scrub typhus (Smadel, 1954); (*b*) the poorer results of penicillin therapy, and lower antibody titres, in protein-depleted rats infected with pneumococci (Skinsnes & Woolridge, 1948); and (*c*) the greater effectivity of quinoxaline-1:4-dioxides in mice against larger doses of lymphogranuloma venereum virus (Hurst *et al.* 1953).

Phagocytes. In humans, the normal accumulation of neutrophil leucocytes at a site of coccal multiplication may be prevented by agranulocytosis, or by suppression of the inflammatory reaction with cortisone. A greater dosage and more prolonged administration of antibacterial agent is then needed to produce a normal curative effect. Similarly in experimental leucopenia induced in guinea-pigs by nitrogen mustard (Skinsnes, 1948) or in mice by 1:4-dimethanesulphonoxybutane (Gowans, 1953*b*) or exposure to X-rays (Smith & Wood, 1956*a*), the therapeutic effect of penicillin on coccal infection may be much reduced. Conversely, a homogenate of immature mouse spleen (a known leucopoietic material) will potentiate streptomycin against Proteus infection in X-irradiated mice (Marston, Ruth & Smith, 1953).

Further indications of the value of phagocytes can be seen in (*a*) the failure of penicillin, if given after the 12th hour, to sterilize streptococci enclosed in agar within the peritoneum of rabbits (Darnell *et al.* 1955), (*b*) the marked advantage, in white rats, of combining surgical drainage of subcutaneous pneumococcal abscesses with penicillin therapy (Smith & Wood, 1956*b*), and (*c*) the adjuvant effect of intrathecal tuberculin in tuberculous meningitis (see Smith, 1953; Waingortin, Herrera & Foley,

1956). In (b) and (c), part of the synergy is logically attributable to an increased access of antibodies or drugs or both, as well as an increased activity of drugs from renewal of conditions for rapid growth.

Certain non-ionic surface-active agents, with no demonstrable effect on mycobacteria *in vitro*, suppress the development, or cause regression, of experimental murine tuberculosis (Hart & Rees, 1955). The agents are taken up by monocytes (Lovelock & Rees, 1955) and almost certainly facilitate intracellular lysis. All those examined so far appear too toxic for human use, but it is of interest that the only one tested in combination with antimycobacterial drugs, Triton A 20 (a non-ionic alkylaryl polyether alcohol), proved synergic with dihydrostreptomycin in murine tuberculosis (Solotorovsky & Gregory, 1952).

Temperature. Very few studies have been made of the influence of temperature on infective disease and fewer still of host-parasite-drug-temperature interaction. In rabbits, 10 hr. of 4° F pyrexia may reduce the curative dose of penicillin for rabbit syphilis about eightfold (Eagle, Magnuson & Fleischman, 1947). But in man, although hyperthermia alone will improve the course of neurosyphilis, and in spite of some uncontrolled evidence of synergy (Epstein & Key, 1949), it seems doubtful if hyperthermia would generally improve the results of penicillin therapy. Similarly, before the introduction of tetracyclines, lymphogranuloma venereum was treated with some success by fever therapy, sulphonamides or both. Yet here, too, no convincing evidence of any synergy has been found. Recently Lützenkirchen & Schoog (1954) and Schoog (1955) have shown that hypothermia in the mouse induced by Largactil [N-(3′-dimethylamino)-propyl-3-chlorophenothiazin] is associated with (a) an enhanced chemotherapeutic action of penicillin on a group A streptococcus infection, and (b) a failure of *Trypanosoma evansi* to grow, and of trypan blue or arsenicals to cure the infection. How far, however, the effect of the Largactil is attributable to a direct chemical action on the parasite or host and how far to the hypothermia has still to be determined.

Exceptionally, the influence of temperature on the course of an infection may exactly reflect a demonstrable action on the growth of the microbe *in vitro*. Thus virulence of pneumococci in the rabbit is correlated with ability to grow *in vivo* and *in vitro* at 40–41°, that is at the temperature quickly reached by an infected rabbit (Rich & McKee, 1936). Comparably, *Mycobacterium balnei* fails to grow *in vitro* at 37° and is almost avirulent for the mouse intraperitoneally and for the chick embryo held at 37°. But it grows well *in vitro* at 33°, kills the chick embryo in 5 days at 33°, and produces lesions in the footpad of the mouse (Fenner, 1956).

At times, the influence of temperature is less obviously direct. Cooling chickens (Pasteur, Joubert & Chamberland, 1878) or warming frogs to 35° (Gibier, 1882) makes them susceptible to anthrax. Taken together these records suggest that the virulence of *Bacillus anthracis* falls sharply above and below 35°; but no one seems to have tested this.

At present, however, the influence of temperature is usually un-predictable. In general, it appears to depend very much on the particular association of parasite and host and is not completely determined by either parasite or host. This certainly applies to rust (Hart, 1949) and virus (Kassanis, 1957) diseases of plants. A raised environmental or body temperature has been shown to increase the resistance of (*a*) rabbits to several bacteria (see McDowell, 1923) and myxoma virus (Parker & Thompson, 1942), (*b*) mice to St Louis encephalitis virus (Lillie, Dyer, Armstrong & Pasternack, 1937), herpes virus (Armstrong, 1942) and typhus rickettsias (Moragues & Pinkerton, 1944), and (*c*) the chick embryo to vesicular stomatitis virus (Sigurdsson, 1943), murine typhus rickettsias (Greiff & Pinkerton, 1945) and *Cryptococcus neoformans* (Kligman, Crane & Norris, 1951). Conversely, an environmental temperature near 35° may reduce the resistance of mice to streptococci (Ritzmann, 1907), pneumococci (Mills & Schmidt, 1942), and influenza A virus (Sulkin, 1945). In contrast, at a very low environmental temperature, chickens are more resistant to Newcastle disease (Sinha, Hanson & Brandly, 1957), rats are much less resistant to *Trypanosoma cruzi* (Kolodny, 1940) and adult mice become as susceptible to Coxsackie (Conn 5) virus as are suckling mice at a normal temperature (Boring, Zu Rhein & Walker, 1956).

Thus in microbial diseases not at present amenable to chemotherapy the interaction of temperature and drugs might be explored with profit.

Synergy with two non-toxic drugs

Hurst and his colleagues have shown that mepacrine markedly inhibits multiplication of equine encephalomyelitis virus in mice, but has no action on the virus *in vitro* or in most other animals (Hurst, 1957). The therapeutic effect of sub-optimal doses of mepacrine in mice is greatly diminished by SKF 525-A, increased by tryptophan and greater in females than males. As Hurst points out, these findings and the knowledge that (i) SKF 525-A can block liver biotransformations (Brodie, 1956), (ii) tryptophan can increase liver enzymes, and

18

(iii) biotransformation varies greatly with sex and species, strongly indicate that mepacrine is converted in the mouse liver to an active metabolite. By analogy with the influence of hormones on other liver transformations (Brodie, 1956) it also seems probable that oestrogens would be synergic with sub-optimal doses of mepacrine in male mice.

Many other substances of therapeutic value appear inactive *in vitro*. These include (*a*) antimalarial agents which are only plasmodistats *in vitro*, such as proguanil (Hawking & Perry, 1948) or pamaquin (Taylor, Josephson, Greenberg & Coatney, 1952), (*b*) antituberculous compounds such as some thiocarbanilides (Eisman, Konopka & Mayer, 1954), 5-amino-7-methyl-1:2:4:6-tetra-azaindene (Francis, Martin, Rose & Spinks, 1954) and ethyl mercaptans (Davies *et al.* 1956) and (*c*) the interesting antibacterial substance 2:3-dimethylquinoxaline 1:4-dioxide (Francis *et al.* 1956). Of these, the last and proguanil (Crowther & Levi, 1953) are known to be converted *in vivo* to an active metabolite and therefore are presumptively susceptible to synergy or antagonism by substances affecting biotransformations. Others may prove to be similarly activated, but some will almost certainly be found to have either (i) a slow direct action on the microbe, as dimidium probably has on trypanosomes (Lock, 1950), or (ii) an action exclusively on the host, or (iii) an action in no-man's land, at the surface of the organism, as polyoxyethylenes appear to have on tubercle bacilli (Lovelock & Rees, 1955) and diethylcarbamazine on microfilaria (Bangham, 1955).

Bauer (1955) has found that the anti-vaccinial activity in mice of isatin thiosemicarbazone may be enhanced by either inactive (e.g. 5-(3-methyl-4-chloro-phenoxy)-thiouracil) or active phenoxypyrimidines. In this case it seems most unlikely that the inactive synergist has any influence on biotransformation of the active component.

Finally, a synergy of great interest in this class has been reported by Fitzpatrick (1955). Nicotinamide may inhibit the intracellular growth of tubercle bacilli (Mackaness, 1956) but neither nicotinamide nor coenzyme I has any direct affect on tubercle bacilli *in vitro*. Nicotinamide, however, if given in huge doses beforehand, will greatly prolong the life of mice infected with tubercle bacilli. Coenzyme I has no therapeutic effect by itself but increases that of nicotinamide.

CONCLUSION

This hasty survey contains few original thoughts, no orginal work and no precepts. But it does at least reassert the undesirability of a too exclusive concentration on drug-parasite interaction, and hence the microbiologist's need in this field of the pharmacologist on one hand and the chemist on the other. And at best it might be seen as a strategic framework for combined therapy. The advantages of combined therapy were well known to its first advocates, Ehrlich and Morgenroth. When recapitulating these Ehrlich (1913) concluded:

For all these reasons I think that combined therapy will in future conquer an ever-increasing field of action....It is precisely in the manifold character of the possibilities of combination that I see a special advantage and peculiar possibilities of development. When once we are acquainted with the majority of the chemo-receptors of a particular kind of parasite, which will be a long piece of work, occupying many hands and heads, we shall have the most far-reaching possibilities of simultaneous attack by various agencies.

REFERENCES

ABRAHAM, E. P. & NEWTON, G. G. F. (1956). A comparison of the action of penicillinase on benzylpenicillin and cephalosporin N and the competitive inhibition of penicillinase by cephalosporin C. *Biochem. J.* **63**, 628.

ALBERT, A. (1951). *Selective Toxicity with Special Reference to Chemotherapy.* London: Methuen.

ALBERT, A. (1956). In discussion on 'Synergy in chemotherapy'. *Proc. R. Soc. Med.* **49**, 871.

ALBERT, A., GIBSON, M. I. & RUBBO, S. D. (1953). The influence of chemical constitution on antibacterial activity. Part VI: The bactericidal action of 8-hydroxyquinoline (oxine). *Brit. J. exp. Path.* **34**, 119.

ALVING, A. S., ARNOLD, J., HOCKWALD, R. S., CLAYMAN, C. B., DERN, R. J., BEUTLER, E. & FLANAGAN, C. L. (1955). Potentiation of the curative action of primaquine in vivax malaria by quinine and chloroquine. *J. Lab. clin. Med.* **46**, 301.

ARMSTRONG, C. (1942). Some recent research in the field of neurotropic viruses with especial reference to lymphocytic choriomeningitis and herpes simplex. *Milit. Surg.* **91**, 129.

ARNSTEIN, H. R. V. & GRANT, P. T. (1956). The metabolism of the penicillia in relation to penicillin biosynthesis. *Bact. Rev.* **20**, 133.

AUSTIN, M. L., WIDMAYER, D. & WALKER, L. M. (1956). Antigenic transformation as adaptive response of *Paramecium aurelia* to patulin; relation to cell division. *Physiol. Zoöl.* **29**, 261.

AVERY, O. T. & DUBOS, R. (1931). The protective action of a specific enzyme against type III pneumococcus infection in mice. *J. exp. Med.* **54**, 73.

AVEZZÙ, G. (1953). Modificazioni indotte dall' aureomicina nella morphologia, nel comportamento colturale, nel patrimonio antigene e nel potere patogeno dell' *Escherichia coli. Riv. ital. Igiene*, **13**, 18.

BANGHAM, D. R. (1955). The mode of action of diethylcarbamazine investigated with ¹⁴C-labelled drug. *Brit. J. Pharmacol.* **10**, 406.

BARRY, V. C., BELTON, J. G., CONALTY, M. L., DENNENY, J. M., EDWARD, D. W., O'SULLIVAN, J. F., TWOMEY, D. & WINDER, F. (1957). A new series of phenazines (rimino-compounds) with high antituberculous activity. *Nature, Lond.* **179**, 1013.

BAUER, D. J. (1955). The antiviral and synergic actions of isatin thiosemicarbazone and certain phenoxypyrimidines in vaccinia infection in mice. *Brit. J. exp. Path.* **36**, 105.

BEERSTECKER, JUN., E. & SHIVE, W. (1947). Prevention of phenylalanine synthesis by tyrosine. *J. biol. Chem.* **167**, 527.

BEILER, J. M., BRENDEL, R. & MARTIN, G. J. (1956). Enzymic modification of blood-brain barrier permeability. *J. Pharmacol.* **118**, 415.

BEYER, K. H. (1954). Factors basic to the development of useful inhibitors of renal transport mechanisms. *Arch. int. Pharmacodyn.* **98**, 97.

BICKEL, G. (1955). Les médications de renfort de la chimiotherapie anti-infectieuse. *Schweiz. med. Wschr.* **85**, 981.

BIGGER, J. W. (1944). Treatment of staphylococcal infections with penicillin by intermittent sterilisation. *Lancet*, ii, 497.

BIGGER, J. W. & WARE, G. C. (1950). Potentiation of sulphonamide by 'L substance'. *Lancet*, ii, 427.

BLISS, E. A., CHANDLER, C. A. & SCHOENBACH, E. B. (1949). *In vitro* studies of polymyxin. *Ann. N.Y. Acad. Sci.* **51**, 944.

BLISS, E. A. & WORTH, P. T. (1950). The effect of surface-active agents on antibiotics: an informal report. *Ann. N.Y. Acad. Sci.* **53**, 38.

BLOCH, H. (1955). Virulence of mycobacteria. *Advanc. Tuberc. Res.* **6**, 49.

BLOCH, H. & NOLL, H. (1953). Studies on the virulence of tubercle bacilli. Variations in virulence effected by Tween 80 and thiosemicarbazone. *J. exp. Med.* **97**, 1.

BLOCH, H. & NOLL, H. (1955). Studies on the virulence of tubercle bacilli. The effect of cord factor on murine tuberculosis. *Brit. J. exp. Path.* **36**, 8.

BONDI, A., KAMINSKI, Z. C., DE ST PHALLE, M., KORNBLUM, J. & MOAT, A. G. (1955). The effect of nutritional conditions on penicillinase production by *Micrococcus pyogenes. Bact. Proc.* p. 48.

BORING, W. D., ZU RHEIN, G. M. & WALKER, D. L. (1956). Factors influencing host-virus interactions. II. Alteration of Coxsackie virus infection in adult mice by cold. *Proc. Soc. exp. Biol., N.Y.* **93**, 273.

BRANHAM, S. E. (1940). The effect of sulphapyridine and sulphanilamide with and without serum in experimental meningococcus infection. *Publ. Hlth Rep., Wash.* **55**, 12.

BREWER, J. H. (1950). Mercurials as antiseptics. *Ann. N.Y. Acad. Sci.* **53**, 211.

BRIGGS, S., CRAWFORD, K., ABRAHAM, E. P. & GLADSTONE, G. P. (1957). Some properties of Gram-negative bacilli obtained from a strain of *Staphylococcus aureus* in the presence of benzylpenicillin. *J. gen. Microbiol.* **16**, 614.

BRODIE, B. B. (1956). Pathways of drug metabolism. *J. Pharm., Lond.* **8**, 1.

BRODIE, B. B. & HOGBEN, C. A. M. (1957). Some physico-chemical factors in drug action. *J. Pharm., Lond.* **9**, 345.

BROWNING, C. H. (1949). Chemotherapy of *T. congolense* infections with phenanthridium compounds: biological aspects. *Nature, Lond.* **163**, 590.

BROWNLEE, G. & WOODBINE, M. (1948). The antibacterial activity of some synthetic compounds related to penicillin. *Brit. J. Pharmacol.* **3**, 305.

BRYER, M. S. (1955). The chemotherapy of bacterial infections refractory to the common antibiotics. *Amer. J. Med.* **18**, 782.

BRYSON, V. & SZYBALSKI, W. (1955). Microbial drug resistance. *Advanc. Genet.* **7**, 1.

BUCK, M. & SCHNITZER, R. J. (1944). Synergistic effect of penicillin and antipneumococcus serum in the experimental pneumococcus infection of mice. *Arch. Biochem.* **5**, 153.

BURCH, T. A. (1949). Experimental therapy of oncocerciasis with suramin and hetrazan. *Bol. Ofic. sanit. pan-amer.* **28**, 233.

BURNS, J. J., YÜ, T. F., RITTERBAND, A., PEREL, J. M., GUTMAN, A. B. & BRODIE, B. B. (1957). A potent new uricosuric agent, the sulphoxide metabolite of the phenylbutazone analogue G-25671. *J. Pharmacol.* **119**, 418.

BUTLER, E. E. (1954). Cited by DEVAY, J. E. (1956). Mutual relationships in fungi. *Annu. Rev. Microbiol.* **10**, 115.

BYRDE, R. J. W. & WOODCOCK, D. (1957). Effect of the interaction between chelating agents on their fungitoxicity. *Nature, Lond.* **179**, 539.

CHAIN, E. & DUTHIE, E. S. (1945). Bactericidal and bacteriolytic action of penicillin on the staphylococcus. *Lancet,* i, 652.

CLARKE, D. A., PHILIPS, F. S., STERNBERG, S. S. & STOCK, C. C. (1954). Effects of 6-mercaptopurine and analogs on experimental tumors. *Ann. N.Y. Acad. Sci.* **60**, 235.

COLE, L. R. (1953). Recovery of aureomycin from the gastrointestinal tract following intravenous administration. *J. Lab. clin. Med.* **41**, 670.

COLEMAN, V. R., GUNNISON, J. B. & JAWETZ, E. (1953). Participation of erythromycin and carbomycin in combined antibiotic action *in vitro. Proc. Soc. exp. Biol., N.Y.* **83**, 668.

CORNFORTH, J. W. & JAMES, A. T. (1954). Structure of a naturally occurring antagonist of dihydrostreptomycin. *Biochem. J.* **63**, 124.

COVELL, G., COATNEY, G. R., FIELD, J. W. & SINGH, J. (1955). *Chemotherapy of Malaria.* Geneva: World Health Organization.

CRAWFORD, K. & ABRAHAM, E. P. (1957). The synergistic action of cephalosporin C and benzylpenicillin against a penicillinase-producing strain of *Staphylococcus aureus. J. gen. Microbiol.* **16**, 604.

CROWTHER, A. F. & LEVI, A. A. (1953). Proguanil—the isolation of a metabolite with high antimalarial activity. *Brit. J. Pharmacol.* **8**, 93.

DARNELL, J. E., PESCH, B. B. & GLASER, R. J. (1955). Effect of penicillin on group A streptococci *in vivo* in the absence of leucocytes. *J. clin. Invest.* **34**, 1237.

DAVIES, G. E., DRIVER, G. W., HOGGARTH, E., MARTIN, A. R., PAIGE, M. F. C., ROSE, F. L. & WILSON, B. R. (1956). Studies in the chemotherapy of tuberculosis: ethyl mercaptan and related compounds. *Brit. J. Pharmacol.* **11**, 351.

DAVIS, B. D. (1952). Drug-parasite interactions. In *Bacterial and Mycotic Infections of Man.* Edited by R. J. Dubos. 2nd ed. p. 726. London: Lippincott.

DEDIC, G. A. & KOCH, O. G. (1956). Aerobic cultivation of *Clostridium tetani* in the presence of cobalt. *J. Bact.* **71**, 126.

DE SOMER, P., VAN DE VOORDE, H., EYSSEN, H. & VAN DIJCK, P. (1955). A study on penicillin toxicity in guinea-pigs. *Antibiot. Chemother.* **5**, 463.

DIETZ, C. C. & BONDI, JUN., A. (1948). The susceptibility of penicillinase-producing bacteria to penicillin. II. The effect of sodium azide. *J. Bact.* **55**, 849.

DOWLING, H. F. (1957). Mixtures of antibiotics. *J. Amer. med. Ass.* **164**, 44.

DUBOS, R. & AVERY, O. T. (1931). Decomposition of the capsular polysaccharide of pneumococcus type III by a bacterial enzyme. *J. exp. Med.* **54**, 51.

DUBOS, R. J. (1954). *Biochemical Determinants of Microbial Disease.* Cambridge, Mass.: Harvard University Press.

DU VIGNEAUD, V., CARPENTER, F. H., HOLLEY, R. W., LIVERMORE, A. H. & RACHELE, J. R. (1946). Synthetic penicillin. *Science,* **104**, 431, 450.

EAGLE, H. (1939). The minimal effective concentrations of arsenic and bismuth compounds on *T. pallidum in vitro* in relation to the therapeutic dose. *Amer. J. Syph.* **23**, 310.

EAGLE, H. (1951). Further observations on the zone phenomenon in the bactericidal action of penicillin. *J. Bact.* **62**, 663.

EAGLE, H., FLEISCHMAN, R. & LEVY, M. (1953). Effect of prior immunization on bactericidal action of penicillin *in vivo. Proc. Soc. exp. Biol., N.Y.* **82**, 201.

EAGLE, H., FLEISCHMAN, R. & MUSSELMAN, A. D. (1950). The bactericidal action of penicillin *in vivo*: the participation of the host, and the slow recovery of the surviving organisms. *Ann. intern. Med.* **33**, 544.

EAGLE, H., MAGNUSON, H. J. & FLEISCHMAN, R. (1947). The effect of hyperpyrexia on the therapeutic efficacy of penicillin in experimental syphilis. *Amer. J. Syph.* **31**, 239.

EAGLE, H. & MUSSELMAN, A. D. (1944). The spirochaeticidal action of penicillin *in vitro* and its temperature coefficient. *J. exp. Med.* **80**, 493.

EHRLICH, P. (1913). Chemotherapeutics: scientific principles, methods and results. *Lancet*, ii, 445.

EISLER, M. VON (1909). Ueber Wirkungen von Salzen auf Bakterien. *Zbl. Bakt.* I Orig. **51**, 546.

EISMAN, P. C., KONOPKA, E. A. & MAYER, R. L. (1954). Antituberculous activity of substituted thioureas. II. Activity in mice. *Amer. Rev. Tuberc.* **70**, 121.

ELEK, S. D. (1956). Principles and problems of combined therapy. *Post. Grad. med. J.* **32**, 324.

ELION, G. B., SINGER, S. & HITCHINGS, G. H. (1954). Antagonists of nucleic acid derivatives. VIII. Synergism in combinations of biochemically related anti-metabolites. *J. biol. Chem.* **208**, 477.

EL-ROOBY, A. & GOHAR, M. A. (1956). The effect of chloramphenicol on the agglutinin titre in enteric fevers. *J. trop. Med.* (*Hyg.*) **59**, 47.

ENGLESBERG, E., GIBOR, A. & LEVY, J. B. (1954). Adaptive control of terminal respiration in *Pasteurella pestis*. *J. Bact.* **68**, 146.

ENGLESBERG, E., LEVY, J. B. & GIBOR, A. (1954). Some enzymatic changes accompanying the shift from anaerobiosis to aerobiosis in *Pasteurella pestis*. *J. Bact.* **68**, 178.

EPSTEIN, N. N. & KEY, J. M. (1949). Treatment of neurosyphilis with penicillin combined with artificial fever. *Arch. Derm. Syph.*, *N.Y.* **60**, 543.

ERLENMEYER, H., BÄUMLER, J. & ROTH, W. (1953). Metallkomplexe und tuberculo-statische Aktivität. *Helv. chim. acta*, **36**, 941.

ESPLIN, D. W. & MARCUS, S. (1954). Relation between antibacterial action of penicillin and mouse host defenses in systemic pneumococcus infection. *Antibiot. Chemother.* **4**, 423.

EYLES, D. E. & COLEMAN, N. (1953). Synergistic effect of sulphadiazine and daraprim against experimental toxoplasmosis in the mouse. *Antibiot. Chemother.* **3**, 483.

FENNER, F. (1956). The pathogenic behaviour of *Mycobacterium ulcerans* and *Mycobacterium balnei* in the mouse and the developing chick embryo. *Amer. Rev. Tuberc.* **73**, 650.

FINLAND, M. (1955). Emergence of antibiotic-resistant bacteria. *New Engl. J. Med.* **253**, 909, 969, 1019.

FISHER, M. W. (1948). Sensitivity of tubercle bacilli to streptomycin. *Amer. Rev. Tuberc.* **57**, 58.

FITZPATRICK, F. K. (1955). Nicotinamide in murine tuberculosis. *Proc. Soc. exp. Biol.*, *N.Y.* **88**, 54.

FLETCHER, F., EPSTEIN, C. & JEWELL, P. I. (1953). The antimycobacterial activity of tissue extracts and surface-active agents in Dubos's medium. *J. gen. Microbiol.* **8**, 323.

FOLEY, F. (1921). Resorption of the cerebrospinal fluid by the choroid plexuses under the influence of intravenous injection of hypertonic salt solutions. *Arch. Neurol. Psychiat.* **5**, 744.

FOUTS, J. R. & BRODIE, B. B. (1955). Inhibition of drug metabolic pathways by the potentiating agent 2,4-dichloro-6-phenyl-phenoxyethyl diethylamine. *J. Pharmacol.* **115**, 68.

FOUTS, J. R. & BRODIE, B. B. (1956). On the mechanism of drug potentiation by iproniazid (2-isopropyl-1-isonicotinyl hydrazine). *J. Pharmacol.* **116**, 480.

FOUTS, J. R. & BRODIE, B. B. (1957). The enzymatic reduction of chloramphenicol, *p*-nitrobenzoic acid and other aromatic nitro compounds in mammals. *J. Pharmacol.* **119**, 197.

FRANCIS, J., LANDQUIST, J. K., LEVI, A. A., SILK, J. A. & THORP, J. M. (1956). 2-Hydroxymethyl-3-methylquinoxaline 1:4-dioxide: a metabolite of 2:3-dimethylquinoxaline 1:4-dioxide active against Gram-negative bacteria. *Biochem. J.* **63**, 455.

FRANCIS, J., MARTIN, A. R., ROSE, F. L. & SPINKS, A. (1954). The absorption, toxicity and experimental antituberculous action of 5-amino-7-methyl-1:2:4:6-tetra-azaindene. *Brit. J. Pharmacol.* **9**, 437.

FRANCIS, JUN., T., TERRELL, E. E., DUBOS, R. & AVERY, O. T. (1934). Experimental type III pneumococcus pneumonia in monkeys. II. Treatment with an enzyme which decomposes the specific capsular polysaccharide of pneumococcus type III. *J. exp. Med.* **59**, 641.

FRIEDEN, E. H. (1945). Synergistic action of nicotinamide upon penicillin. *Proc. Soc. exp. Biol., N.Y.* **60**, 352.

GARROD, L. P. (1953). Combined chemotherapy in bacterial infections. *Brit. med. J.* i, 953.

GIBIER, P. (1882). De l'aptitude communiquée aux animaux à sang froid à contracter le charbon par l'élévation de leur température. *C.R. Acad. Sci., Paris*, **94**, 1605.

GILLISSEN, G. (1954). Die synergistische Wirkung von Isonicotinsäurehydrazid (INH) und Sulphonamid (*in vitro*-Versuche). *Z. Hyg. InfektKr.* **138**, 321.

GOODNER, K., DUBOS, R. & AVERY, O. T. (1932). The action of a specific enzyme upon the dermal infection of rabbits with type III pneumococcus. *J. exp. Med.* **55**, 393.

GOWANS, J. L. (1953a). The action of penicillin and terramycin on pneumococcal infection in normal and leucopenic rabbits. *Brit. J. exp. Path.* **34**, 35.

GOWANS, J. L. (1953b). The effect of some antibiotics on coccal infection in mice. *Brit. J. exp. Path.* **34**, 195.

GRAY, D. F. (1946). Some factors influencing virulence of *Haemophilus pertussis* phase I. *Aust. J. exp. Biol. med. Sci.* **24**, 301.

GREENBERG, J. (1949). Hypersensitivity to sulphadiazine of a chlorguanide-resistant strain of *Plasmodium gallinaceum*. *J. nat. Mal. Soc.* **8**, 80.

GREENBERG, J. & RICHESON, E. M. (1950). Potentiation of antimalarial activity of sulfadiazine by 2,4-diamino-5-aryloxypyrimidines. *J. Pharmacol.* **99**, 444.

GREIFF, D. & PINKERTON, H. (1945). Effect of enzyme inhibitors and activators on the multiplication of typhus rickettsiae. II. Temperature, potassium cyanide and toluidin blue. *J. exp. Med.* **82**, 193.

GUNNISON, J. B., KUNISHIGE, E., COLEMAN, V. R. & JAWETZ, E. (1955). The mode of action of antibiotic synergism and antagonism: the effect *in vitro* on bacteria not actively multiplying. *J. gen. Microbiol.* **13**, 509.

HAHN, F. E., WISSEMAN, JUN., C. L. & HOPPS, H. E. (1954). Mode of action of chloramphenicol. II. Inhibition of bacterial D-polypeptide formation by an L-stereoisomer of chloramphenicol. *J. Bact.* **67**, 674.

HAHN, H. VON, BÄUMLER, J., ROTH, W. & ERLENMEYER, H. (1953). Über Kupferkomplexe von Säureamiden und anderen Verbindungen. *Helv. chim. acta*, **36**, 10.

HAIGHT, T. H. & FINLAND, M. (1952). Observations on mode of action of erythromycin. *Proc. Soc. exp. Biol., N.Y.* **81**, 188.

HANDSCHUMACHER, R. E. & WELCH, A. D. (1956). Microbial studies of 6-azauracil, an inhibitor of uracil. *Fed. Proc.* **15**, 267.

HART, H. (1949). Nature and variability of disease resistance in plants. *Annu. Rev. Microbiol.* **3**, 289.

HART, P. D'A. (1954). The role of the host in the chemotherapy of tuberculosis. *Brit. med. J.* ii, 767.

HART, P. D'A. & REES, R. J. W. (1955). Influence of certain surface-active agents on the host-parasite relationship in experimental tuberculosis. In *Experimental Tuberculosis*. Edited by G. E. W. Wolstenholme & M. P. Cameron, p. 299. London: Churchill.

HAWKING, F. & PERRY, L. M. (1948). Activation of paludrine. *Brit. J. Pharmacol.* 3, 320.

HAYNES, W. C., KUEHNE, R. W. & RHODES, L. J. (1955). The influence of incubation temperature upon the growth response of *Micrococcus pyogenes* to potassium. *Bact. Proc.* p. 47.

HENDERSON, D. W. & GORER, P. A. (1940). The treatment of certain experimental anaerobic infections with sulphapyridine and with immune sera and the problem of synergic action. *J. Hyg., Camb.* 40, 345.

HIRSCH, J. G. (1955). Biochemical factors which may influence the fate of tubercle bacilli in tissues. In *Experimental Tuberculosis*. Edited by G. E. W. Wolstenholme & M. P. Cameron, p. 115. London: Churchill.

HITCHINGS, G. H., ELION, G. B. & SINGER, S. (1955). Effects of combinations of three biochemically-related antimetabolites. *Fed. Proc.* 14, 227.

HOBBY, G. (1954). Synergism, antagonism and hormesis with reference to anti-microbial substances. In *Principles and Practice of Antibiotic Therapy*. Edited by H. Welch. New York: Blakiston.

HOBBY, G. L. & DAWSON, M. H. (1944). Effect of rate of growth of bacteria on action of penicillin. *Proc. Soc. exp. Biol., N.Y.* 56, 181.

HOBBY, G. L., MEYER, K. & CHAFFEE, E. (1942). Observations on the mechanism of action of penicillin. *Proc. Soc. exp. Biol., N.Y.* 50, 281.

HÖBER, R. (1945). *Physical Chemistry of Cells and Tissues*. London: Churchill.

HOLLINGSHEAD, R. G. W. (1956). *Oxine and its Derivatives*. London: Butterworth.

HOLLY, F. W., PEEL, E. W., LUZ, E. L. & FOLKERS, K. (1952). *N*-Phenylacetyl-L-cysteinyl-D-valine. *J. Amer. chem. Soc.* 74, 4539.

HORSFALL, J. G. (1956). *Principles of Fungicidal Action*. Waltham, Mass.: Chronica Botanica Co.

HURST, E. W. (1957). Approaches to the chemotherapy of virus diseases. *J. Pharm., Lond.* 9, 273.

HURST, E. W. & DAVIES, O. L. (1950). Studies on the blood-brain barrier. II. Attempts to influence the passage of substances into the brain. *Brit. J. Pharmacol.* 5, 147.

HURST, E. W., LANDQUIST, J. K., MELVIN, P., PETERS, J. M., SENIOR, N., SILK, J. A. & STACEY, G. J. (1953). The therapy of experimental psittacosis and lymphogranuloma venereum (inguinale). II. The activity of quinoxaline-1:4-dioxide and substituted and related compounds, with a note on the morphological changes induced in lymphogranuloma virus by these compounds and by antibiotics. *Brit. J. Pharmacol.* 8, 297.

JACKSON, G. G., RUBENIS, M. & MELLODY, M. (1957). Synnematin B and penicillin G: relationship of molecular differences to bacterial sensitivity and resistance. *Antibiotics Annual* (1956–7), p. 740.

JANCSÓ, N. VON & JANCSÓ, H. VON (1935). Chemotherapeutische Mittel mit opsoninartiger Wirkung. *Z. ImmunForsch.* 84, 471.

JAWETZ, E. (1956). Antimicrobial chemotherapy. *Annu. Rev. Microbiol.* 10, 85.

JAWETZ, E. & GUNNISON, J. B. (1953). Antibiotic synergism and antagonism: an assessment of the problem. *Pharmacol. Rev.* 5, 175.

JAWETZ, E., GUNNISON, J. B., BRUFF, J. B. & COLEMAN, V. R. (1952). Studies on antibiotic synergism and antagonism. Synergism among seven antibiotics against various bacteria *in vitro*. *J. Bact.* 64, 29.

JOHNSON, F. H. & LEWIN, I. (1946). The growth rate of *E. coli* in relation to temperature, quinine and coenzyme. *J. cell. comp. Physiol.* **28**, 47.

JOHNSON, W. J. (1955a). The inhibition of sulphanilamide acetylation by aromatic and heterocyclic carboxamides and carboxhydrazides. *Canad. J. Biochem. Physiol.* **33**, 107.

JOHNSON, W. J. (1955b). Effects of inhibitors of sulphanilamide acetylation on sulphonamide blood concentrations. *Canad. J. Biochem. Physiol.* **33**, 523.

KÄER, E. & LOEWE, S. (1926). Über Kombinationswirkungen. III. Die Wirkungsvariationen in Veronal-Antipyrin-Gemischen. *Arch. exp. Path. Pharmak.* **114**, 339.

KAIPAINEN, W. J. & FAINE, S. (1954). Toxicity of erythromycin. *Nature, Lond.* **174**, 969.

KAPLAN, H. S., SPECK, R. S. & JAWETZ, E. (1952). Impairment of antimicrobial defenses following total body irradiation of mice. *J. Lab. clin. Med.* **40**, 682.

KASSANIS, B. (1957). Effects of changing temperature on plant virus diseases. *Advanc. Virus Res.* **4**, 221.

KENDALL, S. B. (1956). Synergy between pyrimethamine and sulphonamides used in the control of *Eimeria tenella. Proc. R. Soc. Med.* **49**, 874.

KIDDER, G. W., DEWEY, V. C. & PARKS, JUN., R. E. (1952). Effect of lowered essential metabolites on 8-azaguanine inhibition. *J. biol. Chem.* **197**, 193.

KIRBY, W. W. M. & DUBOS, R. J. (1947). Effect of penicillin on the tubercle bacillus *in vitro. Proc. Soc. exp. Biol., N.Y.* **66**, 120.

KLEIN, P. (1953). Über die Beiden Wirkungsdeterminanten des Terramycin. *Klin. Wschr.* **31**, 1087.

KLIGMAN, A. M., CRANE, A. P. & NORRIS, R. F. (1951). Effect of temperature on survival of chick embryos infected intravenously with *Cryptococcus neoformans* (*Torula histolytica*). *Amer. J. med. Sci.* **221**, 273.

KNIGHT, B. C. J. G. (1952). Physiological background to microbial inhibition. *Bull. World Hlth Org.* **6**, 229.

KNOTHE, H. & BUTENBERG, O. (1955). Zur Frage der Temperaturabhängigkeit von Antibiotica gegenüber gramnegativen Darmbakterien. *Z. Hyg. InfektKr.* **141**, 315.

KNOX, R. (1956). Drug combinations in treatment of bacterial infections. *Proc. R. Soc. Med.* **49**, 879.

KNOX, R. & COLLARD, P. (1952). The effect of temperature on the sensitivity of *Bacillus cereus* to penicillin. *J. gen. Microbiol.* **6**, 369.

KNOX, R., KING, M. B. & WOODROFFE, R. C. (1952). *In vitro* action of isoniazid on *Mycobacterium tuberculosis. Lancet,* ii, 854.

KOCH-WESER, D. (1956). The influence of the metabolic state of tubercle bacilli upon the action of isoniazid *in vitro. J. clin. Invest.* **35**, 718.

KOLODNY, M. H. (1940). The effect of environmental temperature upon experimental trypanosomiasis (*T. cruzi*) of rats. *Amer. J. Hyg.* **32** (C), 21.

LACEY, B. W. (1953). The influence of growth conditions on the antigenic structure of *Haemophilus pertussis, parapertussis* and *bronchisepticus. VI Congr. int. Microbiol.* **2**, 331.

LACEY, B. W. (1954). A new selective medium for *Haemophilus pertussis* containing a diamidine, sodium fluoride and penicillin. *J. Hyg., Camb.* **52**, 273.

LAMBIN, S. & DESVIGNES, A. (1952). Influence de la streptomycine et de la pénicilline sur la phagocytose des bactéries. *C.R. Soc. Biol., Paris,* **146**, 1923.

LANGLADE, Y. M. (1956). Contribution à l'étude de l'action des antibiotiques sur les caractères biochimiques de pathogénicité du staphylocoque doré. *C.R. Soc. Biol., Paris,* **149**, 254.

LAW, L. W., TAORMINA, V. & BOYLE, P. J. (1954). Response of acute lymphocytic leukemias to the purine antagonist 6-mercaptopurine. *Ann. N.Y. Acad. Sci.* **60**, 244.

LEPAGE, G. A. (1953). Effects of chloramphenicol on incorporation of glycine-2-C^{14} into mammalian tumor cell proteins and purines. *Proc. Soc. exp. Biol., N.Y.* **83**, 724.

LETTRÉ, H. (1954). Synergists and antagonists of mitotic poisons. *Ann. N.Y. Acad. Sci.* **58**, 1264.

LIGHTBOWN, J. W. & JACKSON, F. L. (1956). Inhibition of cytochrome systems of heart muscle and certain bacteria by the antagonists of dihydrostreptomycin: 2-alkyl-4-hydroxyquinoline *N*-oxides. *Biochem. J.* **63**, 130.

LILLIE, R. D., DYER, R. E., ARMSTRONG, C. & PASTERNACK, J. G. (1937). Seasonal variation in intensity of brain reaction of the St Louis encephalitis in mice and of endemic typhus in guinea-pigs. *Publ. Hlth Rep., Wash.* **52**, 1805.

LINCOLN, R. E., ZELLE, M. R., RANDLES, C. I., ROBERTS, J. L. & YOUNG, G. A. (1946). Respiratory pathogenicity of *Bacillus anthracis* spores. III. Changes in pathogenicity due to nutritional modifications. *J. infect. Dis.* **79**, 254.

LOCK, J. A. (1950). The chemotherapeutic action of phenanthridine compounds. *Brit. J. Pharmacol.* **5**, 398.

LOEWE, S. (1938). Coalitive action of combined drugs. *J. Pharmacol.* **63**, 24.

LOEWE, S. (1953). The problem of synergism and antagonism of combined drugs. *Arzneim. Forsch.* **3**, 285.

LOEWENTHAL, H. (1939). Combined serum and sulphanilamide in the treatment of streptococcal infections in mice. *Lancet*, i, 197.

LOURIE, E. M. (1943). The blood-brain barrier and cerebro-spinal fluid, in relation to the efficacy of sleeping-sickness drugs. *Trans. Faraday Soc.* **39**, 340.

LOVELOCK, J. E. & REES, R. J. W. (1955). Possible site and mode of action of certain lipotropic macromolecules in tuberculosis. *Nature, Lond.* **175**, 161.

LURIE, M. B. (1955). On the role of hormones in experimental tuberculosis. *Advanc. Tuberc. Res.* **6**, 18.

LÜTZENKIRCHEN, A. & SCHOOG, M. (1954). Wirkungssteigerung von Penicillin durch N-(3′-Dimethylamino)-propyl-3-chlorphenothiazin und Antihistaminica. *Arzneim. Forsch.* **4**, 560.

MAALØE, O. (1948). 1. Pathogenic-apathogenic transformation of *Salmonella typhimurium*. *Acta path. microbiol. scand.* **25**, 414.

McCUNE, JUN., R. M. & TOMPSETT, R. (1956). Fate of *Mycobacterium tuberculosis* in mouse tissues as determined by the microbial enumeration technique. I. The persistence of drug-susceptible tubercle bacilli in the tissues despite prolonged antimicrobial therapy. *J. exp. Med.* **104**, 737.

McCUNE, JUN., R. M., TOMPSETT, R. & McDERMOTT, W. (1956). The fate of *Mycobacterium tuberculosis* in mouse tissues as determined by the microbial enumeration technique. II. The conversion of tuberculous infection to the latent state by the administration of pyrazinamide and a companion drug. *J. exp. Med.* **104**, 763.

McDERMOTT, W. (1952). Host factors in chemotherapy. In *Bacterial and Mycotic Infections of Man*. Edited by R. J. Dubos. 2nd ed., p. 744. London: Lippincott.

McDERMOTT, W., TOMPSETT, R. & STERN, K. (1954). Activation of pyrazinamide and nicotinamide in acidic environments *in vitro*. *Amer. Rev. Tuberc.* **70**, 748.

McDOWELL, C. (1923). The effect of different temperatures and humidities on the resistance of rats to a pneumococcus infection. *Amer. J. Hyg.* **3**, 521.

MACKANESS, G. B. (1952). The action of drugs on intracellular tubercle bacilli. *J. Path. Bact.* **64**, 429.

MACKANESS, G. B. (1956). The intracellular activation of pyrazinamide and nicotin-amide. *Amer. Rev. Tuberc.* **74**, 718.

MACKANESS, G. B. & SMITH, N. (1952). The action of isoniazid (isonicotinic acid hydrazide) on intracellular tubercle bacilli. *Amer. Rev. Tuberc.* **66**, 125.

MACKANESS, G. B. & SMITH, N. (1953). The bactericidal action of isoniazid, strepto-mycin, and terramycin on extracellular and intracellular tubercle bacilli. *Amer. Rev. Tuberc.* **67**, 322.

MACLEAN, I. H., ROGERS, K. B. & FLEMING, A. (1939). M & B 693 and pneumo-cocci. *Lancet*, i, 562.

MARKS, J. (1951). Effects of hyperthermia and antibacterial agents on tubercle bacilli. *Brit. med. J.* ii, 1318.

MARMION, D. E. (1952). The treatment of typhoid fever with chloramphenicol. *Trans. R. Soc. trop. Med. Hyg.* **46**, 619.

MARSTON, R. Q., RUTH, H. J. & SMITH, W. W. (1953). Role of host defenses in streptomycin treatment of X-irradiated mice. *Proc. Soc. exp. Biol., N.Y.* **83**, 289.

MATHIESON, J. M. & CATCHESIDE, G. D. (1955). Inhibition of histidine uptake in *Neurospora crassa*. *J. gen. Microbiol.* **13**, 72.

MATTHEWS, R. E. F. & SMITH, J. D. (1955). The chemotherapy of viruses. *Advanc. Virus Res.* **3**, 49.

MAXWELL, R. E. & NICKEL, V. S. (1954). The antibacterial activity of the isomers of chloramphenicol. *Antibiot. Chemother.* **4**, 289.

MEADOW, P. & KNOX, R. (1956). The effect of isonicotinic acid hydrazide on the oxidative metabolism of *Mycobacterium tuberculosis* var. *bovis* B.C.G. *J. gen. Microbiol.* **14**, 414.

MICKELSON, M. & WERKMAN, C. H. (1938). Influence of pH on the dissimilation of glucose by *Aerobacter indologenes*. *J. Bact.* **36**, 67.

MIDDLEBROOK, G. & DRESSLER, S. H. (1955). Isoniazid resistance. *Lancet*, i, 669.

MILLER, A. K. & VERWEY, W. F. (1954). Effect of probenecid on combined peni-cillin and triple sulphonamides therapy of experimental streptococcal infections. *Antibiot. Chemother.* **4**, 169.

MILLER, C. P. & FOSTER, A. Z. (1944). Studies on the action of penicillin. III. Bac-tericidal action of penicillin on meningococcus *in vitro*. *Proc. Soc. exp. Biol., N.Y.* **56**, 205.

MILLS, C. A. & SCHMIDT, L. H. (1942). Environmental temperatures and resistance to infection. *Amer. J. trop. Med.* **22**, 655.

MITCHISON, D. A. & SELKON, J. B. (1956). The bactericidal activities of anti-tuberculous drugs. *Amer. Rev. Tuberc.* **74**, Suppl. 109.

MORAGUES, V. & PINKERTON, H. (1944). Variation in morbidity and mortality of murine typhus infection in mice with changes in the environmental temperature. *J. exp. Med.* **79**, 41.

MOSS, J. N., BEILER, J. M. & MARTIN, G. J. (1955). Effect of trypsin on levels of antibiotics in the spinal fluid. *Bact. Proc.* p. 80.

MURRAY, E. G. D. (1954). A surmise on some trends in bacteriology. *Lancet*, i, 221.

NOVICK, A. & SZILARD, L. (1952). Anti-mutagens. *Nature, Lond.* **170**, 926.

OESTREICHER, R., DRESSLER, S. H. & MIDDLEBROOK, G. (1954). Peripheral neuritis in tuberculous patients treated with isoniazid. *Amer. Rev. Tuberc.* **70**, 504.

PARK, J. T. & STROMINGER, J. L. (1957). Mode of action of penicillin. *Science*, **125**, 99.

PARKER, R. F. & THOMPSON, R. L. (1942). The effect of external temperature on the course of infectious myxomatosis of rabbits. *J. exp. Med.* **75**, 567.

PASTEUR, JOUBERT & CHAMBERLAND (1878). Sur le charbon des poules. *C.R. Acad. Sci., Paris*, **87**, 47.

PITTILLO, R. F. & FOSTER, J. W. (1954). Potentiation of inhibitor action through determination of reversing metabolites. *J. Bact.* **67**, 53.

POLLOCK, M. R. cited by ROGERS, H. J. & SPENSLEY, P. C. (1955). Selective inhibition of the liberation of extracellular enzymes and protein in cultures of *Staphylococcus aureus*. *Biochem. J.* **60**, 635.

POTTER, V. R. (1951). Sequential blocking of metabolic pathways *in vivo*. *Proc. Soc. exp. Biol., N.Y.* **76**, 41.

QUASTEL, J. H. (1956). Action of drugs on enzyme systems. In *Enzymes: Units of Biological Structure and Function*. *Henry Ford Hosp. Symp.* **4**, 523.

REILLY, H. C. (1956). Effect of test medium upon the demonstration of antimicrobial activities of certain antibiotics. *Bact. Proc.* p. 72.

REINER, L. & LEONARD, C. S. (1932). Studies on the mechanism of chemotherapeutic action. III. Differentiation between parasiticidal and virulence-decreasing action of arsenicals. *Arch. int. Pharmacodyn.* **43**, 10.

RICH, A. R. & MCKEE, C. M. (1936). The mechanism of a hitherto unexplained form of native immunity to the type III pneumococcus. *Johns Hopk. Hosp. Bull.* **59**, 171.

RITZMANN, O. (1907). Über den Einfluss erhöhter Aussentemperatur auf den Verlauf der experimentellen Tetanus- und Streptokokken-infektion. *Arch. Hyg., Berl.* **61**, 355.

ROLLO, I. M. (1955). The mode of action of sulphonamides, proguanil and pyrimethanine on *Plasmodium gallinaceum*. *Brit. J. Pharmacol.* **10**, 208.

RUBBO, S. D., ALBERT, A. & GIBSON, M. I. (1950). The influence of chemical constitution on antibacterial activity. Part V: The antibacterial activity of 8-hydroxyquinoline (oxine). *Brit. J. exp. Path.* **31**, 425.

RUTTEN, F. J., WINKLER, K. C. & DE HAAN, P. G. (1950). The action of sulphanilamide on bacteriophages T_1–T_7. *Brit. J. exp. Path.* **31**, 369.

SACKS, L. E. (1955). Sporostatic action of subtilin and penicillin. *J. Bact.* **70**, 491.

SCHAEFER, W. B. (1954). The effect of isoniazid on growing and resting tubercle bacilli. *Amer. Rev. Tuberc.* **69**, 125.

SCHOOG, M. (1955). Der Einfluss der Hypothermie durch N-(3′-Dimethylamino)-propyl-3-chlorophenothiazin auf die Trypanosomen-Infektion der Maus. *Arzneim. Forsch.* **5**, 327.

SEIBERT, F. B., LONG, E. R. & MORLEY, N. (1933). Two avian tubercle bacillus dissociants and two human tubercle bacillus strains of different virulence. A chemical and biologic study. *J. infect. Dis.* **53**, 175.

SHAFFER, J. M., KUCERA, C. J. & SPINK, W. W. (1953). The protection of intracellular brucella against therapeutic agents and the bactericidal action of serum. *J. exp. Med.* **97**, 77.

SHAPIRO, D. M. & GELLHORN, A. (1951). Combinations of chemical compounds in experimental cancer therapy. *Cancer Res.* **11**, 35.

SHAPIRO, D. M., KREAM, J. & DIETRICH, L. S. (1952). Combination chemotherapy of cancer: potentiation of carcinostatic activity of 8-azaguanine by 6-formyl-pteridine. *Proc. Soc. exp. Biol., N.Y.* **81**, 616.

SHEPARD, C. C. (1956). The use of HeLa cells infected with tubercle bacilli for the assessment of antitubercular drugs. *Bact. Proc.* p. 65.

SHIVE, W., ACKERMANN, W. W., GORDON, M., GETZENDANER, M. E. & EAKIN, R. E. (1947). 5(4)-amino-4(5)-imidazolecarboxamide, a precursor of purines. *J. Amer. chem. Soc.* **69**, 725.

SIEBENMANN, C. O. & PLUMMER, H. (1945). Chemotherapy and antitoxin therapy of experimental *Cl. welchii* infection in mice. *J. Pharmacol.* **83**, 71.

SIGURDSSON, B. (1943). The influence of age of host and temperature of incubation on infection of the chick embryo with vesicular stomatitis virus. *J. exp. Med.* **78**, 17.

SINGH, B. & MITCHISON, D. A. (1954). Bactericidal activity of streptomycin and isoniazid against tubercle bacilli. *Brit. med. J.* i, 130.

SINHA, S. K., HANSON, R. P. & BRANDLY, C. A. (1957). Effect of environmental temperature upon facility of aerosol transmission of infection and severity of Newcastle disease among chickens. *J. infect. Dis.* **100**, 162.

SKINSNES, O. K. (1948). The relationship of biological defense mechanisms to the antibiotic activity of penicillin. II. The modifying influence of penicillin on the histopathological pattern of pneumococcus infection in normal and debilitated rats and guinea-pigs. *J. infect. Dis.* **83**, 100.

SKINSNES, O. K. & WOOLRIDGE, R. L. (1948). The relationship of biological defense mechanisms to the antibiotic activity of penicillin. I. The modifying influence of penicillin on the pattern of pneumococcic infection and the immune response in the protein-depleted rat. *J. infect. Dis.* **83**, 78.

SLONIMSKI, P. P. (1953). A specific relation between enzymic adaptation and cytoplasmic mutation. In *Adaptation in Micro-organisms. Symp. Soc. gen. Microbiol.* **3**, 76.

SMADEL, J. E. (1954). Influence of antibiotics on immunologic responses in scrub typhus. *Amer. J. Med.* **17**, 246.

SMITH, H. V. (1953). Tuberculin in the treatment of tuberculous meningitis and other conditions. *Proc. R. Soc. Med.* **46**, 588.

SMITH, M. R. & WOOD, JUN., W. B. (1956a). An experimental analysis of the curative action of penicillin in acute bacterial infections. II. The role of phagocytic cells in the process of recovery. *J. exp. Med.* **103**, 499.

SMITH, M. R. & WOOD, JUN., W. B. (1956b). An experimental analysis of the curative action of penicillin in acute bacterial infections. III. The effect of suppuration upon the antibacterial action of the drug. *J. exp. Med.* **103**, 509.

SMRT, J., BERÁNEK, J., SICHER, J., HESS, V. F. & ŠORM, F. (1957). Synthesis of L-4-amino-3-isoxazolidinone, the unnatural stereoisomer of cycloserine and its antibiotic activity. *Experientia*, **13**, 291.

SOLOTOROVSKY, M. & GREGORY, F. J. (1952). Antituberculous activity in mice of Triton A-20, a nonionic alkyl-aryl polyether alcohol, used alone and in combination with dihydrostreptomycin. *Amer. Rev. Tuberc.* **65**, 718.

SORKIN, E., ROTH, W. & ERLENMEYER, H. (1951). Über von Cu·· abhängige bakteriostatische Wirkungen. *Experientia*, **7**, 64.

SORKIN, E., ROTH, W. & ERLENMEYER, H. (1953). Über die Beeinflussung tuberculostatischer Wirkungen durch Cu··. *Helv. chim. acta*, **35**, 1736.

SPRICK, M. C. (1956). Phagocytosis of *M. tuberculosis* and *M. smegmatis* stained with indicator dyes. *Amer. Rev. Tuberc.* **74**, 552.

STERBENZ, F. J. & LILLY, D. M. (1956). Factors influencing growth in protozoa. I. Factors influencing abnormal growth in suctorian protozoa. *Trans. N.Y. Acad. Sci.* **18**, 522.

SULKIN, S. E. (1945). The effect of environmental temperature on experimental influenza in mice. *J. Immunol.* **51**, 291.

SUTER, E. (1952). Multiplication of tubercle bacilli within phagocytes cultivated *in vitro*, and effect of streptomycin and isonicotinic acid hydrazide. *Amer. Rev. Tuberc.* **65**, 775.

SWIFT, P. N. (1957). Antibiotics and host resistance. *Brit. med. J.* i, 129.

SZYBALSKI, W. & BRYSON, V. (1952). Genetic studies on microbial cross resistance to toxic agents. I. Cross resistance of *Escherichia coli* to fifteen antibiotics. *J. Bact.* **64**, 489.

SZYBALSKI, W. & BRYSON, V. (1953). Conditional antagonism between isoniazid and other antibacterial agents. *Amer. Rev. Tuberc.* **68**, 280.

TAYLOR, D. J., JOSEPHSON, E. S., GREENBERG, J. & COATNEY, G. R. (1952). The *in vitro* activity of certain antimalarials against erythrocytic forms of *Plasmodium gallinaceum*. *Amer. J. trop. Med. Hyg.* **1**, 132.

TOMPSETT, R., SHULTZ, S. & McDERMOTT, W. (1947). Influence of protein-binding on the interpretation of penicillin activity *in vivo*. *Proc. Soc. exp. Biol., N.Y.* **65**, 163.

VAN ESELTINE, W. P. & RAHN, O. (1949). The effect of temperature upon bacteriostasis. *J. Bact.* **57**, 547.

VELDSTRA, H. (1956). Synergism and potentiation. *Pharm. Rev.* **8**, 339.

WAIN, R. L. (1953). Plant growth substances. Royal Institute of Chemistry Monograph No. 2.

WAINGORTIN, E., HERRERA, V. A. & FOLEY, J. A. (1956). The use of tuberculin in the treatment of tuberculous meningitis. *Amer. Rev. Tuberc.* **74**, 277.

WASZ-HÖCKERT, O., McCUNE, JUN., R. M., LEE, S. H., McDERMOTT, W. & TOMPSETT, R. (1956). Resistance of tubercle bacilli to pyrazinamide *in vivo*. *Amer. Rev. Tuberc.* **74**, 572.

WASZ-HÖCKERT, O., McCUNE, JUN., R. M. & TOMPSETT, R. (1956). Concurrent administration of pyridoxine and isoniazid. *Amer. Rev. Tuberc.* **74**, 471.

WATT, D. & WERKMAN, C. H. (1951). Modification of the enzyme system of *Micrococcus pyogenes*. *Arch. Biochem.* **31**, 383.

WEBB, J. E. (1949). The permeability of insect cuticle. In *Selective Toxicity and Antibiotics*. *Symp. Soc. exp. Biol.* **3**, 143.

WEED, L. H. & McKIBBEN, P. S. (1919). Experimental alteration of brain bulk. *Amer. J. Physiol.* **48**, 531.

WEIL, A. J. (1952). Inhibition of pigment formation of *Serratia marcescens* by chloramphenicol, aureomycin and terramycin. *Proc. Soc. exp. Biol., N.Y.* **79**, 539.

WEINBERG, E. D. (1957). The mutual effects of antimicrobial compounds and metallic cations. *Bact. Rev.* **21**, 46.

WELCH, A. D. (1956). Interference with nucleic acid metabolism. In *Enzymes: Units of Biological Structure and Function*. *Henry Ford Hosp. Symp.* **4**, 547.

WELCH, A. D., PRUSOFF, W. H. & LAJTHA, L. G. (1955). Azathymidine, the deoxyriboside of an analogue of thymine: an antagonist of the utilization of thymidine and of the reproduction of certain cells. *Trans. Ass. Amer. Phycns*, **68**, 112.

WELSCH, M. (1955). La résistance bactérienne aux antibiotiques. Antibiotica et Chemotherapia, Progr. **2**, 34. Bâle/New York: S. Karger.

WHITE, H. J. (1939). The relationship between temperature and the streptococcidal activity of sulphanilamide and sulphapyridine *in vitro*. *J. Bact.* **38**, 549.

WILLIAMSON, G. M. & WHITE, F. (1956). Dihydrostreptomycin and anaerobiosis—comparison with other antibiotics and its selectivity with regard to obligate anaerobes. *J. gen. Microbiol.* **14**, 637.

WILSON, G. S. & MILES, A. A. (1955). *Topley and Wilson's Principles of Bacteriology and Immunity*. 4th ed. London: Arnold.

WOLINSKY, E. & STEENKEN, JUN., W. (1953). Infrequent appearance of drug resistant strains of tubercle bacilli in experimental animals treated with streptomycin and *p*-aminosalicylic acid. *J. Bact.* **66**, 229.

WOOD, JUN., W. B. & SMITH, M. R. (1956). An experimental analysis of the curative action of penicillin in acute bacterial infections. I. The relationship of bacterial growth rates to the antimicrobial effect of penicillin. *J. exp. Med.* **103**, 487.

WOODS, L. A. (1956). The pharmacology of nalorphine (*N*-allylnormorphine). *Pharmacol. Rev.* **8**, 175.

WOOLLEY, D. W., VAN WINKLE, E. & SHAW, E. (1957). A method for increasing brain serotonin without incurring some of the peripheral effects of the hormone. *Proc. nat. Acad. Sci., Wash.* **43**, 128.

WORK, T. S. & WORK, E. (1948). *The Basis of Chemotherapy*. London: Oliver & Boyd.

YOUMANS, A. S. (1947). Studies on the delay in the bacteriostatic action of sulphanilamide on *Escherichia coli*. *J. Bact.* **54**, 5.

YOUMANS, A. S. & YOUMANS, G. P. (1955). The inactivation of isoniazid by filtrates and extracts of mycobacteria. *Amer. Rev. Tuberc.* **72**, 196.

YOUMANS, A. S. & YOUMANS, G. P. (1956). The effect of the 'anti-isoniazid' substance produced by mycobacteria on the chemotherapeutic activity of isoniazid *in vivo*. *Amer. Rev. Tuberc.* **73**, 764.

ZIPF, H. F. & HALBEISEN, TH. (1954). Bakteriostatische und bakterizide Kombinationswirkungen verschiedener Antibiotica *in vitro*. *Arzneim. Forsch.* **4**, 463.

THE CHEMOTHERAPY OF BACTERIAL INFECTIONS

R. KNOX

Bacteriology Department, Guy's Hospital Medical School, London

Strategy has been described as 'the art of concentrating an effective fighting force at a given place at a given time, and tactics as the art of using it when there' (Webster, 1928). In the chemotherapy of bacterial infections strategy is concerned with the broad principles of concentrating the right drug at the right place and time, while tactics is more concerned with day to day and local problems, though the precise distinction between strategy and tactics is not worth labouring too far. What is more important is that, just as in war even global strategy may be influenced and determined by a long sequence of events leading from fundamental physical, chemical, or biological research to the development of new weapons or new ways of increasing the effectiveness of old ones, so, in theory at least, it is with chemotherapy. To understand the principles of this we need to learn more about those fundamental aspects of microbiology, some of which have been dealt with already by earlier speakers in this Symposium. These are the discoveries which should lead to the development of new drugs or new ways of using existing drugs, and thereby should dominate and determine the strategy and tactics of chemotherapy.

Unfortunately this is not the way in which the subject of chemotherapy has in fact developed. Far more commonly a drug has first been found to be effective against a group of organisms, and this has then been the stimulus to fundamental research on the mode of action of the drug. The sulphonamides, penicillin, streptomycin, chloramphenicol, the tetracyclines, isoniazid—all these are good examples of this sequence of events.

At first sight it would seem that empirical screening of drugs and antibiotics has been more worth while than any attempts at a rational approach to the problem. This may have appeared to be true in the past but there are signs today that things are changing. Other contributors are dealing with viruses, protozoa and fungi, but so far as bacteria are concerned, the emphasis is shifting now from the drugs themselves to their rational and effective use. We now have at our disposal drugs effective against most of the important pathogenic bacteria, and fundamental microbiological research may be expected to give us help in understanding better how to use these drugs separately and together. I do not mean to imply that fundamental research may not produce many more completely new classes of antibacterial drug, but only that it seems more likely at the present time to help in the development of existing drugs rather than in the discovery of new ones.

Table 1. *Different levels in the strategy of chemotherapy*

I. *Fundamental level*

Molecular level, e.g.   chemical and physical factors
 specific enzyme inhibitors
 antimetabolites

Subcellular level, e.g.   organization of enzymes
 lethal synthesis

Cellular level, e.g.   cell-wall synthesis
 permeability
 biochemical differences between sensitive and resistant strains

Genetic level, e.g.   genotype and phenotype
(statistical,   mutation rates
bacterial   'potency' of genes (streptomycin *v* penicillin)
populations)   differences between growth rates of sensitive and resistant strains
 mixed bacterial populations

II. *Level of interaction between micro-organism and individual host*

Pharmacological level, e.g.   selective absorption, excretion, toxicity

'Pathological' level, e.g.   pathogenicity of drug sensitive and resistant strains
 defence mechanisms of host—immune response, physical and
 chemical changes (temperature, pH, etc.)

Laboratory control of chemotherapy, e.g.   drug sensitivity tests
 methods of assessing proportion of resistant
 organisms

Clinical level, e.g.   collaboration between clinician and laboratory
 effectiveness of combined chemotherapy in preventing drug resistance
 clinical tests of new drugs

III. *Epidemiological level*, e.g.   spread of micro-organisms through communities
 ecology of sensitive and resistant strains
 reversibility of drug resistance
 rational use of promising drugs
 methods of control: isolation; control of drug distribution

Contributors to this part of the Symposium, it was suggested, should 'survey drugs which have been used with success; examine the success or otherwise of the approaches discussed in the earlier papers; discuss properties of the organisms which might be used as sites of attack in further search, and speculate on the lines along which future research might usefully be directed'. I will try to keep within these general terms of reference in discussing the chemotherapy of bacterial infections.

It is probably true to say that the greatest single obstacle to successful chemotherapy is the development of drug resistance, and it is therefore natural that this should figure largely in discussions on the strategy of chemotherapy. But there are many other facets to the subject and it is often difficult for workers in one branch to understand the thoughts or even the language of workers in other branches. At the inaugural meeting of this Society in 1945, Dr Marjory Stephenson defined five levels of microbiology (Woods, 1953), and particularly emphasized that these represented a spectrum rather than a ladder. I think it is helpful to consider the strategy of chemotherapy in a similar way at different levels—at the 'fundamental' (biochemical, genetic, microbiological) level, at the level of the interactions between micro-organisms and the individual host (pharmacological, experimental or clinical level) and at the epidemiological level (Table 1). There has been too little exchange of ideas between these different disciplines, and this is certainly one of the reasons why the strategy of chemotherapy has been so conspicuously absent up till now. Yet just as a polyglot alliance of many different nations cannot function without interpreters, so the strategy of chemotherapy can be fully developed only by a Grand Alliance of many different disciplines and proper interpretation and liaison between them. It is good for the microbiologists, chemists, biochemists, geneticists, pharmacologists, physiologists, pathologists, immunologists, clinicians and epidemiologists to get together and hear something of each other's problems, and if this Symposium does nothing more than give each of them a sense of humility and an appreciation of the many facets of the subject, it will certainly have done something worth while.

SUCCESSES AND FAILURES OF ANTIBACTERIAL CHEMOTHERAPY

First, I should like to review briefly what has already been achieved. To anyone with clinical experience of bacterial infections before the days of chemotherapy the transformation in the last few years has been astonishing. Up to about 1935 it was probably true to say that syphilis was the only bacterial infection against which there was any effective specific chemotherapy. The sulphonamides, despite the toxicity of the drugs first used, soon brought under control a large group of common and serious infections—streptococcal, pneumococcal, meningococcal, gonococcal and even some infections due to Gram-negative coliform organisms and dysentery bacilli, even though with some of these infections the problem of drug resistance soon arose (Finland, 1955).

Penicillin added many more to the list of bacterial infections which could be effectively treated. Because of its great potency, its low toxicity and for various other reasons it attracted even more attention than the sulphonamides, though for many infections these are probably just as effective and for some even more so. But a rapid increase in the frequency of penicillin-resistant staphylococci was soon detected (Barber 1947 a, b; Barber & Rozwadowska-Dowzenko, 1948) and it is now well known that in hospitals where penicillin is in constant use resistant strains of staphylococci are becoming more common than sensitive strains. (See Finland, 1955, for a full list of references.) The discovery of streptomycin for the first time brought the chemotherapy of tuberculosis within reach, though here too drug resistance was soon encountered (Steenken & Wolinsky, 1949; Mitchison, 1954). Streptomycin, besides being effective against tuberculosis, was found also to be active against a wide variety of other bacteria. Soon after, there followed the tetracyclines—aureomycin, terramycin, tetracycline—and chloramphenicol. All of these are active against a wide range of bacteria and are known as broad spectrum antibiotics. Many new drugs have been discovered which have similar properties or which are useful against particular genera—for example, polymyxin against *Pseudomonas aeruginosa*, the erythromycin group of antibiotics against staphylococci, isoniazid and *p*-aminosalicylic acid against the tubercle bacillus, and many others.

The array of drugs now available is bewildering and confusing, and there is little sign of any strategic principles governing their use. The present position may be summed up in this way.

(1) There are now very few bacterial infections which cannot be controlled by some specific drug or antibiotic.

(2) Often a hit or miss policy of ringing the changes on a series of drugs, one of which has a good chance of success, has greater attractions than a more leisurely and rational approach dependent on laboratory drug sensitivity tests.

(3) The drug resistance which may spell the failure of an originally successful drug is peculiarly selective in its development at the clinical level. For all practical purposes gonococci rapidly become resistant to sulphonamides but meningococci do not. Resistance to penicillin has developed in staphylococci but hardly at all in *Streptococcus pyogenes*, or, so far, in gonococci, meningococci or pneumococci.

(4) The two outstanding examples of infections in which drug resistance develops are staphylococcal infections and tuberculosis. In both of these the development of drug-resistant strains is a really serious problem.

(5) There remains a number of bacterial infections for which a really effective drug has not yet been found. Perhaps the most important are brucella, salmonella, proteus and pseudomonas infections, Johne's disease, and leprosy.

THE DIFFERENT LEVELS OF CHEMOTHERAPY

It has already been mentioned that the strategy of chemotherapy can be approached at several different levels and it will be useful to discuss the different contributions which each of these can make.

The fundamental approach

It has been stressed that many of the most spectacular successes of chemotherapy have had a large element of chance or at the best intelligent guesswork about them, but that we must not therefore dismiss the rational approach as a waste of time. In war, it may be that an intelligent amateur might think of new types of weapon which did not involve a complete departure from existing principles, but atomic or nuclear weapons could never have been evolved without years of pioneering fundamental work in the field of 'pure' science. In chemotherapy the inter-dependence of fundamental research and empirical screening has been abundantly shown—for example, in Dubos's work on tyrothricin (Dubos, 1939), in McIlwain's studies of the antagonism between panto-thenate and pantoyl taurine (McIlwain, 1942), in the discovery of ison-iazid by Fox & Gibas (1952) as a sequel to the known antituberculous activity of nicotinamide and thiosemicarbazones, and many other examples could be quoted. But there are two fields of fundamental work which can be picked out as being of outstanding importance for the development of chemotherapy—one biochemical, and the other genetic.

The Woods–Fildes (Woods, 1940; Fildes, 1940) concept of competi-tive antagonism together with the work of Quastel, McIlwain, Woolley, Gale, and many others (Work & Work, 1948; Albert, 1951; Woolley, 1952) has stimulated research at many different levels into the mode of action of antibacterial drugs both in intact cells and in isolated enzyme systems, and we are only just beginning to realize the many practical consequences which may arise from this fundamental approach. If we knew more about the specific substrates required for the development of specific enzymes, or of the enzymes, coenzymes or vitamins necessary for the development of other enzymes, then it would perhaps be easy to devise drugs of great specificity and potency capable of blocking these by competitive or non-competitive antagonism.

Other contributors to the Symposium have dealt mainly with these and other biochemical aspects of the strategy of chemotherapy, at the molecular, subcellular and cellular levels. In addition to discussion of general principles we have heard at the molecular and subcellular levels about metal-binding agents, the design of antimetabolites, lethal synthesis, inhibitors of protein and nucleic acid synthesis and inhibitors of energy production and utilization, while at the cellular level we have learned about surface-active substances, inhibitors of cell-wall synthesis, and membrane effects.

We have heard, however, little or nothing about the genetic aspects of drug resistance, or the dynamics of shifting bacterial populations. Yet the study of genetics has made fundamental contributions to the whole strategy of chemotherapy. The work of Demerec, Luria and Delbrück, Lederberg and many others has firmly established the genetic basis of drug resistance in micro-organisms (Demerec, 1945; 1948; Luria & Delbrück, 1943; Luria, 1946; Lederberg & Lederberg, 1952). These concepts have had a profound influence on our thinking about drug resistance but have so far had much less influence on our routine practice. Theoretically, if we consider drugs A, B, C and D and if we suppose that mutants resistant to a given concentration of each of these drugs are likely to arise with a frequency of 1 in 10^5 cell divisions, the chances of a mutant arising resistant to all four of the drugs will be 1 in 10^{20}. In the treatment of patients it is likely that such an astronomically large number of organisms as 10^{20} would never occur—and so mutants resistant to all four drugs should never arise, because the presence of all four drugs would prevent a population of this size from ever being reached. It would seem logical then to use combined chemotherapy whenever possible in the hope of preventing drug-resistant mutants from ever appearing.

In practice this ideal state of affairs is not always easy to achieve for a number of reasons. *In vivo* it may not be possible to maintain consistently high drug concentrations in all the sites in the body in which pathogenic micro-organisms may be living. Too high a drug concentration, while eliminating all but the most highly resistant organisms, might have toxic effects on the tissues of the host and in fact reduce their ability to dispose of the surviving drug-resistant micro-organisms (Munoz & Geister, 1950). Too low a drug concentration on the other hand merely increases selection pressure in favour of drug-resistant at the expense of drug-sensitive members of the microbial population. In some cases, individual cells in a bacterial population may survive the action of a drug, not because they are truly resistant, but merely because they have adapted themselves physiologically to the drug or are not in a state of active metabolism (Jawetz, 1956). Bigger (1944) in his work on the killing of staphylococci by penicillin called such cells persisters, and similar examples have been frequently reported since. It seems to be generally true that micro-organisms which are in an active metabolic state are more susceptible, certainly to drugs which are mainly bactericidal, though not perhaps to mainly bacteriostatic drugs, than organisms which are in a 'resting' stage. Clinically it is often found that fulminating infections associated with the rapid multiplication of micro-organisms in the blood-stream are more easily treated by chemotherapy than more indolent and localized infections. The subject is well discussed by Eagle & Saz (1955) and Jawetz (1956).

Combined chemotherapy then does not always come up to theoretical expectations, even in cases where each drug in the combination acts quite independently of the others. The 'genetic' theory of combined chemotherapy, as outlined above, in fact could approximate to the ideal state of affairs only where the individual drugs attacked separate unrelated systems in the bacterial cell. The term 'synergism' is loosely used to indicate that two or more drugs in combination have an effect out of all proportion to the effect which might be expected from similar concentrations of the single drugs. To attempt to define 'synergism' any more precisely than that would be unwise. If two drugs act on identical enzymes or enzyme sites in a bacterial cell, then their combined effect could only be additive. If they act on different enzyme systems then the effects they produce are qualitatively different and therefore cannot be summated. It is in fact doubtful whether there are any true examples of synergism between antibacterial drugs (Eagle & Saz, 1955). The term, however, could be used in at least two more precise ways. In a biochemical sense it can be used to indicate that where each of two drugs produces a partial block in a particular metabolic pathway, but at different points, the two drugs together may have a quite disproportionate effect by producing a complete block in that pathway, or else, where each separately blocks alternative pathways, by blocking both of them at the same time. In a genetic sense it can be used to describe the combined effect of two or more drugs in enormously reducing the risk of drug-resistant mutants arising—a paradoxical genetic 'synergism a non synergendo' (to coin a horrible hybrid) resulting from a completely independent action of the individual drugs.

The subject of synergism has been more fully dealt with by Dr Lacey, and I only want here to stress the importance of trying to keep clear in our minds this difference between what may be called the biochemical action of drug combinations and their effect in delaying the emergence of resistant organisms. But although it may be possible to be clear about this distinction in theory, in practice it is often not at all easy to decide whether a reinforcing action of two drugs does indicate some more than additive effect on the enzymes of the bacterial cell or whether the effect can all be explained in fact simply in terms of the greatly reduced frequency of double or multiple mutants. This is clearly a field which demands further research and a carefully designed experimental approach.

Interactions between micro-organism and host

When we turn from the purely microbiological to the pharmacological or clinical aspects, things are at once much more complex. We have to consider now not only the interaction between drug and micro-organism, but also the effect of the tissues of the host on that interaction and the pharmacological action of the drug. The ultimate object in antibacterial chemotherapy is the production and correct use of drugs which will control infections in the living host. But *in vivo* experiments are time-consuming and expensive, and *in vitro* tests are often used to give preliminary information and for much fundamental work on the mode of action of antibacterial drugs. But we must always be careful not to let our tests lead us astray. At the screening and experimental level, there are many examples of drugs with great antibacterial activity *in vitro* but quite ineffective when tested *in vivo*. Even more interesting are drugs whose antibacterial activity is not shown in the test-tube but only in the experimental animal or man (Cornforth, Hart, Rees & Stock, 1951; Hart, 1954).

There are many possible reasons for discrepancies between *in vitro* and *in vivo* results. A drug may be converted in the body into another substance which may be more or less active than the parent drug; it may be unable to penetrate into the tissues where it is needed; it may act only in association with antibacterial defences of the body, or on the other hand it may, through its very effectiveness in inhibiting bacterial growth, cut short the immune response which is essential for rapid elimination of the invading micro-organism.

This last effect deserves to have a good deal of attention paid to it. In typhoid fever it is often stated that if chloramphenicol is given early the typhoid bacilli can be almost completely eliminated but that the survivors (which are still chloramphenicol-sensitive but have in some way survived the drug) multiply when the drug is stopped, and that relapses are in fact more common than in patients who reach the same sort of stage without drug treatment (Keefer & Weinstein, 1954). In general, the timing of drug treatment is not an easy matter. If a drug is given at the very earliest possible moment, the patient may be cured, but has little or no immunity. The ideal treatment would be to allow sufficient organisms to multiply to produce a powerful antigenic stimulus resulting in active immunity and then to use the drug to reinforce the defences of the body. A patient who had recovered from an infection would then have some immunity against further attacks. But often we are not in a position to take risks of this kind. This is a field of experimental research which certainly deserves much more attention than it has had.

Harrison (1946) found that the production of antipneumococcal anti-bodies in rabbits given sulphonamides or penicillin showed interesting differences which depended on the drug and also on the time interval between the infecting dose and the treatment. The literature is reviewed by Joseph (1957) who has also compared the survival rates of mice injected with pneumococci and treated with single or multiple doses of sulphadimidine and penicillin.

On the other hand the reactions of the body against bacteria are not always beneficial, and sometimes result in chronic inflammatory or fibrotic lesions which harbour organisms in positions inaccessible to antibodies and even to drugs. There is some evidence that cortisone, by suppressing the inflammatory reaction, may make micro-organisms in the tissues more vulnerable to chemotherapy (Johnson & Davey, 1954; Johnson, 1955).

Another reason for discrepancies between the response of bacteria to drugs *in vitro* and in the body may lie in the very nature of the tests we use. As commonly used the routine drug-sensitivity tests tell us either that a given drug concentration inhibits the growth of a given inoculum of micro-organisms after a certain period of incubation in a suitable medium in the laboratory (serial dilution tests), or that a drug diffusing into a solid medium from a reservoir produces inhibition zones of different sizes depending on the concentration of drug in the reservoir and the sensitivity of the micro-organism (diffusion tests). In many cases the information so given is of great value and enables us to carry out treatment of infectious disease rationally and with every expectation that the infection will respond to the chosen drug.

But sometimes we may need fuller information which simple tests of this kind do not, and from their nature cannot, give. There are three main ways in which these routine tests may fail:

(1) They tell us little about the distribution of drug-resistant indi-viduals in a given bacterial population. In most cases it is probably true

that if the great majority of micro-organisms in a culture are sensitive to a clinically useful concentration of a drug, the few resistant mutants that exist can be dealt with by the defences of the body. But a patient may perhaps be infected with a mixture of strains—one drug-sensitive, the other drug-resistant, or there may even be within a species considerable variation from strain to strain not only in the average drug sensitivity but also in the 'skewness' or the scatter of the distribution of drug resistance. In parts of the body which for various reasons may be inaccessible to antibiotics and other body defences, a few drug resistant survivors may rapidly establish themselves. It is therefore important to know at the earliest possible moment if such organisms are present in abnormally high proportions, and this can only be determined by further more elaborate tests.

(2) Our routine tests tell us nothing about the bactericidal power of drugs—they merely give us at the best a 'minimum inhibitory concentration' (M.I.C.). In most cases, this information is enough but, again, in some parts of the body it is not enough that a drug should be efficient in arresting bacterial growth. In subacute bacterial endocarditis, for example, where *Streptococcus viridans* or *S. faecalis* may be multiplying in fibrinous, almost avascular lesions in the heart valves, a drug to be effective must be bactericidal and not merely bacteriostatic. Penicillin is effective in such situations when the pathogen is fully sensitive, but when the organisms are even moderately resistant to penicillin it is unable to kill them. It was hoped that in such cases the tetracyclines would be useful, because *S. faecalis* is sensitive to these in low concentrations according to serial dilution tests. But these drugs failed because they were only bacteriostatic and not bactericidal (Jawetz, 1956).

(3) Our tests tell us nothing about the effectiveness of drug combinations. Subacute bacterial endocarditis due to *Streptococcus faecalis* has been cured only by combinations of penicillin and streptomycin. Each of these separately has little bactericidal effect on *S. faecalis* but the two drugs together are fully bactericidal. As Garrod (1953) has pointed out, the laboratory work involved in determining the bactericidal effect of several drugs alone and in combination is quite outside the scope of ordinary routine work, and of the ordinary sensitivity tests. Yet sometimes that information is vital for the proper use of drugs, and accurate tests of drug sensitivity certainly play an important part in the strategy of chemotherapy. The subject of combined chemotherapy in clinical medicine has been discussed by Dowling (1957).

Whatever else our tests tell us, to be of any practical value they must give information about the susceptibility of pathogenic organisms to drug concentrations likely to be maintained in the tissues of the patient. When careful inquiries are made, a number of unexpected explanations for failure may be unearthed. Quite frequently the simplest of all explanations is the correct one—that the patient has either not been taking the drug at all, or perhaps even worse, taking it so erratically as to give drug-resistant organisms a chance to emerge. Sometimes a mixed infection may be responsible for a paradoxical result—as when a penicillinase-producing staphylococcus makes penicillin quite ineffective against a penicillin-sensitive streptococcus (Rountree, 1955; Gray, 1956), or in other mixed infections with cocci and coliform organisms. At the clinical level, progress in chemotherapy can be made only by close collaboration between clinicians and laboratory workers, and by careful and painstaking investigation of all cases of unexpected failure of chemotherapy.

The epidemiological level

The failure of a drug through the development of drug resistance is often the result of neglecting sound epidemiological principles. Infectivity is the outstanding feature of infectious diseases, and the epidemiological approach is vital to the grand strategy of chemotherapy.

Finland (1955) in an exhaustive review of the emergence of antibiotic-resistant bacteria stresses the need to distinguish clearly in our minds between drug-resistant variants of an originally susceptible strain arising in the patient during treatment, and resistant strains taking the place, or appearing after the suppression, of sensitive strains (substitution). But, as he points out, while it is easy enough to distinguish these in principle, it is not always so easy to decide in any given case which kind of resistance we are dealing with.

Tuberculosis gives perhaps the clearest examples of drug resistance developing within the original host. This has occurred with each of the three most commonly used antituberculous drugs (streptomycin, p-amino-salicylic acid, and isoniazid), both when used alone and in combination, though combined chemotherapy greatly delays the speed with which resistance develops and its incidence (Medical Research Council, 1952; 1955; Joiner et al. 1952; 1956). But tuberculosis also illustrates the other way in which resistant strains can spread. Drug-resistant strains are being increasingly often isolated from patients who themselves have not had any chemotherapy but who have been in contact with patients excreting drug-resistant strains (Fox et al. 1957; Mitchison & Selkon, 1957).

Apart from tuberculosis, unequivocal examples of drug resistance developing in one patient during the course of treatment are not easy to find. Dowling, Hirsch & O'Neil (1946) described a patient with endocarditis from whose blood was isolated a strain of streptococcus which showed an increase in penicillin resistance from 0·0007 to 1·43 μg./ml. during treatment. Garrod (1951) reported a similar case, in which during the administration of several thousand pounds worth of penicillin (up to a rate of 40 million units daily) the resistance of the strain of streptococcus isolated slowly rose from a level of 2 up to 20 units penicillin/ml. Garrod also observed a tenfold increase in the penicillin resistance of the causal organism in cases of actinomycosis and believed that this must have been the result of 'habituation' and not substitution. He also mentions the very rapid increase in resistance to streptomycin which often occurs in coliform infections of the urinary tract. This too would seem usually to be a clear case of the rapid selection, in the presence of the drug, of a small proportion of highly resistant cells present in the original streptomycin-sensitive population. This was shown to occur during streptomycin treatment of *Haemophilus influenzae* meningitis by Alexander & Leidy (1947), and in general streptomycin seems to be a drug to which many organisms develop drug resistance readily within the tissues of the treated patient (Finland, 1955). To what extent this feature of streptomycin resistance is connected with the one step character of streptomycin resistance *in vitro* described by Demerec (1948) and others is an interesting question that has not yet been answered.

Erythromycin resistance in staphylococci seems to be of a similar nature. Lepper *et al.* (1953–4) and Wise, Voigt, Collin & Cranny (1955) stated that strains of staphylococci steadily increased in resistance to erythromycin both in patients during the course of their treatment and in those who acquired erythromycin-resistant strains from others.

On the other hand substitution of drug-sensitive by drug-resistant strains has frequently been reported. These may be naturally drug-resistant genera or drug-resistant variants of originally sensitive strains. For example, in place of the penicillin-sensitive *Streptococcus pyogenes* which was formerly a common invader of wounds and burns, we now find more commonly genera such as *Proteus* and *Pseudomonas*, most strains of which are naturally resistant to penicillin (Pulaski, 1954; Lowbury, 1955), and often also penicillin-resistant strains of *Staphylococcus aureus* (Editorial, 1953). In the lungs and in the intestinal tract of patients receiving broad spectrum antibiotics 'superinfection' with drug-resistant bacteria and fungi is a quite common and serious

complication (Finland, 1955). In recent years an acute entero-colitis
with a very high mortality has been frequently reported as a sequel to ab-
dominal operations. This condition has often, though not always, been
associated with the use before and after operation of broad spectrum
antibiotics, especially terramycin. It is quite clearly an example of
cross-infection, since the organisms isolated are staphylococci resistant
to the antibiotic used and the patient may die in 1–2 days (Finland, 1955;
Cook *et al.* 1957).

Other examples of substitution are the replacement of sulphon-
amide-sensitive by sulphonamide-resistant *Streptococcus pyogenes*
(found to be of different serological type from the original sensitive
strain) and the replacement of penicillin-sensitive by penicillin-resistant
staphylococci of a different phage type (Barber & Whitehead, 1949).

The distinction between these two types of drug resistance—resistance
from within and from without—has been discussed at some length
because of its obvious epidemiological importance. It is true that the
distinction does not explain how the resistance arose in the first instance.
Presumably where drug-resistant strains have steadily increased in a
community such as a hospital without detection of the actual process in
any individual, there must have been a gradual build-up of resistance
through many 'generations' of patients or carriers. But whatever the
origin of drug-resistant strains may be in the individual, their epidemiological importance lies in their capacity to infect other people and spread
through the community.

From this point of view, a good deal of attention is now being directed
to the 'virulence' or 'pathogenicity' of drug-resistant strains. In many
cases drug-resistant bacteria differ greatly in their metabolism from
sensitive bacteria. One of the most interesting examples of this is the
behaviour of isoniazid-resistant tubercle bacilli. As compared with
isoniazid-sensitive tubercle bacilli, many strains resistant to 10 or
20 μg. isoniazid/ml. show an apparent dependence on haemin (Fisher,
1954; Knox, 1955), a lack of catalase (Middlebrook, 1954; Knox,
Meadow & Worssam, 1956) and greatly reduced virulence for some
experimental animals (Mitchison, 1953).

It has even been suggested that in the treatment of tuberculosis it
might not be a bad thing if virulent isoniazid-sensitive organisms were
replaced by avirulent isoniazid-resistant organisms. It may even be true
that in a naturally drug-sensitive species there is always some selection
pressure operating in favour of the drug-sensitive 'normal' cells and
against the drug-resistant 'mutant' cells, and that it is this controlling
mechanism which keeps the frequency of resistant mutants down to

very low levels. Some interesting results suggesting some such mechanism were reported by Welsch (1949) with artificial mixtures of sensitive and resistant strains. In the presence of the drug selection at once occurs in favour of the resistant cells. If these have once become dominant, however, it may be a long time before drug-sensitive mutants can multiply sufficiently, by a process of reverse mutation or by any other mechanism, to restore the 'normal' equilibrium which existed before the drug was used. Even in cases where the virulence of the drug-resistant organisms is less than that of their normal sensitive parents, this weakness in their power of attack may be more than offset by their immunity from attack by chemotherapy. And in many infections there is not a shred of evidence to suggest that drug resistance is associated with loss of virulence. At the present time many infections due to drug-resistant staphylococci seem just as severe as similar infections in the days before chemotherapy.

USEFUL LINES FOR FUTURE RESEARCH

Advances in chemotherapy of bacterial infections are likely to come about in at least two ways—as a result of a general increase in our knowledge of micro-organisms and their spread through communities, or as a result of concentrated attack on certain special lines which at the moment seem to be particularly promising.

So far as fundamental research is concerned, it is almost impossible to single out any one line which seems more promising than others. The earlier contributors to the Symposium have themselves discussed future exploitation of work in their own fields. All the lines which they have discussed represent active growing points in our knowledge of bacteria and all of them will undoubtedly continue to make essential contributions to the strategy of chemotherapy. I have mentioned earlier the outstanding contributions that have been made in the last few years by bacterial genetics, and it seems clear that there are several ways in which bacterial genetics may make special contributions in the future.

(1) We need to know more about the patterns of mutation to drug resistance that can occur with different drugs and organisms and about the general validity of the difference between streptomycin, isoniazid and perhaps erythromycin on the one hand, and penicillin and other drugs on the other.

(2) We need to know more about the relative growth rates of drug-sensitive and drug-resistant strains. This involves more detailed study of the nutritional requirements of such strains, and more especially a study

of their growth rates in different conditions of culture—both separately and in mixed culture. Saz & Eagle (1953) have described the interesting phenomenon of co-killing activated by penicillin, and I have recently described some curious differences in the apparent rate of mutation to isoniazid resistance of *Mycobacterium tuberculosis* in different media (Knox, 1957). Continued studies on these lines, and especially studies of the interactions between drug-sensitive and drug-resistant organisms, are certain to be valuable.

(3) Further work on the genetic aspect of drug combinations is urgently needed. As has been remarked earlier, apparent 'synergism' of two drugs in combination can sometimes be explained simply as a result of their combined effect in reducing the chances of doubly resistant mutants arising. The general validity of this 'genetic synergism' can only be established by further experiments with different drug combinations.

(4) This may need the development of new techniques since one of the difficulties in studying different concentrations of drugs in different combinations not only for bacteriostatic but also for bactericidal effect is the enormous scale on which experiments must be done to be significant. Diffusion techniques, though they have many drawbacks, offer many advantages for this kind of work. By means of blotting-paper strips, disks, etc. it is possible to distinguish between the direct bacteriostatic effects of drugs separately and in combination and the effect that such combinations may have in delaying the development of resistance (King, Knox & Woodroffe, 1953). The value of such methods is increased by combining them with the replica plating methods of Lederberg & Lederberg (1952) as in the experiments described by Elek and his colleagues (Elek & Hilson, 1954). A particularly promising, though at first sight rather complex, combination of diffusion method, gradient plates, and replica plating has recently been described by Streitfeld (1957).

(5) But perhaps the most important contribution that genetics can make in the future will be in the biochemical field. Biochemical genetics in microbiology has already proved a powerful tool in discovering metabolic pathways of micro-organisms and will have many more applications at both the biochemical and the genetic level. But in many other fields we are profoundly ignorant of the biochemical basis of genetic mechanisms—of transformation, transduction, recombination and mutation, of the relation between genetic make-up and biosynthesis of enzymes, of the roles of DNA and RNA in determining genotype and phenotype, and of the chemical processes by which genes and

enzymes themselves are synthesized. Fundamental advances on these lines are certain to open up new approaches to the control of drug-resistant infections.

At the level of the individual host there are several interesting lines on which the strategy of chemotherapy may be expected to develop in the future.

We may hope to exploit conditions in the host which might make the drug even more effective against micro-organisms than in artificial media. The importance of immune mechanisms has already been mentioned. While it is already clear that the wrong dose of a drug at the wrong time may depress antibody production, the right dose at the right time may even enhance it (Slanetz, 1953; Stevens, 1953). Resistant organisms, which would grow in the test-tube, and in the body would be unaffected by the drug, could then be disposed of by phagocytosis and other immune mechanisms.

Another way of exploiting the contribution which the host can make is by creating conditions in which the micro-organisms would be unable to by-pass the action of a drug. For example, a change in body-temperature may profoundly affect the response of bacteria to drugs. The biosynthesis of some adaptive enzymes, for example tetrathionase, is suppressed at temperatures much above 37° (Pollock, 1945), and this sensitivity to heat has been shown to have biological importance (Knox, 1950). In the case of the adaptively formed penicillinase of *Bacillus cereus* (Pollock, 1950), it was found that the organism was able to grow in the presence of penicillin concentrations 10–100 times greater at 37° than at 42° (Knox & Collard, 1952). In this case increase of temperature makes the drug far more effective by preventing the organism from elaborating an adaptive enzyme necessary for its survival. Artificial increase of temperature, both locally and systemically, has for some years been used clinically in the treatment of a number of infections, and the effectiveness of chemotherapy may well be increased by the potentiating action of raised temperatures. The effect of raised tempera-ture could be fairly direct—as in the example of penicillinase where it prevents the micro-organism from destroying the drug, or it could be more indirect—by preventing micro-organisms from synthesizing enzymes needed for an alternative pathway to the one blocked by the drug. Formation of specific enzymes necessary for multiplication of organisms in the animal body might also be blocked by other chemical or physical changes in the tissues. This kind of approach has been developed by Dubos and his colleagues (Dubos, 1954; 1955), and obviously opens up a field of great interest.

Other lines which would seem to be promising are the investigation of
rates of 'reversion' *in vitro* to drug sensitivity in different mixtures of
drug-resistant and -sensitive strains (Welsch, 1949), and the possible use
in vivo of transforming principles (DNA) from sensitive strains to
accelerate a change from resistance to sensitivity.

At the epidemiological level, there are several interesting lines of
attack. The most important is really part of a general attack on cross-
infection. Any measures which will reduce the amount of cross-infection
occurring in closed communities such as hospitals and schools or even in
the community as a whole will tend to reduce the rate at which drug-
resistant strains spread.

As part of this general plan there are two specific measures worth
special consideration—isolation of patients and the control of the distribution of chemotherapeutic drugs. Isolation is particularly important
when a new antibiotic is just coming into use, and if patients receiving
this are carefully separated from others and are nursed with strict
precautions against cross-infection there is hope that the useful life of
that drug will be greatly prolonged.

Alarm at the serious consequences of drug resistance developing has
led some to recommend compulsory control of the sale and dispensing
of certain antibiotics. In New Zealand the use of erythromycin was for-
bidden except for special indications. There is little doubt that measures
of this kind, coupled with isolation, could greatly reduce the risk of drug-
resistant organisms spreading quickly through the community. But so
far as erythromycin is concerned, an interesting if somewhat alarming
situation has arisen. In this country, as a result of fears that erythromycin would soon become ineffective if it were indiscriminately used,
the drug has in fact been used with restraint. But it looks as though
erythromycin-resistant strains are now beginning to appear as it were
by the back door—through the use of other, sometimes less effective,
drugs which can give rise to cross-resistance with erythromycin (Garrod
& Waterworth, 1956; Garrod, 1957).

CONCLUSION

These are but a few suggestions as to the lines on which future progress
may be made. It is easy to forget how new the subject of chemotherapy
is and how rapidly it is advancing. Progress has been most spectacular
in the bacterial field where the elimination of many of the most severe
bacterial infections has had far-reaching social consequences throughout
the world. There is every reason to think that similar progress will be

made in other branches of microbiology, and no microbiologist of whatever species can afford to ignore advances being made by other species of microbiologists and other genera of scientists. In fact, in a field in which dynamic processes and genetic exchanges are so important, it is to be hoped that strenuous efforts will be made to break down any rigid classification of the workers concerned into genera and species. It is even possible that by free exchange of ideas as in this Symposium we may by a single transformation convert microbiologists into bio-chemists and the other way round, by a double transformation turn geneticists into both microbiologists and biochemists, and by carefully selective recombination produce races of healthy hybrids with interests not only in the biochemical and genetic but also in the medical, veterinary, agricultural and epidemiological field.

Of course it is obvious that no one individual can hope to cover all those fields in any detail, but I should like to end with a plea for a serious attempt to co-ordinate our efforts in the field which is the subject of this Symposium. One way of achieving this, apart from meetings and discussions of this kind, is to create at least one or two centres in the country where it will be possible to combine in one unit or department both fundamental biochemical and genetic work and its applications at the levels of animal experiment, clinical research and epidemiology.

It is even possible that commercial firms which are prepared to spend vast sums of money on screening programmes in the hope of discovering new antibiotics or synthetic drugs might feel it worth while to devote some of their research funds to projects of this kind. Something of this sort is essential for the full development of the strategy of chemotherapy.

REFERENCES

ALBERT, A. (1951). *Selective Toxicity with Special Reference to Chemotherapy.* London: Methuen.

ALEXANDER, H. E. & LEIDY, G. (1947). Mode of action of streptomycin on type b *H. influenzae*. I. Origin of resistant organisms. *J. exp. Med.* **85**, 329.

BARBER, M. (1947a). Coagulase-positive staphylococci resistant to penicillin. *J. Path. Bact.* **59**, 373.

BARBER, M. (1947b). Staphylococcal infection due to penicillin-resistant strains. *Brit. med. J.* ii, 863.

BARBER, M. & ROZWADOWSKA-DOWZENKO, M. (1948). Infection by penicillin-resistant staphylococci. *Lancet*, ii, 641.

BARBER, M. & WHITEHEAD, J. E. M. (1949). Bacteriophage types in penicillin-resistant staphylococcal infection. *Brit. med. J.* ii, 565.

BIGGER, J. W. (1944). Treatment of staphylococcal infections with penicillin by intermittent sterilization. *Lancet*, ii, 497.

COOK, J., ELLIOTT, C., ELLIOT-SMITH, A., FRISBY, B. R. & GARDNER, A. M. N. (1957). Staphylococcal diarrhoea with an account of two outbreaks in the same hospital. *Brit. med. J.* i, 542.

CORNFORTH, J. W., HART, P. D'A., REES, R. J. W. & STOCK, J. A. (1951). Antituberculous effect of certain surface-active polyoxyethylene ethers in mice. *Nature, Lond.* **168**, 150.

DEMEREC, M. (1945). Production of staphylococcus strains resistant to various concentrations of penicillin. *Proc. nat. Acad. Sci., Wash.* **31**, 16.

DEMEREC, M. (1948). Origin of bacterial resistance to antibiotics. *J. Bact.* **56**, 63.

DOWLING, H. F. (1957). Mixtures of antibiotics. *J. Amer. med. Ass.* **164**, 44.

DOWLING, H. F., HIRSH, H. L. & O'NEIL, C. B. (1946). Studies on bacteria developing resistance to penicillin fractions X and G *in vitro* and in patients under treatment for bacterial endocarditis. *J. clin. Invest.* **25**, 665.

DUBOS, R. J. (1939). Studies on a bactericidal agent extracted from a soil bacillus. I. Preparation of the agent. Its activity *in vitro*. *J. exp. Med.* **70**, 1.

DUBOS, R. J. (1954). *Biochemical Determinants of Microbial Diseases.* Harvard University Press.

DUBOS, R. J. (1955). Properties and structures of tubercle bacilli concerned in their pathogenicity. In *Mechanisms of Microbial Pathogenicity. Symp. Soc. gen. Microbiol.* **5**, 103.

EAGLE, H. & SAZ, A. K. (1955). Antibiotics. *Annu. Rev. Microbiol.* **9**, 173.

EDITORIAL (1953). The antibiotic-resistant staphylococci. *Antibiot. Chemother.* **3**, 561.

ELEK, S. D. & HILSON, G. R. F. (1954). Combined agar diffusion and replica plating techniques in the study of antibacterial substances. *J. clin. Path.* **7**, 37.

FILDES, P. (1940). The mechanism of the anti-bacterial action of mercury. *Brit. J. exp. Path.* **21**, 67.

FINLAND, M. (1955). Emergence of antibiotic-resistant bacteria. *New Engl. J. Med.* **253**, 909.

FISHER, M. W. (1954). Hemin as a growth factor for certain isoniazid-resistant strains of *Mycobacterium tuberculosis*. *Amer. Rev. Tuberc.* **69**, 797.

FOX, H. H. & GIBAS, J. T. (1952). Synthetic tuberculostats. IV. Pyridine carboxylic acid hydrazides and benzoic acid hydrazides. *J. org. Chem.* **17**, 1653.

FOX, W., WIENER, A., MITCHISON, D. A., SELKON, J. B. & SUTHERLAND, I. (1957). The prevalence of drug-resistant tubercle bacilli in untreated patients with pulmonary tuberculosis: a national survey, 1955–56. *Tubercle*, **38**, 71.

GARROD, L. P. (1951). The reactions of bacteria to chemotherapeutic agents. *Brit. med. J.* i, 205.

GARROD, L. P. (1953). Combined chemotherapy in bacterial infections. *Brit. med. J.* i, 953.

GARROD, L. P. (1957). The erythromycin group of antibiotics. *Brit. med. J.* ii, 57.

GARROD, L. P. & WATERWORTH, P. M. (1956). Behaviour *in vitro* of some new antistaphylococcal antibiotics. *Brit. med. J.* ii, 61.

GRAY, J. D. A. (1956). Outbreak of streptococcal infection in a maternity unit. *Lancet*, ii, 132.

HARRISON, P. E. (1946). Comparative effect of penicillin and sulfonamide drugs on the immune response of rabbits to pneumococcus infection and the relation of immunity to bacterial chemotherapy. *J. infect. Dis.* **79**, 101.

HART, P. D'A. (1954). The role of the host in the chemotherapy of tuberculosis. *Brit. med. J.* ii, 767.

JAWETZ, E. (1956). Antimicrobial chemotherapy. *Annu. Rev. Microbiol.* **10**, 85.

JOHNSON, J. R. (1955). Tuberculous meningitis: use of corticotrophin as an adjunct to chemotherapy. *Amer. Rev. Tuberc.* **72**, 825.

JOHNSON, J. R. & DAVEY, W. N. (1954). Cortisone, corticotropin, and antimicrobial therapy in tuberculosis in animals and man. *Amer. Rev. Tuberc.* **70**, 623.

JOINER, C. L., MACLEAN, K. S., MARSH, K., CARROLL, J. D. & KNOX, R. (1956). Prolonged chemotherapy in chronic pulmonary tuberculosis with combinations of isoniazid, para-aminosalicylic acid and streptomycin. *Lancet,* ii, 165.

JOINER, C. L., MACLEAN, K. S., PRITCHARD, E. K., ANDERSON, K., COLLARD, P., KING, M. B. & KNOX, R. (1952). Isoniazid in pulmonary tuberculosis. Its use with and without streptomycin. *Lancet,* ii, 843.

JOSEPH, M. C. (1957). Single dose therapy in acute respiratory infection in children. Thesis for M.D. University of Cambridge.

KEEFER, C. S. & WEINSTEIN, L. (1954). Urinary and intestinal tract infections. In *Principles and Practice of Antibiotic Therapy,* p. 453. New York: Medical Encyclopedia Inc.

KING, M. B., KNOX, R. & WOODROFFE, R. C. (1953). Investigation of antituberculous substances. An agar diffusion method using *Mycobacterium smegmatis. Lancet,* i, 573.

KNOX, R. (1950). Tetrathionase: the differential effect of temperature on growth and adaptation. *J. gen. Microbiol.* **4**, 388.

KNOX, R. (1955). Haemin and isoniazid resistance of *Mycobacterium tuberculosis. J. gen. Microbiol.* **12**, 191.

KNOX, R. (1957). Distribution of drug resistant individuals in cultures of *Mycobacterium tuberculosis.* In *Drug Resistance in Micro-organisms. Mechanisms of Development. Ciba Foundation Symp.* London: Churchill.

KNOX, R. & COLLARD, P. (1952). The effect of temperature on the sensitivity of *Bacillus cereus* to penicillin. *J. gen. Microbiol.* **6**, 369.

KNOX, R., MEADOW, P. M. & WORSSAM, A. R. H. (1956). The relationship between the catalase activity, hydrogen peroxide sensitivity and isoniazid resistance of mycobacteria. *Amer. Rev. Tuberc.* **73**, 726.

LEDERBERG, J. & LEDERBERG, E. M. (1952). Replica plating and indirect selection of bacterial mutants. *J. Bact.* **63**, 399.

LEPPER, M. H., MOULTON, B., DOWLING, H. F., JACKSON, G. G. & KOFMAN, S. (1953–54). Epidemiology of erythromycin-resistant staphylococci in a hospital population—effect on therapeutic activity of erythromycin. *Antibiotics Annual,* p. 308.

LOWBURY, E. J. L. (1955). Cross infection of wounds with antibiotic-resistant organisms. *Brit. med. J.* i, 985.

LURIA, S. E. (1946). A test for penicillin sensitivity and resistance in staphylococcus. *Proc. Soc. exp. Biol., N.Y.* **61**, 46.

LURIA, S. E. & DELBRUCK, M. (1943). Mutations of bacteria from virus sensitivity to virus resistance. *Genetics,* **28**, 491.

MCILWAIN, H. (1942). Bacterial inhibition by metabolite analogues. 3. Pantoyltaurine. The antibacterial index of inhibitors. *Brit. J. exp. Path.* **23**, 95.

MEDICAL RESEARCH COUNCIL (1952). The treatment of pulmonary tuberculosis with isoniazid. *Brit. med. J.* ii, 735.

MEDICAL RESEARCH COUNCIL (1955). Various combinations of isoniazid with streptomycin or with P.A.S. in the treatment of pulmonary tuberculosis. *Brit. med. J.* i, 435.

MIDDLEBROOK, G. (1954). Isoniazid resistance and catalase activity of tubercle bacilli. *Amer. Rev. Tuberc.* **69**, 471.

MITCHISON, D. A. (1953). The ecology of tubercle bacilli resistant to streptomycin and isoniazid. In *Adaptation in Micro-organisms. Symp. Soc. gen. Microbiol.* **3**, 253.

MITCHISON, D. A. (1954). Problems of drug resistance. *Brit. med. Bull.* **10**, 115.

MITCHISON, D. A. & SELKON, J. B. (1957). Bacteriological aspects of a survey of the incidence of drug-resistant tubercle bacilli among untreated patients. *Tubercle*, **38**, 85.

MUNOZ, J. & GEISTER, R. (1950). Inhibition of phagocytosis by aureomycin. *Proc. Soc. exp. Biol., N.Y.* **75**, 367.

POLLOCK, M. R. (1945). The influence of temperature on the adaptation of 'tetrathionase' in washed suspensions of *Bact. paratyphosum B. Brit. J. exp. Path.* **26**, 410.

POLLOCK, M. R. (1950). Penicillinase adaptation in *B. cereus*: adaptive enzyme formation in the absence of free substrate. *Brit. J. exp. Path.* **31**, 739.

PULASKI, E. J. (1954). Surgical infections. In *Principles and Practice of Antibiotic Therapy*, p. 421. New York: Medical Encyclopedia Inc.

ROUNTREE, P. M. (1955). *Streptococcus pyogenes* infections in a hospital. *Lancet*, ii, 172.

SAZ, A. K. & EAGLE, H. (1953). The co-killing of penicillin sensitive and penicillin resistant bacteria at low concentrations of the antibiotic. *J. Bact.* **66**, 347.

SLANETZ, C. A. (1953). The influence of antibiotics on antibody production. *Antibiot. Chemother.* **3**, 629.

STEENKEN, W. & WOLINSKY, E. (1949). Resistance of tubercle bacilli to streptomycin. In *Streptomycin: Nature and Practical Applications*, p. 618. Edited by S. A. Waksman. Baltimore: The Williams & Wilkins Co.

STEVENS, K. M. (1953). The effect of antibiotics upon the immune response. *J. Immunol.* **71**, 119.

STREITFELD, M. M. (1957). The replica strip gradient plate technique for determination of synergism or antagonism of antibiotics paired in various concentration ratios: a bacteriostatic and bactericidal assay. *Antibiotics Annual*, p. 906. Medical Encyclopedia Inc.

WEBSTER, N. (1928). *New International Dictionary of the English Language.* London: G. Bell & Sons Ltd.

WELSCH, M. (1949). Quelques aspects de la résistance du staphylocoque à la streptomycine. *C.R. Soc. Biol., Paris*, **143**, 1282.

WISE, R. I., VOIGT, A. E., COLLIN, M. V. & CRANNY, C. L. (1955). Origin of erythromycin-resistant strains of *Micrococcus pyogenes* in infections. *Arch. intern. Med.* **95**, 419.

WOODS, D. D. (1940). The relation of *p*-aminobenzoic acid to the mechanism of the action of sulphanilamide. *Brit. J. exp. Path.* **21**, 74.

WOODS, D. D. (1953). The integration of research on the nutrition and metabolism of micro-organisms. *J. gen. Microbiol.* **9**, 151.

WOOLLEY, D. W. (1952). *A Study of Antimetabolites.* New York: John Wiley & Sons Inc.

WORK, T. S. & WORK, E. (1948). *The Basis of Chemotherapy.* Edinburgh and London: Oliver & Boyd Ltd.

THE CHEMOTHERAPY OF
FUNGAL DISEASES

R. J. W. BYRDE

Long Ashton Research Station, University of Bristol

AND

G. C. AINSWORTH

Commonwealth Mycological Institute, Kew, Surrey

The mechanisms of fungicidal action *in vitro* are in general similar for both saprophytic and parasitic fungi. A consideration of pathogenic fungi *in vivo* introduces the host as a third term in the fungicide-fungus equation and it is at once apparent that this has resulted in a marked dichotomy in the approach to the control of fungal diseases of plants on the one hand, and of mycoses of man and animals on the other. For example, inspection of a recent annual index to the *Review of Applied Mycology* shows, in round numbers, 380 different chemicals or fungicidal preparations to have been recorded during 1955 as being used against plant pathogenic fungi. A similar inspection of the general index to the *Review of Medical and Veterinary Mycology* (1943–53) shows 270 chemicals or preparations to have been used in the therapy of mycoses of man and animals. Only thirty items are common to the two lists.

This pattern is possibly in part due to the lack of contacts between those interested in the chemotherapy of fungal diseases of man and animals (who tend to be drawn from specialists on the chemotherapy of bacterial and virus diseases) and plant pathologists, and to the fact that, generally speaking, fungi pathogenic for plants are not pathogenic for animals. In addition there are fundamental differences between the plant and the animal hosts and in the host-parasite relations. In plants, infection by fungi is frequently superficial when it may often be controlled by the external application of fungicides. In animals and man the infection is more frequently deep-seated and an additional complication is the development of an immunological response in the host. Further, a number of fungicides which are not unduly phytotoxic are very poisonous for man and animals.

These differences necessitate the separate consideration of fungi pathogenic for plants and fungi pathogenic for man and higher animals, after an introductory section on mechanisms of fungicidal action in general.

One further point perhaps merits attention. Many of the most useful fungicidal preparations have been developed empirically. The chance discovery of Bordeaux Mixture some seventy-five years ago is a familiar story (see Large, 1940) and Whitfield's Ointment, which is still one of the most reliable and popular of the many panaceas against ringworm in man, also owed its origin to chance (Whitfield, 1912). During recent years attempts have been made in both plant pathology and medicine to develop new fungicides in the light of studies on fungal metabolism and host-parasite relations. This more rational approach, which holds great promise for the future, must be taken as the justification of certain digressions into aspects of fungal physiology and host-parasite inter-action which, though not strictly chemotherapy, may eventually provide the clues which will lead to major advances in that field.

MECHANISM OF FUNGICIDAL ACTION

To be active as a 'fungicide' (in the broad sense which includes fungi-static agents; see McCallan & Wellman, 1942), a compound must possess two properties: first, the ability to penetrate to, and accumulate at, the site of action within or at the surface of the fungal cell and secondly, the power to interfere with at least one vital process.

Accumulation at the site of action

Miller & McCallan (1956) have pointed out that, when evaluated on a weight/weight basis, fungicides in current use display comparatively low biological activity. Thus the approximate ED_{50} value for penicillin against staphylococci is of the order of 2 μg./g. whilst the values they obtained for a selection of fungicides against fungus spores ranged from 85 to 10,000 μg./g. The ability of most fungicides to inhibit the growth of fungi seems rather to arise from their rapid uptake by the organism from dilute aqueous solutions and, in this respect, their action resembles that of DDT and certain other insecticides (Metcalf, 1955). For example, Miller, McCallan & Weed (1953b) using radioactive tracers to study fungicide uptake, showed that spores of *Neurospora sitophila* accumu-lated a 10,000-fold concentration of 2-heptadecyl-2-imidazoline from an aqueous solution of 2 p.p.m., and similar, if slightly less spectacular, data on uptake were recorded with other fungi and other compounds. The action of sulphur is somewhat anomalous (see p. 313).

The problems of differentiation between inherent toxicity and accumu-lation have been clarified by the now classical paper of Ferguson (1939), who sought to distinguish, on a thermodynamic basis, between substances acting by a chemical mechanism and those which exert their physiological effects through a physical mechanism. The effect of the latter is thought to arise solely from their accumulation at the site of toxic action (the 'biophase') as a result of a favourable phase distribution, either between two homogeneous phases, or between a single homogeneous phase and a surface, such as a cell membrane. Chemical toxicity, on the other hand, involves a reaction in the biophase which prevents the establishment of any such equilibrium.

Surprisingly few fungicides have been examined in the light of this hypothesis. McCallan (1957), on the basis of the uptake studies already mentioned, suggested that many fungicides may well act by physical toxicity according to the Ferguson Principle, and Ross & Ludwig (1957) were able to demonstrate its validity for a homologous series of N-n-alkylethylenethioureas: in this series, fungicidal activity based on applied concentration rose to a peak as the series was ascended, and subsequently declined as aqueous solubility became a limiting factor. Rich & Horsfall (1952), however, concluded that physical toxicity was not the only factor involved in the activity of certain 4-nitroso-pyrazoles.

Whilst Ferguson's Principle is strictly applicable only when equilibrium within the system is attained, it is clear that distribution phenomena remain of great importance in the accumulation of toxicants entering into a reaction in the biophase. It follows that, subject to a limiting effect of aqueous solubility, the fungicidal activity of a given structure may be increased by the addition of groups favouring the distribution of the material out of the external aqueous phase. The effect of methylene groups in homologous series has already been mentioned; another example of a group which probably increases activity in this way is afforded by the —$SCCl_3$ group of N-trichloromethylmercapto-4-cyclohexene-2:3-dicarboximide ('captan') (Horsfall, 1956, p. 73), whilst the high activity of 2:2′-(2:2:2-trichloro-ethylidene)*bis*(4-chlorophenol) found by Corey & Shirk (1955) in studies on bisphenols may be attributed to a similar effect of the hydrophobic —$CHCCl_3$ grouping. The role of ionization in the activity of electrolytes has been ably demonstrated by Simon & Blackman (1949) and other relevant examples of this phenomenon were cited by Albert (1951, Table 7): undissociated molecules, by virtue of their physical properties, are in general more active than the corresponding ions. It may be noted that chelation also exerts a marked influence on distribution properties, and this is probably a factor not only in the high bactericidal activity of the 1:2 copper-oxine complex (Albert, Gibson & Rubbo, 1953) but also in its fungicidal activity (Block, 1955). (For a full discussion of the role of chelation in toxicity, see Albert, 1958.)

Interference with vital processes

Having entered the biophase, a fungicide must interrupt at least one vital process. Some of the ways in which this is achieved are:

(i) *Inhibition of enzyme systems.* There is now ample evidence that the application of many fungicides results in a derangement of fungal enzyme systems, and that this is one of the mechanisms involved in fungicidal action; nevertheless, the full significance of such effects *in vivo* is still obscure. A detailed survey of the inhibition of fungal enzymes by fungicides is outside the scope of this review, but a few examples will serve to illustrate the complexity of the subject and the difficulties in interpretation of the data obtained.

Owens (1953 a) investigated the effect of a range of twenty fungicides on four enzyme systems—pancreatic and malt amylases, catalase and polyphenol oxidase. At fungicide concentrations of 10^{-3} M about half the possible enzyme-fungicide combinations showed at least 50 % reduction in enzyme activity. This finding indicates that fungicidal effects are probably relatively non-specific, a conclusion also reached by McCallan (1957) in the light of the uptake studies already cited. Owens (1953 b) also showed that a wide range of quinones, tested at low concentrations, was inhibitory to pancreatic and malt amylases: whilst the data obtained for enzyme inhibition were consistent with the known chemical effects of substituents and ring structure, they were not well correlated with toxicity data from spore germination of two test fungi. Difficulties in assessing the *in vivo* significance of the enzyme inhibition data also arose in Owens' earlier paper.

It appears, therefore, that fungicides in current use tend to inactivate a number of enzymes, rather than an individual system, probably due to reaction with common prosthetic groups. A good example is afforded by the familiar effect of quinones and heavy metals on thiol and amino groups, which is thought to be the basis of their fungicidal activity. There is also evidence that active halogen atoms are capable of undergoing displacement reactions with these prosthetic groups; the significance of such reactions was demonstrated by Burchfield & Storrs (1956, 1957) in relation to the fungicidal activity of 2:4-dichloro-6-(o-chloroanilino)-s-triazine and related compounds towards conidia of *Neurospora sitophila*. It was also concluded, however, that a more critical factor in determining fungicidal activity, on the basis of applied concentration, was the amount of the compounds accumulated by the spores. Gero & Reese (1956) pointed out that many drugs displaying high activity contain functional groups separated by a distance of 5.5 Å, which happens to be the distance between two turns of the α-protein helix, and suggested that hydrogen bonding on the enzyme protein might be an important factor.

The mechanism of the fungicidal action of elemental sulphur is not clear. Sulphur is not accumulated by spores, but is taken up in large amounts and converted to hydrogen sulphide, which was long thought to be the toxic agent. Recent studies suggest that this is not so and the fungicidal action of sulphur is now attributed to an interference in normal hydrogenation and dehydrogenation processes (Miller, McCallan & Weed, 1953a).

Another approach to the study of fungicide-enzyme interactions was made by Byrde, Martin & Nicholas (1956), who demonstrated a deranged enzyme pattern in mycelium of *Sclerotinia laxa* grown in the presence of four fungicides at sublethal concentrations; whilst such a method avoids the need to interpret *in vitro* results, it is difficult to distinguish between primary effects induced by the fungicide, and resulting secondary changes in enzyme pattern (cf. Fry, 1955, p. 145), and also to differentiate the inhibition of enzyme formation from the inhibition of enzyme activity.

Partly as a consequence of the relatively non-specific nature of most fungicides in current use, it is impossible to present a comprehensive yet brief summary of the chemical groupings associated with toxicity. Those which have received recent study include the dithiocarbamates (Van der Kerk, 1956), quinones (McNew & Burchfield, 1951), heterocyclic nitrogen compounds (Horsfall & Rich, 1951), *bis*-phenols (Corey & Shirk, 1955), substituted *s*-triazines (Schuldt & Wolf, 1956) and substituted pyrazoles (McNew & Sundholm, 1949).

One fungicide in current use—2-heptadecyl-2-imidazoline—may owe its activity to competitive enzyme inhibition, in interfering with histidine or purine synthesis (West & Wolf, 1955). Other examples of fungal antimetabolites not exploited as fungicides have been cited by Horsfall (1956, p. 111); this approach appears to be one of the most promising for future development (see p. 319).

(ii) *Cytological disorganization.* Some fungicides appear to act by disorganizing the structure or function of cellular components. There is evidence, for example, that the permeability of the cell membrane is markedly altered by a number of fungicides. Miller & McCallan (1957), using ^{31}P in tracer experiments with spores of *Aspergillus niger*, showed that silver, and to some extent copper, induced a large release of cell contents, whilst zinc, cadmium and mercuric ions completely inhibited germination without a comparable effect on permeability. Burchfield & Storrs (1957) noted that disorganization of the cell membrane of spores of *Neurospora sitophila* was one of the primary effects of *s*-triazine fungicides at sublethal concentrations, and considered that permeability changes probably arose through reaction of these compounds with thiol and amino groups on the membrane proteins. However, doses which caused release of intracellular phosphorus did not necessarily have significant effects on either spore germination or respiration, and it was concluded that continuous maintenance of selective permeability may not be as critical to survival as had been supposed.

An effect of a different nature on the cell wall itself has been described by Brian (1949), who studied the effect on a wide range of fungi of the antibiotic griseofulvin, which is produced by three species of *Penicillium*. This compound induces morphogenic changes which include stunting, branching, distortion, and a characteristic spiral twisting of the hyphae. Although the mechanism of these effects remains obscure it is thought to involve the physical properties, particularly the plasticity, of the cell wall; it is significant that all fungi sensitive to griseofulvin have chitinous cell walls, whilst insensitive fungi (Oomycetes) have cellulose or other non-chitinous cell walls. Somewhat similar morphogenic effects are also induced by a range of compounds (see also Horsfall, 1956, pp. 98–101), but griseofulvin appears exceptional in its ability to act at applied concentrations of the order of 0·1 μg./ml. and to induce the spiral curling.

Effects of fungicides on fungal nuclei have been well summarized by Horsfall (1956, pp. 91–6), who suggested that many compounds acting as mitotic poisons, such as ketones, phenols or amino compounds, owe their activity to their ability to react with thiol, keto or amino groups on chromosome protein. Others may act by a physical mechanism.

Antimitotic action is clearly one possible mechanism of the inhibition of sporulation of fungi. Horsfall (1956, pp. 102–4) reported that the sporulation of *Sclerotinia* (*Monilinia*) *fructicola* was markedly depressed by aromatic hydrocarbons and also by chelating agents. An example of the former group which has found practical application by virtue of antisporulant properties (against *Botrytis cinerea*) is afforded by the chlorinated nitrobenzenes (Reavill, 1954).

Detoxication of fungicides

An outline of the fungus-fungicide relation involves not only a consideration of the effects of fungicides on fungi but also the converse–fungal metabolism of foreign molecules. The term 'detoxication' is used here in its broadest sense, to cover all metabolism of foreign molecules whether or not associated with a decrease in toxicity (Williams, 1947). The importance of detoxication in biological systems is becoming increasingly apparent: for example, the selective herbicidal action of certain substituted γ-phenoxy-n-butyric acids arises from their enzymic β-oxidation by susceptible species to the corresponding phenoxyacetic acids, which are highly active (Wain, 1955), whilst there is evidence that *ortho*-hydroxylation is a factor in the carcinogenic properties of 2-naphthylamine (Boyland & Watson, 1956).

The metabolism of foreign molecules by fungi, however, has received comparatively little attention. Rich & Horsfall (1954) demonstrated the significance of polyphenol oxidases in the fungicidal activity of phenols and quinones towards two fungi with different enzymic constitution. Byrde, Harris & Woodcock (1956) studied the metabolism of ω-(2-naphthyloxy)-n-alkylcarboxylic acids by *Aspergillus niger* and showed that these acids underwent both β-oxidation and nuclear hydroxylation. The latter process, in the two specific acids studied, was accompanied by a decrease in fungicidal activity, probably due to the less favourable phase distribution properties of the hydroxy acids. This finding by no means precludes the possibility of breakdown by the fungus sometimes resulting in a metabolite of greater toxicity, although it suggests that nuclear hydroxylation may not be the most suitable mechanism to be exploited.

There is now strong evidence of the ability of fungi to become adapted to fungicides, and it is possible that, as with insects, detoxication mechanisms may be involved; on the other hand such processes are probably of little importance in the acquirement of drug resistance by bacteria (Abraham, 1953).

PLANT PATHOGENIC FUNGI

The plant-parasite-fungicide relation: the theoretical basis of selective toxicity

The introduction of a third factor—in this case the host plant—into the fungus-fungicide relation results in a series of complex interactions. The problem of chemotherapy of plant disease is clearly to develop compounds with the ability to inhibit the fungal parasite without causing injury to the host. The fact that both host and parasite are plants makes selectivity the more difficult to achieve (Marsh, 1954). A further complication arises from the desirability of using fungicides of low mammalian toxicity as a safeguard to grower and consumer.

The general principles to be considered in achieving selective toxicity formed the subject of a monograph by Albert (1951). Some of the differences between higher plants and their fungal pathogens which have been, or might be, exploited are:

(i) *Selective accumulation.* A consideration of the evidence available suggests that selectivity in current practice in plant protection is often achieved as a result of selective accumulation, i.e. in many cases the absence of phytotoxicity is due simply to the failure of a toxic amount of the fungicide to accumulate in the plant cells. This effect may result from widely differing causes—for example, anatomical differences may be such that fungus spores are penetrated by fungicides which are kept from contact with the plant cells by the host's protective layers. A somewhat similar effect was postulated by Martin (1955) in a consideration of the possible use of mutagenic substances against micro-organisms. It was pointed out that the large ratio of somatic tissue to reproductive organs in higher plants and animals would result in a much higher dilution than would be possible in micro-organisms: these compounds might thus exert a selective effect.

Also, there are clear chemical differences between the lipids of fungi and those of plants, and this is bound to affect phase distribution phenomena. These differences probably account for our ability to utilize modifications in chemical structure of fungicides to attain selective action: an excellent example is afforded by the homologous series of 2-alkyl-2-imidazolines examined by Wellman & McCallan (1946). These workers showed that the fungistatic activity of the series, on the basis of applied concentration, reached a maximum at an alkyl chain length of 17 carbon atoms. Phytotoxicity, on the other hand, was greatest at a chain length of about 13 carbon atoms; hence, by utilizing the 17-carbon homologue, the fungitoxicity/phytotoxicity ratio was at a maximum. In view of the fact that the activity of these compounds arises, at least in part, through their rapid accumulation by the cell (Miller, McCallan & Weed, 1953*b*), it seems reasonable to conclude that the selectivity of the 17-carbon homologue is a reflexion of different rates of absorption by plant and fungus.

(ii) *Selective detoxication.* The possible exploitation of selective detoxication for the inhibition of plant pathogenic fungi appears to have been neglected. An example of selective herbicidal activity on this basis has already been cited: the same principle was utilized by Hebborn & Danielli (1956), who demonstrated the selective antitumour effect of enzyme-activated nitrogen mustards. Any systematic exploitation of comparative detoxication must, however, await a fuller knowledge of the mechanisms involved in fungi and higher plants.

(iii) *Selective interference with metabolism.* The relatively non-specific effect of most fungicides in current use has already been discussed. It follows that such compounds are unlikely to display high selectivity in their action on fungal and plant enzyme systems: quinones, for instance, are likely to inactivate thiol groups in both by the same mechanism. The usefulness of such compounds as crop protectants probably arises rather from differences in accumulation, and often such differences are barely sufficient to obviate the risk of phytotoxicity: 2:3-dichloro-1:4-naphthaquinone is a good example of a quinone of high fungicidal activity, the use of which has been limited by crop damage and its tendency to cause dermatitis of spray operators (McNew & Burchfield, 1951).

A more promising approach is the use of competitive inhibitors against a fungal enzyme system not present in the host and two such systems appear to merit further investigation along these lines.

Broadly speaking, similarity rather than difference is a feature of the enzymic constitution of fungi and higher plants. On the other hand, physiological differences exist, and one of the most obvious concerns the parasitic habit of the fungus. It is fortunate that in the Fifth Symposium of this Society three reviews should have dealt so adequately with current knowledge of the parasitism of plants.

As stated by Wood (1955) there is now a substantial body of evidence that the secretion of pectic enzymes plays an important part in the invasion and breakdown of plant tissue by facultative pathogens; on the other hand, it does not follow that because a fungus secretes pectolytic enzymes it is necessarily pathogenic to plants. There is good reason to think that the fate of a would-be parasite is decided at a very early stage in the process of infection (Kern, 1956). Moreover, Lapwood (1957), in studies on the parasitic vigour of four bacteria towards potato tubers, found that the only organism showing marked pathogenicity had the ability to secrete pectolytic enzymes at a much earlier stage than three organisms of low pathogenicity; subsequently, there was little difference in the pectolytic activity of all four bacteria.

It should therefore be of interest to examine the effect of inhibitors of pectic enzymes on the pathogenicity of fungi causing plant disease. In general, pectic enzymes are particularly resistant to the action of the usual enzyme poisons, but there is evidence that inhibitory compounds occur naturally in plants (Weurman, 1953; Cole, 1956), and that they may account for varietal differences in susceptibility to disease (Byrde, 1957). In the latter instance, however, the inhibitors, which were formed on wounded tissue, were probably of the nature of phloba-tannins, and acted by virtue of protein precipitation, i.e. by a non-selective mechanism.

An approach likely to be of more value to chemotherapy is that of Smith (1955), who reported preliminary studies on γ-pectin glycosidase and pectin methylesterase with a view to the development of specific inhibitors of pectic enzymes secreted by bacterial plant pathogens. Whilst our present inadequate knowledge of the chemistry of the pectic substances is a handicap, it is at least encouraging that Conchie & Levvy (1957) have demonstrated the competitive inhibition of β-glycosidases by aldono-lactones of corresponding configuration. Moreover, competitive inhibitors of pectic enzymes would be likely to be of low mammalian toxicity.

The second possible line of approach turns on the peculiar role which the nitrogen metabolism of the host often plays in determining the plant's susceptibility to fungal attack: both quantitative and qualitative effects of nitrogen status have been cited (e.g. Gäumann, 1950, p. 387; Last, 1953; Grümmer, 1955). It is possible that such an association may stem partly from the critical effect of nitrogen level on the secretion of pectic enzymes, which has been amply demonstrated in vitro (e.g. Cole, 1956), and which may be regarded as a specific example of the general function of amino acids as enzyme precursors (cf. Spiegelman & Halvorson, 1953). It is significant, for example, that Vasudeva (1930) showed that a fungus not normally parasitic on apple was able to invade this tissue when a nitrogen source was added to the inoculum. Thus, an interference with the nitrogen metabolism of the fungus might well disturb the delicately balanced host-parasite relation by interfering with the formation (as distinct from the activity) of pectolytic enzymes by the pathogen.

There is clearly a need for a rational biochemical approach to the comparative nitrogen metabolism of host and parasite for a wide range of plant diseases. The development of chromatography, radio-active tracer and biochemical mutant techniques in the last decade has greatly facilitated such studies (e.g. Fry, 1955). Keitt and his associates have already utilized biochemical mutants to assess the significance of various metabolites in the host-parasite relationship of apple scab, caused by

Venturia inaequalis. In experiments on the growth responses of such mutants, it was found that deficiencies of certain vitamins, nitrogen bases and amino acids were absolute; such mutants with complete deficiencies must obviously depend on the host or another source of required substances (Lamey, Boone & Keitt, 1956). Earlier pathogenicity tests of a preliminary nature had shown that a large number of mutants, particularly those deficient for nitrogen bases and amino acids, including arginine, were unable to infect the hosts, indicating that the ability of *V. inaequalis* to synthesize these compounds may be of critical importance in its pathogenicity (Keitt & Boone, 1954). A similar approach was followed by Garber & Hackett (1954) in their studies of the parasitism of potato by *Erwinia aroideae*.

The pathways of nitrogen metabolism of host and parasite will diverge at some point, and it is the subsequent stages in the metabolism of the fungus on which attention should primarily be focused. Antimetabolites of compounds present in both host and parasite are unlikely to be useful chemotherapeutic agents.

Current developments in antimetabolites of amino acids should lend a stimulus to such research: Horowitz & Srb (1948), for example, demonstrated the toxicity of canavanine, an arginine antimetabolite, to the fungus *Neurospora crassa*; Walker (1955) showed that homoarginine, another antimetabolite of arginine, was highly effective in inhibiting the growth of the yeast *Candida utilis* in the absence of arginine, whilst Halvorson & Spiegelman (1952) demonstrated the effects of amino acid analogues on the induction of enzyme synthesis in yeasts. In the light of these reports, it may be significant that Kuc, Williams & Shay (1957) found that D-phenylalanine and also its DL-isomer, but not the naturally occurring L-isomer, when injected into apples, inhibited the growth of *Venturia inaequalis* but were ineffective *in vitro*. There seems sufficient evidence, therefore, to justify the view that studies of comparative nitrogen metabolism of host and parasite, with a view to competitive inhibition of processes restricted to the fungus, offer great promise as topics for long-term investigation.

(iv) *Inactivation of fungal toxins.* The role of fungal toxins in plant parasitism was comprehensively reviewed by Brian (1955). There have been several attempts to mitigate the effects of plant diseases with an antidote for these toxins, and a measure of success has been claimed for the use of 8-hydroxyquinoline salts and diaminoazobenzenes. Clearly, however, a rational use of such compounds must await a fuller knowledge of the nature and role of toxins (Horsfall, 1956, p. 223).

The application of fungicides to plants: selective toxicity in practice

Fungicides may be divided into three categories on the basis of their application to plants: *Residual* ('*protectant*') *fungicides*, which are applied to the healthy plant surface with a view to protecting it from infection; *Contact* ('*eradicant*') *fungicides*, which are applied externally to the host, with a view to killing the parasite on or within the host tissues; and *Systemic fungicides*, which are applied to the plant with a view to their being absorbed by the plant and acting within it. These three categories will now be considered in more detail.

(i) *Residual* ('*protectant*') *fungicides* depend for their effect on inhibition of the germination of spores alighting on the plant surface. The field performance of a compound used in this way will thus depend not only on its inherent fungicidal activity, but also on the amount and distribution of its residue at the time when the fungus spore attempts to germinate. This may be days, or even weeks, after application, and in the meantime the residue is exposed to the effects of rain, sun, plant growth, etc. Consequently, such factors as water solubility and photostability are of great practical importance. Tetrachlorobenzoquinone affords an example of a compound of high fungicidal activity, which finds extensive use as a seed dressing, but fails as a residual fungicide on foliage through its instability in sunlight (McNew & Burchfield, 1951). For a more detailed consideration of the problems involved see Martin (1940) and Horsfall (1956).

The epidermal cells of the plant are frequently protected by a waxy layer, and so often do not come into direct contact with the applied chemical. Fungal spores alighting on such a surface are, however, exposed to the fungicide, which is able to prevent their germination, and thus infection of the host.

It has therefore been possible to utilize compounds of relatively low specificity as residual fungicides. Copper, for example, has been used since the nineteenth century (Large, 1940), and the 'pest-averting' value of sulphur was mentioned by Homer (Horsfall, 1956, p. 2). These simple and inexpensive fungicides are still the most important in crop protection. The present trend, however, is towards the use of organic compounds, which provide great scope for variation of chemical structure, and which tend to be more selective in their effects. Whilst toxicity needs to be selective as between plant and fungus, too much selectivity between fungal genera is undesirable. For example, the substitution of captan for lime sulphur for the control of apple scab (caused by *Venturia inaequalis*) has often been followed by a substantial increase in the incidence of apple mildew (caused by *Podosphaera leucotricha*), which was previously kept in check by lime sulphur (e.g. Bush, 1956). A useful list of crop protection chemicals, including fungicides, has been compiled by Martin (1953).

(ii) *Contact* ('*eradicant*') *fungicides* must exert a fungicidal, as distinct from fungistatic, effect; they are usually compounds of relatively low selectivity. The danger of injury to the host is generally obviated by application whilst the latter is dormant; an excellent example of the successful use of a contact fungicide is the practice of seed dressing with organo-mercurial compounds. The small amount of host material to be treated results in great economy and efficiency in the use of the fungicide, whilst selectivity is ensured by the relative impermeability of the seed coat, by comparison with the spore membrane. The spraying of blighted potato haulm with sulphuric acid to prevent infection of the tubers by *Phytophthora infestans* may also be regarded as the application of a particularly non-specific contact fungicide. Many attempts to utilize contact fungicides have not met general success, for the reasons cited by Horsfall (1956).

(iii) *Systemic fungicides* are still used only experimentally; they act within the living plant following intake through roots or foliage. This more intimate contact between plant and fungicide results in a greater need for selective toxicity, and lessens the possibility of exploiting selective accumulation.

The need for systemic fungicides to be distributed uniformly throughout the plant has stimulated studies on their absorption and translocation. An apparent correlation between the rate of translocation of a given compound within the plant and its R_F value in certain paper chromatography systems led Crowdy & Rudd Jones (1956) to postulate that partition might be a factor in the transverse movement across the cortical cells of the root. Earlier studies on the translocation of antibiotics and sulphonamides in various plants had shown clearly that it is impossible to generalize from the behaviour of a single substance in a single species of plant (e.g. Crowdy, 1957).

Several compounds appear to act as systemic fungicides by direct inhibition of fungal growth in the host tissues. Griseofulvin, for example, has been reisolated from treated plants in amounts sufficient to provide inhibition of fungal growth *in vitro* (Crowdy, 1957). On the other hand, there is ample evidence that other compounds act, not directly, but rather by altering host resistance to disease by modifying the host-parasite relation in some way. Thus streptomycin, virtually inactive *in vitro* against *Phytophthora infestans* has been found to check its spread on tomato plants (Müller, Mackay & Friend, 1954); an interesting example of an opposite effect is the apparent increase in susceptibility to *Didymella lycopersici* of tomato plants treated with 2:4:6-trichlorophenoxyacetic acid (Croxall, Norman & Gwynne, 1957).

Whilst a wide range of compounds has been tested as systemic fungicides, two main groups have received particular attention—antibiotics, both from micro-organisms and from higher plants and, secondly, compounds related to plant growth substances.

The possibility of utilizing antibiotics of microbial origin as systemic fungicides was demonstrated by Brian, Wright, Stubbs & Way (1951), who controlled *Botrytis cinerea* on lettuce leaves and *Alternaria solani* on tomato foliage by griseofulvin applied to the soil. Since then much energy has been devoted to the large-scale screening of organisms for the production of antifungal antibiotics. Nevertheless, as Harington (1955) pointed out, there is ample scope for basic biological investigations on antibiotics, particularly with reference to mode of action: such studies may also be valuable in directing synthetic chemical work. In the field of antifungal substances a comprehensive study along these lines is illustrated by the work of Grove (1953) on the structure and fungistatic activity of gladiolic acid.

The biological control of plant diseases by the use of antagonistic organisms was reviewed by Wood & Tveit (1955), and interesting progress continues along these lines. For example, Wright (1956) obtained chromatographic evidence for the presence of three antibiotics in coats of seeds inoculated with fungi known to produce antibiotics *in vitro*. In addition, she demonstrated for the first time the production of a known antibiotic in an unsterilized soil by a member of the natural microflora, thereby providing a welcome rational basis for future development.

There is increasing interest in the possible exploitation of compounds occurring naturally in higher plants and associated with disease resistance. Their very presence in plant tissues suggests that they might be non-toxic to a range of plants at concentrations sufficient for antifungal activity. For example, Kirkham & Flood (1956), on the basis of earlier work on the significance of phenolic acids in the host-parasite relation of apple scab, tested a number of cinnamic acids against the fungus *in vitro*. They found that cinnamic acid itself was more active than its naturally occurring hydroxy-derivatives, and that its sodium salt, injected into apple shoots, gave marked protection against scab infection without being appreciably phytotoxic. A further instance of the natural occurrence of an antifungal substance which might lead to the development of a systemic fungicide was reported by Spencer, Topps & Wain (1957), who demonstrated the presence of such a phenolic compound in the tissues of *Vicia faba*.

Another approach to the development of systemic fungicides is due to Crowdy & Wain (1951) who examined a number of aryloxyalkyl-carboxylic acids for their ability to act as systemic fungicides against chocolate spot of bean (caused by *Botrytis fabae*). They chose these compounds in view of their ability to be translocated within plants, and selected those acids showing little or no growth-promoting activity. Initially it was thought that the compounds acted by virtue of their fungistatic properties. Later studies on these and related acids indicated, however, that their ability to act as systemic fungicides (using the term in a broad sense) probably arises from their ability to induce biochemical changes within the host plant which increase its resistance to disease (Fawcett, Spencer & Wain, 1957). The nature of these effects is still obscure, but it was suggested that they might involve modifications in protein or carbohydrate structure. Davis & Dimond (1953) had earlier reported the ability of certain growth substances to alter the resistance of tomato to *Fusarium oxysporum* f. *lycopersici*.

Economic considerations, and critical environmental factors affecting absorption by the plant, may well result in the use of systemic fungicides being restricted to valuable crops under controlled conditions, as in glasshouses. Moreover it is unlikely that they will supplant conventional fungicides against diseases such as superficial foliage infections readily controlled by the latter: their value will probably be for systemic diseases and those caused by wound parasites, which are at present intractable.

FUNGI PATHOGENIC FOR MAN AND ANIMALS

'Despite the great advances which have been made during the past twenty years in the treatment of many infections with chemotherapy and antibiotics, the natural defence mechanisms of the body remain our chief safeguard against infection.'

This statement from the *Report of the Medical Research Council for the year 1954–55* (p. 16) may be used to illustrate an essential difference between fungal diseases of plants and those of higher animals. In spite of the widespread use of resistant cultivars of many economic plants and the manipulation of the environment in the host's favour, the use of protective fungicides is a major aspect of the control of fungal diseases of plants. Further, the fungicides used as a safeguard against infection in plants are sometimes of equal use for eradicating the infection, which is frequently superficial. This is a marked contrast to the treatment of mycotic diseases of man and animals in which the natural defences of the body seem to play a more important part in the inhibition both of infection and of the subsequent growth of a pathogenic fungus in the host. As a clearer understanding of the mechanisms involved in the inhibition of the growth of pathogenic fungi in the host should contribute towards a more rational approach to the chemotherapy of mycoses, which up to the present has been largely empirical, certain aspects of the fungus-host relation will be very briefly indicated before considering the chemotherapy of such infections.

Some fungus-host relations

Many fungi are characteristically pathogenic for plants and a large number of these are obligate parasites. Relatively few fungi are pathogenic for man and higher animals and probably none is an obligate parasite. Most fungi are filamentous (mycelial) and plant pathogenic fungi typically have a mycelial parasitic phase in the course of which they may grow profusely and sporulate freely. Some fungi pathogenic for man have a mycelial parasitic phase but if so the growth is usually less vigorous than that of the saprophytic phase. Others have a yeast-like parasitic phase, a growth form virtually unknown among plant pathogens.

If in a systemic mycosis the growth of the pathogen is mycelial, the mycelium frequently does not spread freely throughout the infected tissues but is limited and forms more or less globose masses (mycetomas) similar to the well-known 'granules' characteristic of tissues and exudates from cases of actinomycosis. These structures, which have no close parallel in plant infections, clearly result from an inhibition of the growth of the fungus by the host. This inhibition may be even more extreme. A number of the major systemic mycoses of man, such as histoplasmosis (*Histoplasma capsulatum*), North American blastomycosis (*Blastomyces dermatitidis*), and sporotrichosis (*Sporotrichum schencki*) are caused by fungi which are mycelial as saprophytes but occur in the host tissues as yeast-like cells. During recent years these so-called 'dimorphic' fungi have received much attention and it is now possible to effect the yeast-mycelial and mycelial-yeast transformations *in vitro* at will (Scherr & Weaver, 1953).

Another contrast between fungal infections of plants and higher animals is that in the latter there may be a marked serological response resulting in lifelong immunity to subsequent infection. One very characteristic immunological feature of mycoses of man is the development of a skin hypersensitivity which allows the use in diagnosis and epidemiological studies of tests similar to the tuberculin test, and there is some evidence that this skin hypersensitivity is linked with other defence mechanisms. For example, Henrici (1940) claimed that in experimental *Aspergillus fumigatus* infections of rabbits the pathogen at first spreads freely through the tissues and that mycetoma formation coincides with the development of the skin hypersensitivity.

A further series of factors which influence fungal infection in man are concerned with the physiological condition of the host. For example, head ringworm in children caused by the dermatophyte *Microsporum audouini* tends to be very persistent but clears spontaneously at puberty while generalized moniliasis (caused by *Candida albicans*) is frequent in diabetics and has been claimed to be associated with a high glucose tolerance of the skin (Rothman, 1949).

Finally there is the inhibition of pathogenic fungi by other components of the microflora of the oral cavity or the alimentary tract as indicated by the numerous records during recent years of mycotic infection complicating therapy with antibacterial antibiotics.

Chemotherapy of superficial infections

The only superficial mycotic infection which will be considered is ringworm. This complex of diseases caused by a number of closely related species (the dermatophytes) has been known since classical times and the panaceas which have been advocated for its control are legion. In clinical trials of fungicides against ringworm the species of dermatophyte involved was, all too frequently, not established and as certain ringworm infections show a tendency to heal spontaneously, the efficacy of many of the materials tested is very uncertain; the few examples cited in this review have been chosen to illustrate several of the more rational procedures developed.

Self-limiting ringworm infections of the scalp are typically caused by dermatophytes derived from infected animals (the so-called 'animal dermatophytes'). They are frequently inflammatory and as a result the infected hairs or hair stumps are shed thus eliminating the infection (or at least a source of reinfection). The principle involved in this natural phenomenon is similar to that underlying both the somewhat barbaric but at one time widely used treatment of scalp ringworm by injecting croton oil into the hair follicles, and thus inducing inflammation, and the more humane and more complete epilation which follows the oral administration of thallium sulphate or the irradiation of the scalp with a suitable dose of X-rays.

Scalp ringworm of children caused by *Microsporum audouini* is usually of the non-inflammatory type. It tends, as already noted, to be persistent but to clear spontaneously at puberty. Infection of adults by *M. audouini* is less frequent than in children and when infection does occur it is more usually of the glabrous skin than of the scalp. This suggests a difference in susceptibility between children and adults. Rothman, Smiljanic, Shapiro & Weitkamp (1947) found that the hair of children below the age of eleven contained approximately 2·5–3·0 % of ether-soluble fat compared with 3·5–4·5 % for adult hair and that the hair fat for adults was approximately five times more fungistatic to *M. audouini* than the fat from pre-pubertal hair. They also showed the fungistatic activity to be confined to the fatty acid fraction which contained odd-numbered saturated fatty acids ranging from C_7 to C_{13}. Some of these findings have been questioned by Kligman & Ginsberg (1950) who were unable to demonstrate that post-pubertal sebum possessed decisively superior fungistatic activity but the usefulness of fatty acids in the therapy of dermatomycoses has been abundantly confirmed: propionic and undecylenic acids and their derivatives are the active principles of many therapeutic preparations.

Observations on the effects of fatty acids have been made since 1910 (see Drouhet, 1957) and it was Peck & Rosenfeld (1938) who first noted the greater efficacy of fatty acids containing an odd number of carbon atoms than those with an even number. As Horsfall (1956) points out, fungi appear to synthesize fats from 2-carbon fragments and fungus fats tend to be composed of 16- or 18-carbon compounds, and he suggests that odd-carbon fatty acids possibly act as antimetabolites for the even-carbon acids. Chattaway, Thompson & Barlow (1956) have recently shown that the inhibition of endogenous respiration of *Microsporum audouini* and the related *M. canis* by the homologous series of saturated straight-chain fatty acids from C_2 to C_{14} increased with increasing chain length and was greatest at acid pH values. They also noted that the inhibitory effect of undecylenic acid (an unsaturated acid) was no greater than that of a saturated acid of the same chain length.

Respiratory studies on dermatophytes by Nickerson and Chadwick in 1946 showed water soluble zinc salts to have a very marked inhibiting effect on respiration and this led Dolce and Nickerson in the following year to undertake clinical trials against dermatophyte infections of the scalp and glabrous skin with dilute aqueous solutions of zinc chloride (see Nickerson, 1947). The results were inconclusive but as the authors emphasized the point of the trial was to put to the test substances for which there was evidence on experimental grounds indicative of potential value. Such a result suggests that the evidence from respiratory studies, like that from the more usual agar plate screening of compounds for fungistatic or fungicidal activity, may bear little relation to clinical performance.

In vitro the growth of dermatophytes may be inhibited by a wide range of substances and as a group they do not appear to differ greatly from other fungi. They appear to be more sensitive to fatty acids than other moulds and they are more resistant to such substances as potassium tellurite (Gentles & Dawson, 1956) and the antibiotic cycloheximide (actidione) (Georg, Ajello & Papageorge, 1954) which are of use in selective media for isolating dermatophytes from heavily contaminated clinical material; but such characteristics are probably of very minor importance compared with the problem of bringing the fungicide into contact with the pathogen during the parasitic phase. *In vivo* the dermatophytes are mycelial and riddle the superficial layers of the skin. Their activity is, however, restricted to keratinized tissues and in an infected hair shaft, for example, downward growth of the dermatophyte ceases in the region above the bulb where keratinization is taking place. Keratin is not easily permeated by fungicides and part at least of the success of Whitfield's Ointment—a mixture of salicylic and benzoic acids in white paraffin base—is due to the keratolytic action of the salicylic acid, while during recent years diverse fungicides have been applied to ringworm lesions in a variety of surface-active bases such as 'Carbowax' and 'Intraderm'. In this connexion the clinical successes claimed by Nickerson & White (1948) in the treatment of *Trichophyton rubrum*-infected nails by the use of ammoniacal silver nitrate, which is both fungicidal and has the property of penetrating keratin, may be noted. More recently Barlow & Chattaway have made some novel attempts at therapy. First (Barlow & Chattaway, 1955a), they studied the effects of dermatophytes upon hair modified by breaking the di-sulphide bridges and hydrogen bonds between the polypeptide chains of adjacent keratin molecules; or by strengthening the cross-linkages on the side chains by cross-linking the amino groups and the free carboxyl groups of adjacent molecules; or by inserting a trimethylene group between the sulphur atoms of the disulphide bridges. In general they found that breaking the disulphide bridges or the hydrogen bonds en-hanced degradation of the hair by the dermatophytes employed, while strengthening the cross-linkages rendered the hair less susceptible to attack; none of the four dermatophytes was able to attack hair after the insertion of trimethylene groups in the disulphide bridges. On the basis of these findings Barlow & Chattaway (1955 b) undertook a clinical trial on five cases of resistant *Trichophyton rubrum* infection of the feet. One foot on each subject was treated by soaking for 6 hr. in an aqueous solution of urea (to rupture the hydrogen bonds), sodium bisulphite (to break the disulphide bridges) and phenyl mercuric nitrate (as a fungi-cide), thus increasing the permeability of the keratin. The treated feet were then kept continuously moist for 2 hr. by spraying with an alcoholic solution of ninhydrin (to increase the bonding and so render the keratin more resistant to fungal attack) and phenyl mercuric nitrate. The whole treatment was repeated after 48 hr. and the feet were not washed for a week. Penetration, as estimated by that of ninhydrin in scrapings taken after 5 days, was superficial but the treated feet showed considerable clinical improvement after 6 weeks, when scrapings contained very much less mycelium than at the beginning of treatment and compared with the opposite untreated feet, a result which would appear to encourage further studies on these lines.

Chemotherapy of systemic infections

One of the striking characteristics of mycotic infections and particularly of systemic mycoses, is the lack of any reliable treatment. According to the current edition of Conant *et al., Manual of Clinical Mycology*, 1954, 'There is no specific therapy for generalized cryptococcosis caused by the yeast *Cryptococcus neoformans* and prognosis is invariably poor once meningitis is established', for histoplasmosis (a major disease of world-wide distribution caused by the dimorphic *Histoplasma capsulatum*) there is again 'As yet no specific treatment', while progressive cocci-dioidomycosis (a dust-borne infection by *Coccidioides immitis* in certain arid parts of North and South America) is 'very resistant to treatment' and 'the prognosis is almost hopeless'; and such examples could be multiplied. Possible reasons for the refractory nature of mycoses have been briefly discussed by Drouhet (1957) in a comprehensive review of fungicides and the therapy of mycoses. As for dermatophytes, the growth of fungi responsible for systemic mycoses is readily inhibited *in vitro* by a wide range of fungicides and the ineffectiveness *in vivo* of those which are neither toxic to the host nor inactivated by blood or serum is certainly due, as in their use against ringworm, to a failure to establish adequate contact with the pathogen. The cells of *Cryptococcus neoformans* are surrounded by exceptionally thick polysaccharide capsules while the capsule of the yeast-like cells of the parasitic phase of *Blastomyces dermatitidis* is of a lipid nature. The pathogen may be localized in poorly vascularized tissue (e.g. *Cryptococcus neoformans* in the central nervous system), intracellularly in giant cells (*Blastomyces dermatitidis*) or in the reticulo-endothelial system (*Histoplasma capsulatum*), or in necrotic abscesses or mycetomas. A further handicap is the difficulty sometimes experienced of simulating human infections in experimental animals.

In spite of this rather depressing picture, there are a few reliable chemotherapeutic treatments for systemic mycoses. The best known of these is potassium iodide which was first used against 'actinomycosis' in cattle in 1885 and in 1903 was introduced by de Beurmann and Gougerot (at Sabouraud's suggestion) for the therapy of sporotrichosis (a subcutaneous infection of lymphatics by *Sporotrichum schencki*). Orally administered iodides are specific for sporotrichosis, useful against moniliasis (*Candida albicans*), aspergillosis (*Aspergillus fumigatus*), and chromoblastomycosis (*Phialophora* spp.) and they have probably been used in the attempted treatment of every systemic mycosis. Their mode of action is, however, unknown. *In vitro*, potassium iodide is non-toxic to *Sporotrichum schencki*. An attempt by Sternberg *et al.* (1955) to discover the fate of iodine administered for the therapy of experimental sporotrichosis (susceptible to iodides) and coccidioidomycosis (resistant to iodides) in mice by the use of radioactive iodine (^{131}I) showed the uptake of iodine by the thyroid gland to be less in the infected animals than in the controls. In *Coccidioides immitis* infections there was an accumulation of iodine in the granulomatous tissues. Iodine (in KI) is used as an external application to sporotrichosis abscesses and it is also extensively used on ringworm lesions. One disadvantage of the administration of iodine or iodides is the intolerance shown by some patients and it is also considered essential before beginning the iodide therapy of North American blastomycosis or moniliasis to desensitize patients found to be hypersensitive to an antigen prepared from the pathogen.

Among other compounds successfully used against mycotic infections, gentian violet and stilbamidine deserve mention. Gentian violet is most valuable against moniliasis. Infections of the nail bed by *Candida albicans* usually respond quickly to a 1/10,000 aqueous solution of gentian violet which is also used against similar infections of the vagina and the oral cavity, and even of the lungs. Malachite green, Brilliant green and other triphenylmethane derivatives have similar properties.

One of the major chemotherapeutic advances in medical mycology during the past decade has been the introduction of stilbamidine against disseminated North American blastomycosis, a treatment which has given excellent results in cases in which the prognosis would otherwise have been poor.

The outstanding success of the antibacterial antibiotics penicillin (which though without effect on fungi is now the drug of choice against classical actinomycosis caused by *Actinomyces israelii*) and streptomycin has encouraged the search for antifungal antibiotics. Many have been found. Among these gliotoxin (from *Trichoderma viride*) and patulin (*Penicillium patulum* and other species) which are derived from fungi, have found limited use against plant pathogenic fungi, but the most important series of antifungal antibiotics are those produced by actinomycetes, particularly species of *Streptomyces*. Of more than a dozen which have shown promise *in vitro* and in experimental infections of animals, few have come at all generally into clinical use. By far the most interest has been attracted by nystatin (mycostatin), produced by *Streptomyces noursei*, which was first described by Hazen and Brown in 1950 (see Brown & Hazen, 1957).

The structure of nystatin is complex and has not yet been fully elucidated. The molecule includes a chromophore group containing four conjugated double bonds and a diene system ($-CH=CH-CH=CH-$) while there are four C-methyl groups and the nitrogen is present as a primary amino group. Nystatin, which is without action on bacteria and viruses, inhibits the growth of fungi with sensitive sugar-utilizing systems (e.g. *Candida albicans*) (see Brown & Hazen, 1957) while Stewart (1956) found *in vitro* that $-CHO$ or $-CHOH$ groups in sugars were antagonistic to nystatin, the activity of which was enhanced by $-CH_2-$ chains in alcohols. It is rather unstable and only slightly soluble in water. When used parenterally it is injected as a suspension; adequate levels in the blood are difficult to maintain. It has been widely used against a variety of conditions, but especially in various types of moniliasis. Nystatin has also been used to supplement broad spectrum antibacterial antibiotics for which an all too frequent side-effect has been the development of a mycotic infection. Further details of nystatin and of the already quite extensive literature are given in the series of papers on nystatin in Sternberg & Newcomer (1955), by Drouhet (1957), and by Brown & Hazen (1957).

It is clear that our knowledge of the biochemical nature of the plant-fungus and the animal-fungus relations is woefully inadequate. There is ample scope for fundamental studies which will ultimately lead to a more rational approach to the chemotherapy of mycotic infections.

REFERENCES

ABRAHAM, E. P. (1953). The development of drug resistance in micro-organisms. An introductory discussion. In *Adaptation in Micro-organisms. Symp. Soc. gen. Microbiol.* **3**, 201.

*ALBERT, A. (1951). *Selective Toxicity with Special Reference to Chemotherapy.* London: Methuen.

ALBERT, A. (1958). Contribution to this Symposium.

ALBERT, A., GIBSON, M. I. & RUBBO, S. D. (1953). The influence of chemical constitution on antibacterial activity. Part VI. The bactericidal action of 8-hydroxyquinoline (oxine). *Brit. J. exp. Path.* **34**, 119.

BARLOW, A. J. E. & CHATTAWAY, F. W. (1955a). The attack of chemically modified keratin by certain dermatophytes. *J. invest. Derm.* **24**, 65.

BARLOW, A. J. E. & CHATTAWAY, F. W. (1955b). Persistent fungus infections of skin, hair, and nails. *Lancet*, ii, 1269.

BLOCK, S. S. (1955). Fungitoxicity of the 8-quinolinols. *J. agric. fd Chem.* **3**, 229.

BOYLAND, E. & WATSON, G. (1956). 3-Hydroxyanthranilic acid, a carcinogen produced by endogenous metabolism. *Nature, Lond.* **177**, 837.

BRIAN, P. W. (1949). Studies on the biological activity of griseofulvin. *Ann. Bot., Lond.* **13**, 59.

BRIAN, P. W. (1955). The role of toxins in the etiology of plant diseases caused by fungi and bacteria. In *Mechanisms of Microbial Pathogenicity. Symp. Soc. gen. Microbiol.* **5**, 294.

BRIAN, P. W., WRIGHT, J. M., STUBBS, J. & WAY, A. M. (1951). Uptake of antibiotic metabolites of soil micro-organisms by plants. *Nature, Lond.* **167**, 347.

*BROWN, R. & HAZEN E. (1957). Present knowledge of nystatin, an antifungal antibiotic. *Trans. N.Y. Acad. Sci.* Ser. 2, **19**, 447.

BURCHFIELD, H. P. & STORRS, E. E. (1956). Chemical structures and dissociation constants of amino acids, peptides, and proteins in relation to their reaction rates with 2,4-dichloro-6-(o-chloroanilino)-s-triazine. *Contr. Boyce Thompson Inst.* **18**, 395.

BURCHFIELD, H. P. & STORRS, E. E. (1957). Effects of chlorine substitution and isomerism on the interactions of s-triazine derivatives with conidia of *Neurospora sitophila*. *Contr. Boyce Thompson Inst.* **18**, 429.

BUSH, R. (1956). Spraying trials with captan against apple scab. *Agric. Rev. (Lond.),* **2**, 38.

BYRDE, R. J. W. (1957). The varietal resistance of fruits to brown rot. II. The nature of resistance in some varieties of cider apple. *J. hort. Sci.* **32**, 227.

BYRDE, R. J. W., HARRIS, J. F. & WOODCOCK, D. (1956). Fungal detoxication. The metabolism of ω-(2-naphthyloxy)-n-alkylcarboxylic acids by *Aspergillus niger*. *Biochem. J.* **64**, 154.

BYRDE, R. J. W., MARTIN, J. T. & NICHOLAS, D. J. D. (1956). Effect of fungicides on fungus enzymes. *Nature, Lond.* **178**, 638.

CHATTAWAY, F. W., THOMPSON, C. C. & BARLOW, A. J. E. (1956). The action of inhibitors on dermatophytes. *Biochem. J.* **63**, 648.

COLE, J. S. (1956). Studies in the physiology of parasitism. XX. The pathogenicity of *Botrytis cinerea*, *Sclerotinia fructigena*, and *Sclerotinia laxa*, with special reference to the part played by pectolytic enzymes. *Ann. Bot., Lond.* **20**, 15.

*CONANT, N. F., SMITH, D. T., BAKER, R. D., CALLAWAY, J. L. & MARTIN, D. S. (1954). *Manual of Clinical Mycology*, 2nd ed. Philadelphia: Saunders.

CONCHIE, J. & LEVVY, G. A. (1957). Inhibition of glycosidases by aldonolactones of corresponding configuration. *Biochem. J.* **65**, 389.

COREY, R. R. & SHIRK, H. G. (1955). The influence of chemical structure on fungal activity. IV. The effect of bisphenolic-type compounds. *Arch. Biochem. Biophys.* **56**, 196.

CROWDY, S. H. (1957). The uptake and translocation of griseofulvin, streptomycin and chloramphenicol in plants. *Ann. appl. Biol.* **45**, 208.

CROWDY, S. H. & RUDD JONES, D. (1956). Partition of sulphonamides in plant roots: a factor in their translocation. *Nature, Lond.* **178**, 1165.

CROWDY, S. H. & WAIN, R. L. (1951). Studies on systemic fungicides. I. Fungicidal properties of the aryloxyalkylcarboxylic acids. *Ann. appl. Biol.* **38**, 318.

CROXALL, H. E., NORMAN, T. M. & GWYNNE, D. C. (1957). Effect of 2:4:6-trichlorophenoxyacetic acid on the susceptibility of tomato plants to *Didymella lycopersici*. *Plant Pathology*, **6**, 27.

DAVIS, D. & DIMOND, A. E. (1953). Inducing disease resistance with plant growth-regulators. *Phytopathology*, **43**, 137.

*DROUHET, E. (1957). Antifongiques et thérapeutiques des mycoses. *Sem. Hôp., Paris*, **33**, 843.

FAWCETT, C. H., SPENCER, D. M. & WAIN, R. L. (1957). Investigations on fungicides. II. Aryloxy- and arylthio-alkanecarboxylic acids and their activity as fungicides and systemic fungicides. *Ann. appl. Biol.* **45**, 158.

FERGUSON, J. (1939). The use of chemical potentials as indices of toxicity. *Proc. roy. Soc. B*, **127**, 387.

FRY, B. A. (1955). *The Nitrogen Metabolism of Micro-organisms*. London: Methuen.

GARBER, E. D. & HACKETT, A. J. (1954). Virulence of auxotrophic mutants of *Erwinia aroideae*. *Nature, Lond.* **173**, 88.

GÄUMANN, E. (1950). *Principles of Plant Infection*. London: Crosby Lockwood.

GENTLES, J. C. & DAWSON, C. O. (1956). Isolation of dermatophytes from clinical materials. *Trans. Brit. mycol. Soc.* **39**, 465.

GEORG, L., AJELLO, L. & PAPAGEORGE, C. (1954). Use of cycloheximide in the selective isolation of fungi pathogenic to man. *J. Lab. clin. Med.* **44**, 422.

GERO, A. & REESE, V. J. (1956). Chemical model of drug action. *Science*, **123**, 100.

GROVE, J. F. (1953). Gladiolic acid, a metabolic product of *Penicillium gladioli*. 2. Structure and fungistatic activity. *Biochem. J.* **54**, 664.

GRÜMMER, G. (1955). Die Beziehungen zwischen dem Eiweißstoffwechsel von kultur-pflanzen und ihrer Anfälligkeit gegen parasitische Pilze. *Phytopath. Z.* **24**, 1. (*Rev. appl. Mycol.* **35**, 115.)

HALVORSON, H. O. & SPIEGELMAN, S. (1952). The inhibition of enzyme formation by amino acid analogues. *J. Bact.* **64**, 207.

HARINGTON, C. (1955). Modern trends in chemotherapy. *Nature, Lond.* **176**, 420.

HEBBORN, P. & DANIELLI, J. F. (1956). Selectivity of enzyme-activated nitrogen mustards. *Nature, Lond.* **177**, 25.

HENRICI, A. T. (1940). Characteristics of fungous diseases. *J. Bact.* **39**, 113.

HOROWITZ, N. H. & SRB, A. M. (1948). Growth inhibition of *Neurospora* by canavanine and its reversal. *J. biol. Chem.* **174**, 371.

*HORSFALL, J. G. (1956). *Principles of Fungicidal Action*. Waltham, Mass.: Chronica Botanica.

HORSFALL, J. G. & RICH, S. (1951). Fungitoxicity of heterocyclic nitrogen compounds. *Contr. Boyce Thompson Inst.* **16**, 313.

KEITT, G. W. & BOONE, D. M. (1954). Induction and inheritance of mutant characters in *Venturia inaequalis* in relation to its pathogenicity. *Phytopathology*, **44**, 362.

KERN, H. (1956). Problems of incubation in plant diseases. *Annu. Rev. Microbiol.* **10**, 351.

KIRKHAM, D. S. & FLOOD, A. E. (1956). Inhibition of *Venturia* spp. by analogues of host metabolites. *Nature, Lond.* **178**, 422.

KLIGMAN, A. M. & GINSBERG, D. (1950). Immunity of the adult scalp to infection with *Microsporum audouini. J. invest. Derm.* **14**, 345.

KUC, J., WILLIAMS, E. B. & SHAY, J. R. (1957). Increase of resistance to apple scab following injection of host with phenylthiourea and D-phenylalanine. *Phytopathology*, **47**, 21. (Abstract.)

LAMEY, H. A., BOONE, D. M. & KEITT, G. W. (1956). *Venturia inaequalis* (Cke.) Wint. X. Growth responses of biochemical mutants. *Amer. J. Bot.* **43**, 828.

LAPWOOD, D. H. (1957). Studies in the physiology of parasitism. XXIII. On the parasitic vigour of certain bacteria in relation to their capacity to secrete pectolytic enzymes. *Ann. Bot., Lond.* **21**, 167.

*LARGE, E. C. (1940). *The Advance of the Fungi.* London: Cape.

LAST, F. T. (1953). Some effects of temperature and nitrogen supply on wheat powdery mildew. *Ann. appl. Biol.* **40**, 312.

MCCALLAN, S. E. A. (1957). Mechanisms of toxicity with special reference to fungicides. *Proc. Plant Protection Conference*, 1956, p. 77. London: Butterworth.

MCCALLAN, S. E. A. & WELLMAN, R. H. (1942). Fungicidal versus fungistatic. *Contr. Boyce Thompson Inst.* **12**, 451.

MCNEW, G. L. & BURCHFIELD, H. P. (1951). Fungitoxicity and biological activity of quinones. *Contr. Boyce Thompson Inst.* **16**, 357.

MCNEW, G. L. & SUNDHOLM, N. K. (1949). The fungicidal activity of substituted pyrazoles and related compounds. *Phytopathology*, **39**, 721.

*MARSH, R. W. (1954). Modern developments in research on fungicides. *J. roy. Soc. Arts*, **102**, 555.

*MARTIN, H. (1940). *The Scientific Principles of Plant Protection*, 3rd ed. London: Arnold & Co.

*MARTIN, H. (1953). *Guide to the Chemicals used in Crop Protection*. Canada: Dept. of Agriculture. (Mimeographed.)

MARTIN, H. (1955). Some basic problems in the application of chemistry to crop protection. *Ann. appl. Biol.* **42**, 275.

METCALF, R. (1955). *Organic Insecticides*. London: Interscience Publishers.

MILLER, L. P. & MCCALLAN, S. E. A. (1956). Use of radioisotopes in tracing fungicidal action. *Peaceful Uses of Atomic Energy. Proc. International Conference in Geneva, August, 1955.* **12**, 170. New York: United Nations.

MILLER, L. P. & MCCALLAN, S. E. A. (1957). Toxic action of metal ions to fungus spores. *J. agric. fd Chem.* **5**, 116.

MILLER, L. P., MCCALLAN, S. E. A. & WEED, R. M. (1953*a*). Quantitative studies on the role of hydrogen sulfide formation in the toxic action of sulfur to fungus spores. *Contr. Boyce Thompson Inst.* **17**, 151.

MILLER, L. P., MCCALLAN, S. E. A. & WEED, R. M. (1953*b*). Rate of uptake and toxic dose on a spore weight basis of various fungicides. *Contr. Boyce Thompson Inst.* **17**, 173.

MÜLLER, K. O., MACKAY, J. H. E. & FRIEND, J. N. (1954). Effect of streptomycin on the host-pathogen relationship of a fungal phytopathogen. *Nature, Lond.* **174**, 878.

NICKERSON, W. J. (1947). Respiration and fermentation of pathogenic fungi. In *Biology of Pathogenic Fungi*. Edited by W. J. Nickerson. Waltham, Mass.: Chronica Botanica.

NICKERSON, W. J. & WHITE, S. J. (1948). Therapeutic value of ammoniacal silver nitrate in fungous infections of the nails. *Arch. Derm. Syph., Chicago*, **57**, 935.

OWENS, R. G. (1953a). Studies on the nature of fungicidal action. I. Inhibition of sulfhydryl-, amino-, iron-, and copper-dependent enzymes in vitro by fungicides and related compounds. *Contr. Boyce Thompson Inst.* **17**, 221.

OWENS, R. G. (1953b). Studies on the nature of fungicidal action. II. Chemical constitution of benzenoid and quinonoid compounds in relation to fungi-toxicity and inhibition of amino- and sulfhydryl-dependent enzymes. *Contr. Boyce Thompson Inst.* **17**, 273.

PECK, S. M. & ROSENFELD, H. (1938). The effects of hydrogen ion concentration, fatty acids and vitamin C on the growth of fungi. *J. invest. Derm.* **1**, 237.

REAVILL, M. J. (1954). Effect of certain chloronitrobenzenes on germination, growth and sporulation of some fungi. *Ann. appl. Biol.* **41**, 448.

RICH, S. & HORSFALL, J. G. (1952). The relation between fungitoxicity, permeation and lipid solubility. *Phytopathology*, **42**, 457.

RICH, S. & HORSFALL, J. G. (1954). Relation of polyphenol oxidases to fungi-toxicity. *Proc. nat. Acad. Sci., Wash.* **40**, 139.

ROSS, R. G. & LUDWIG, R. A. (1957). A comparative study of fungitoxicity and phytoxicity in an homologus series of N-n-alkylethylenethioureas. *Canad. J. Bot.* **35**, 65.

ROTHMAN, S. (1949). Susceptibility factors in fungus infections in man. *Trans. N.Y. Acad. Sci.* Ser. 2, **12**, 27.

ROTHMAN, S., SMILJANIC, A., SHAPIRO, A. L. & WEITKAMP, A. W. (1947). The spontaneous cure of tinea capitis in puberty. *J. invest. Derm.* **8**, 81.

SCHERR, G. H. & WEAVER, R. H. (1953). The dimorphism phenomenon in yeasts. *Bact. Rev.* **17**, 51.

SCHULDT, P. H. & WOLF, C. N. (1956). Fungitoxicity of substituted s-triazines. *Contr. Boyce Thompson Inst.* **18**, 377.

SIMON, E. W. & BLACKMAN, G. E. (1949). The significance of hydrogen-ion con-centration in the study of toxicity. In *Selective Toxicity and Antibiotics. Symp. Soc. exp. Biol.* **3**, 253.

SMITH, W. K. (1955). The pectic enzymes of bacterial pathogens of plants. *J. gen. Microbiol.* **13**, xi.

SPENCER, D. M., TOPPS, J. H. & WAIN, R. L. (1957). Fungistatic properties of plant tissues. An antifungal substance from the tissues of *Vicia faba*. *Nature, Lond.* **179**, 651.

SPIEGELMAN, S. & HALVORSON, H. O. (1953). The nature of the precursor in the induced synthesis of enzymes. In *Adaptation in Micro-organisms. Symp. Soc. gen. Microbiol.* **3**, 98.

STERNBERG, T. H. & NEWCOMER, V. D. (1955). *Therapy of Fungus Diseases. An International Symposium.* Boston and Toronto: Little, Brown & Co.

STERNBERG, T. H., NEWCOMER, V. D., STEFFEN, C. G., FIELDS, M. & LIBBY, R. L. (1955). The distribution of radioactive iodine (I-131) in experimental coccidi-oidomycosis and sporotrichosis. *J. invest. Derm.* **24**, 397.

STEWART, G. T. (1956). Laboratory and clinical studies with nystatin in post-anti-biotic mycotic infections. *Brit. med. J.* i, 658.

*VAN DER KERK, G. J. M. (1956). The present state of fungicide research. *Meded. LandbHoogesch. Gent,* **21**, 305.

VASUDEVA, R. S. (1930). Studies in the physiology of parasitism. XI. An analysis of the factors underlying specialisation of parasitism with special reference to the fungi *Botrytis allii* Munn. and *Monilia fructigena* Pers. *Ann. Bot., Lond.* **44**, 469.

WAIN, R. L. (1955). A new approach to selective weed control. *Ann. appl. Biol.* **42**, 151.

WALKER, J. B. (1955). Canavanine and homoarginine as antimetabolites of arginine in yeast and algae. *J. biol. Chem.* **212**, 207.

WELLMAN, R. H, & McCALLAN, S. E. A. (1946). Glyoxalidine derivatives as foliage fungicides. I. Laboratory studies. *Contr. Boyce Thompson Inst.* **14**, 151.

WEST, B. & WOLF, F. T. (1955). The mechanism of action of the fungicide 2-hepta-decyl-2-imidazoline. *J. gen. Microbiol.* **12**, 396.

WEURMAN, C. (1953). Pectinase inhibitors in pears. *Acta Bot. neerl.* **2**, 107.

WHITFIELD, A. (1912). Eczematoid ringworm of the extremities and groins. *Proc. R. Soc. Med.* **5** (1), Dermat. Sect., 36.

WILLIAMS, R. T. (1947). *Detoxication Mechanisms.* London: Chapman & Hall.

WOOD, R. K. S. (1955). Pectic enzymes secreted by pathogens and their role in plant infection. In *Mechanisms of Microbial Pathogenicity. Symp. Soc. gen. Microbiol.* **5**, 263.

WOOD, R. K. S. & TVEIT, M. (1955). Control of plant diseases by use of antagonistic organisms. *Bot. Rev.* **21**, 441.

WRIGHT, J. M. (1956). The production of antibiotics in soil. IV. Production of antibiotics in coats of seeds sown in soil. *Ann. appl. Biol.* **44**, 561.

* Reference providing a general survey of the topic.

THE CHEMOTHERAPY OF SOME
PROTOZOAL INFECTIONS

L. G. GOODWIN

Wellcome Laboratories of Tropical Medicine, London

Diseases caused by the parasitic protozoa were among the first to be controlled effectively by chemotherapy. The knowledge of the existence of potent alkaloids in cinchona and ipecacuanha was an encouragement to pioneers in the search for remedies against other pathogenic organisms. As a result of many years of experiment most of the protozoal diseases can now be controlled by several drugs of diverse chemical structure, and the problems now associated with the major protozoal diseases of man— malaria and trypanosomiasis—are different. It is no longer necessary for communities to sustain great loss of life from these infections; with the requisite trained staff and money the diseases can be prevented or cured. One must expect that resources of self-preservation are to be encountered in species threatened with extinction. Until the transmission rate of an infection becomes so low that a parasite dies out because it lacks the opportunity to infect, it is necessary to continue the search for active drugs of new chemical types in order to deal with drug-resistant variants. The study of new substances also yields information on the biological processes which they inhibit in both parasite and host.

The demands of those working on the control of malaria and of African trypanosomiasis in the field are becoming more exacting. They ask for long-acting prophylactics and for substances which do not allow the development of drug-fast strains of parasite. As a result, the worker in the laboratory has had to 'raise his sights'; a new antimalarial or trypanocidal drug must possess special advantages over the existing remedies. It has perhaps been the tendency in the past to view the strategy of chemotherapy in too much isolation. Chemotherapy must be integrated with measures of public health and hygiene and must take advantage of the immunological responses of the host, however weak these may appear. Hawking (1955) has reviewed the knowledge available upon the immunity caused by protozoa and has shown how important it may be.

In the days when most drugs in the Pharmacopoeia were of vegetable origin and only a few contained active principles, it was the fashion to make polypharmaceutical preparations so that the virtues of several drugs were combined. With the development of more potent remedies there has been some reluctance to mix them. However, once the field of usefulness of a particular drug has been established it would appear logical to use adjuvants to supplement its action; combinations of drugs are often of great advantage. Aspirin, phenacetin, caffeine and codeine have been used in various mixtures as analgesics for many years; the effect of streptomycin in tuberculosis is greatly enhanced by supplements of *p*-aminosalicylate and isoniazid which have the effect of preventing the rapid development of drug-resistant strains of the pathogen. In the field of protozoal diseases it has long been the practice to give 'blunderbuss treatments' for amoebiasis and combined courses of pentamidine and tryparsamide for trypanosomiasis. Some unexpected accidents occurred when pamaquin and mepacrine were used together in malaria, and it became customary to treat the disease with a single antimalarial drug. Recent trends in both chemotherapy and pharmacodynamics have been to use mixtures of active substances to a greater extent and it is likely that a better understanding of the potentialities of known remedies, as well as the development of new ones, will result in improvements in treatment and prophylaxis.

The aim of the present review is to consider what may be achieved by chemotherapy in the eradication of some protozoal diseases of man and animals by a more effective use of the host-parasite relationship and by suitable combinations of drugs.

MALARIA

From the large number of substances which have been introduced for the treatment of malaria (Findlay, 1951), a few have survived the selection process which resulted from use in the field. For the prompt control of an acute malarial attack, a quick-acting schizonticide of the 4-aminoquinoline group, such as chloroquine or amodiaquine, or the related acridine derivative mepacrine, rarely fails to bring the infection under control within 24 hr. In populations with natural immunity, proguanil and pyrimethamine are also effective, but they act slowly in those without immunity. For the suppression of malaria, doses of a 4-aminoquinoline or of pyrimethamine once-weekly or of proguanil given daily are effective. For the eradication of the tissue forms of *Plasmodium vivax* in people travelling from malarious to non-malarious zones the 8-aminoquinoline drug primaquine is available. The only advantage which is still possessed by quinine is in the treatment of cerebral malaria by intravenous injection.

The drugs used for the suppression of malaria have proved to be effective and to be sufficiently free from undesirable side-effects to make them safe for continuous administration at the proper dose for years at a time. They are also manufactured on a large scale, which makes them relatively cheap. A new antimalarial drug has exacting criteria to fulfil.

Drug-resistant strains

The development of resistant strains of plasmodia in man and in experimental animals has been reviewed by Goodwin & Rollo (1956) and Schnitzer & Grunberg (1957). Resistance is very rarely observed with quinine or the 4-aminoquinoline derivatives, although occasional infections are encountered in man which fail to respond adequately to these drugs. It develops more readily against proguanil and pyrimethamine, and the selection of drug-fast strains of *Plasmodium falciparum* has become evident in Malaya and East Africa in recent years. West African strains appear to be less prone to develop drug-resistance. The practice of giving small doses of drug at long intervals to indigenous populations on the grounds of economy favours the development of resistance. It would seem obvious in these circumstances to follow the advice of the Malaria Sub-Committee of the Colonial Medical Research Committee (1954) and alternate treatments with different types of drug which do not show cross-resistance. Basic suppression can be maintained by one of the cheaper drugs and a periodic dose of one of the more expensive 4-aminoquinoline derivatives would ensure that any surviving parasites are eliminated.

Mass-suppression of malaria

In recent years large eradication schemes have been in operation in many parts of the world, sponsored and financed by local government, and by the World Health Organization. In favourable circumstances where the areas are limited by the sea or by other natural barriers to the insect vector, success has been achieved by the use of insecticides. In larger areas such as the continent of Africa, where it is impossible to spray all the breeding grounds of the mosquito and where the development of resistance of the insect to the insecticide has assumed serious proportions, these measures have been less successful. There is also the constant difficulty of the introduction of fresh sources of infection by people migrating from untreated zones. It is evident that for large-scale campaigns, reduction of the mosquito population by insecticides should be accompanied by removal of malaria parasites from the blood of the population. There is some hope that, as in western Europe and in the southern United States, it might be possible to reduce transmission of the infection to a level which is uneconomic to the parasite, leaving an area in which there is 'anophelism without malaria'. Operations of this kind have been successful in Mauritius and in parts of the Belgian Congo, but constant vigilance is required if they are to be maintained. The danger of reintroduction of the disease has been successfully countered in the United States by the routine treatment of people returning from malarious areas of the Far East with primaquine which eradicates the surviving tissue-forms of *Plasmodium vivax*.

In territories in which malaria is epidemic and where the spread of the infection coincides with the breeding of mosquitoes in the rainy season it is sometimes possible to control the disease with a minimal expenditure of public funds by giving a single dose of drug to all members of a village community or labour force at a carefully selected time (Roberts, 1956).

A recent proposal by the World Health Organization to distribute salt containing pyrimethamine or chloroquine for the prophylaxis of malaria in indigenous populations would appear to be less well advised. The amount of salt consumed by individuals varies considerably and the methods in which salt is prepared for sale in different parts of the tropics would ensure a further profound variation in dose of the drug. There is the possibility not only of inadequate medication, with the encouragement of drug-fast strains, but also of overdosage and toxic side-effects in poorly nourished communities. Native communities are often mistrustful of medicines administered compulsorily or presented to them free of charge; for any scheme to be likely to succeed it is essential to gain their goodwill and co-operation. An example of unsatisfactory relations which led to both under- and overdosage with pyrimethamine among the workers at an Assam tea estate was recently reported by Laing (1957).

Long-acting prophylactics

The frequency with which antimalarial drugs have to be administered is a drawback to operations of mass-control and there is a need for a drug or combination of drugs which could afford protection from malaria for several months at a time (Bruce-Chwatt, 1956). Attempts to control malaria by giving doses of pyrimethamine at monthly intervals in endemic areas have succeeded for a time in keeping the malaria rate low, but the method favours the emergence of drug-fast strains because the antimalarial activity of the blood falls to a sublethal level 1 to 2 weeks after the dose. The action of the 4-aminoquinolines is even more short-lived. It has been known for many years that when an 8-amino-quinoline drug such as pamaquin is given together with mepacrine there is danger of toxic effects of mepacrine to the host. This is because the 8-aminoquinoline interferes with enzyme reactions which normally metabolize mepacrine. Potential dangers may often be turned to good account. It is possible that a drug which protects an antimalarial from degradation so that it persists in a concentration which is toxic to the parasite and safe for the host could provide the basis for a long-acting prophylactic. It might be rewarding to examine other enzyme-inhibitors which are known to prolong the effectiveness of drugs.

Drug potentiation

The effect of pamaquin on the toxicity of mepacrine exemplifies one way in which one drug may potentiate the action of another. A further example is provided by the administration of pyrimethamine with a sulphonamide. These drugs act by blocking different stages in a single metabolic pathway and the resultant effect is greater than would be expected from the arithmetic sum of their individual actions. The phenomenon is demonstrable in organisms which synthesize folinic acid from *p*-aminobenzoic acid; these include some species of bacteria, laboratory malaria parasites, *Eimeria tenella* and *Toxoplasma gondii*. The effect has been used to advantage in the treatment of human toxo-plasmosis and caecal coccidiosis of chicken. A trial in human malaria is at present in progress.

A recent claim that the 8-aminoquinoline drug primaquine potentiates the action of pyrimethamine against *Plasmodium relictum* infection in pigeons is less well substantiated. The published results do not give any conclusive evidence that more than a simple additive effect is produced (Soberon y Parra & Perez Reyes, 1956). The work has nevertheless pro-vided the basis for mass-treatment operations in Mexico. Reports of controlled clinical trials in man have not so far been published and it is not possible to judge whether potentiation occurs in human malaria.

The malarial sporozoite has always proved resistant to chemotherapy. Some regard it as a resting stage in the life-cycle of the parasite and there-fore unlikely to be greatly affected by drugs which interfere with meta-bolic processes. Terzian, Stahler & Weathersby (1948) found that the sporozoites were killed if infected *Aedes* mosquitoes were fed on sugar solutions containing 8-aminoquinoline drugs. However, these com-pounds are valueless as causal prophylactics in man and there is not as yet any known medicament which will kill sporozoites before they invade the tissue cells and begin to multiply. The sporozoite is in the same happy position as the microfilariae of *Wuchereria bancrofti*, which, as Hawking (1955) says: 'are so well adapted to their host that they are not noticed by it'. The action of diethylcarbamazine on microfilaria is to change the surface of the parasite in such a way that it becomes recognizable to the host as an intruder. The microfilariae are promptly trapped in the sinusoids of the liver and destroyed by histiocytes. It is possible that a true causal prophylactic for malaria may be found among compounds which act on the surface membrane of the sporozoite.

Immunity in malaria

In areas of the world in which malaria is transmitted all the year round the local population acquires tolerance to the local strains of parasite. Babies at the breast are protected for a few months against malarial fever by the absence of adequate quantities of *p*-aminobenzoate and the presence of specific antibodies in the mother's milk. When the milk begins to fail the child contracts a primary attack of malaria and may die. If he survives, he acquires sufficient immunity of his own to establish a balanced host-parasite relationship; in hyperendemic areas it is very rare to see malarial fever in an adult. If an antimalarial drug is taken the host-parasite relation is destroyed and immunity is lost; failure to continue taking the drug inevitably results in fever. A study by MacGregor and his colleagues (1956) of the effect of regular treatment from birth of babies in villages of Gambia has shown that treated babies escape the primary attack and grow more steadily than untreated controls. However, at the age of 18 months the untreated, having come to terms with the parasite, begin to catch up and there is little difference in weight and physique between the control and treated groups when the children are 3 years old. The children who have received the drug must continue to take it to avoid malaria while those who have not are immune. The judicious treatment of malarial attacks in infants will save life but it is doubtful if any good service has been done to a child who has been made dependent upon a drug instead of being allowed to develop a state of premunity.

It is clear that half-measures in the control of malaria are unsatisfactory (Colbourne & Wright, 1955). To be beneficial, control should be pushed to the point at which transmission is brought to an end.

TRYPANOSOMIASIS

The picture of the chemotherapy of human trypanosomiasis in Africa is in many respects similar to that of malaria; curative drugs are available and there are good long-acting prophylactics. The problem of drug-resistance is important in some regions. An additional problem is that the immunological response of the host is less satisfactory than in malaria and prolonged and untreated infection eventually kills the host because of invasion of the central nervous system. All the trypanocidal drugs at present available must be administered by injection; none is effective when given by mouth.

Prophylaxis of African trypanosomiasis in man

Suramin and pentamidine, which are used for the prophylaxis of trypanosomiasis caused by *Trypanosoma gambiense* and *T. rhodesiense*, have the advantage that they persist in effective concentrations for several months. Pentamidine is preferred because it acts for a longer time and rarely produces toxic side-effects; it is used widely in areas in which *T. gambiense* is endemic. The more acute *T. rhodesiense* infection is often epidemic in nature, and suramin is considered superior to pentamidine for its treatment (Willett, 1955). It was shown by Gui-maraes & Lourie (1951) that when suramin and pentamidine were given together in experimental animals, the immediate unpleasant pharmaco-dynamic effects of pentamidine were abolished. The combination has been used in the field with promising results but it is not yet known whether the trypanocidal action is enhanced. The work of Williamson & Rollo (1952) on drug-resistant strains of *T. rhodesiense* in mice suggests that the mixture should offer valuable advantages because diamidine-resistant strains do not show cross-resistance to suramin, and vice versa. The modes of action of the drugs are different and the use of both ought to reduce the chance of producing drug-fast strains of trypanosome.

A different type of prophylactic, which persists for many months in experimental animals, is Friedheim's melaminyl antimony compound 'MSb'. This has not been used extensively in the field, although Friedheim (1953) claims that a 'detoxicated' compound of MSb and dimercaprol is effective when given by mouth. If this is confirmed it is the first step in the development of a new class of trypanocide which will dispense with the paraphernalia of injection.

It should be possible to make economies in the use of prophylactics by a closer study of the seasonal transmission of trypanosomiasis.

Mulligan (1955) reports that in northern Nigeria, where there is a limited season of transmission, it should be possible to ensure control with a single dose of pentamidine given once a year at the appropriate time.

Treatment of advanced trypanosomiasis

Trypanocidal drugs other than the organic arsenical compounds do not penetrate the 'blood-brain barrier' and are therefore of little value in the treatment of long-standing trypanosomiasis in which the central nervous system has become invaded by the parasites. There is need for an advance in this difficult field. Although the melaminyl arsenicals and tryparsamide are useful and effective drugs, the margin of safety is narrow, and toxic effects to the host are common. It is not difficult to render trypanosomes resistant to these drugs by inadequate treatment, and organisms which are resistant to the melaminyl derivatives are unaffected by all other known trypanocides when they become entrenched in central nervous tissue. In view of the many chemical groupings which are known to cross the blood-brain barrier and to have a selective effect on the central nervous system, it seems conceivable that such a group could be used as a 'carrier' for an effective trypanocidal configuration. The present widespread interest in psychopharmacology is providing a large number of new drugs with stimulating, tranquillizing and other effects. One of these which penetrates but which is pharmacologically inactive may provide a beginning for advances in the chemotherapy of neural trypanosomiasis.

South American trypanosomiasis

Human trypanosomiasis caused by *Trypanosoma cruzi* has so far defied effective chemotherapy. Many and varied compounds which have been shown to have some effect upon the infection in laboratory animals have proved disappointing when tested clinically. The life-history of the parasite is different from that of the African species in that multiplication takes place in the tissues and not in the blood, and the damage caused to the heart muscle is responsible for the serious effects of the disease. At present the only satisfactory means of control is by the destruction of the reduviid bug which transmits the infection.

There is reason to believe that the lesions may be aggravated by sensitization reactions of the host tissue. Gonçalves, Carmo & Tavares (1956) regard histamine as the chief cause of the lesions and although there is at present little evidence to support this view, it has the virtue of being a new approach to a difficult problem.

Trypanosomiasis in cattle

The chemotherapy of animal trypanosomiasis has been reviewed recently by Davey (1957). The chief requirement is for a prophylactic which remains active for a long period against *Trypanosoma vivax* and *T. congolense*. During the African dry season, when grazing in the upland areas is poor, cattle are herded into the valleys in search of grass and water and are exposed to infection from the tsetse fly which lives in the shade of trees and bushes. It is impractical to inject doses of drug at frequent intervals and already advances have been made in the development of trypanocidal preparations of low solubility, which form depots and remain effective for two or more months. Antrycide prosalt and prothidium are in this category. Recently Williamson & Desowitz (1956) have prepared complexes of various drugs with suramin, which are claimed to remain effective for much longer periods.

The slowly diminishing blood-concentration of a trypanocide during its absorption from a depot of sparingly soluble material carries with it the possibility of creating drug-fast strains of trypanosome. It is fortunate that parasites which are resistant to the quaternary ammonium compounds such as antrycide and the phenanthridine derivatives do not show any cross-resistance to the new diamidine compound, berenil. So far, combined prophylaxis with these two types of compound has not been tried. Berenil, like antrycide and the phenanthridinium drugs, forms a complex with suramin and could be given together with one of the quaternary compounds in the form of a depot preparation. One would expect such a combination to render the development of drug-resistant strains less likely. Suramin itself has no action upon *Trypanosoma vivax* or *T. congolense*.

Immunity in trypanosomiasis

Although human serum contains a substance lethal *in vitro* to *Trypanosoma rhodesiense*, there is no evidence that effective immunity can be attained by man. Many animals, on the other hand, possess a natural immunity or succeed in establishing a satisfactory balance with parasitic trypanosomes. The wild creatures which serve as a reservoir of the trypanosomes which destroy domestic animals are apparently unaffected by the parasites. Indigenous breeds of small African cattle such as the Ndama, live and thrive in areas of heavy fly-density which are closed to other breeds. These animals are uneconomical from the point of view of milk and meat production and therefore a number of attempts have been made to induce immunity in other breeds. Crosses between resistant Ndama and susceptible Zebu cattle have an intermediate degree of immunity. Fiennes (1953) protected Zebu calves from fatal infection by injections of antrycide and kept them in tsetse fly country; they developed a host-parasite balance and thrived. Cattle protected for 28 months by injections of antrycide in a tsetse fly area developed a lasting immunity and remained free from trypanosomes in the blood when treatment was discontinued (Soltys, 1955). It is clear that there may be much to gain by taking advantage of the potentialities of cattle to develop immunity under the protective effect of a drug, and further investigations of this kind hold the greatest hope for opening the fly-belts to domestic animals.

It must not be forgotten that this process has its dangers. The soil of the tropics is thin and infertile and a balance between the flora and wild migratory fauna has been reached after centuries of natural selection. Disturbances of balance by cattle-ranching on poor grassland has already turned large tracts of the earth's surface into desert, through over-grazing and soil erosion. The lessons from the recent expensive large-scale attempts to introduce methods of farming suited to temperate countries into Africa should have been learned. No effort should be spared to integrate the chemotherapy of cattle trypanosomiasis with a comprehensive agricultural policy suited to the country (Hornby, 1952).

COCCIDIOSIS

The treatment of caecal coccidiosis in chicken provides a further example of how controlled treatment with drugs may be used to supplement immunological response. The heavy mortality among young chicks infected with *Eimeria tenella* is a result of extensive damage to the wall of the bowel which accompanies the development of second generation schizonts. The first generation schizonts cause less damage because they are not so numerous. If the infection is light and the bird survives without treatment, it enjoys an effective degree of immunity to subsequent infection. Large doses of sulphonamide given at an early stage of the disease will suppress the development of parasites but, on stopping treatment the chick is not found to possess any immunity and is likely to die from recrudescence or reinfection. Smaller doses of sulphonamide which suppress second generation schizogony but are not large enough to affect the less susceptible first generation, will tide the bird over the dangerous phase of the disease and leave it with a degree of immunity which is adequate to ensure survival (Kendall & McCullough, 1952).

The parasite makes use of the metabolic synthesis of folinic acid from
p-aminobenzoate and therefore the action of sulphonamides is potentiated by diaminopyrimidine derivatives such as pyrimethamine (Lux,
1954; Joyner & Kendall, 1956). By giving small doses of the two drugs
it is possible to control coccidiosis and to avoid the toxic side-effects
which sometimes occur with an adequate dose of the sulphonamide
alone.

Other drugs such as nitrofurazone are effective against *Eimeria tenella*
and there is no doubt that an effective combination of drugs will be
found that will exploit the chemotherapeutic and immunological
responses to the full.

THEILERIA

East Coast Fever of cattle in Africa, caused by *Theileria parva* and
transmitted by ticks, is a serious disease which is relatively resistant to
chemotherapy. Parasites are found in the erythrocytes and also in the
reticuloendothelial cells of the lymph glands where they undergo
schizogony. Neitz (1950) found that the antimalarial drug pamaquin
had an effect upon the erythrocytic parasites. The 8-aminoquinoline
compounds are also effective against experimental infections of *T.
mutans* in cattle and *Aegyptianella pullorum* in chicks; both of these
piroplasms are confined to the erythrocytes and do not invade the lymph
glands. Schizonts of *Theileria parva* in the lymph glands are unaffected
by pamaquin which therefore cannot prevent the fatal outcome of the
disease. Early and continuous treatment with chlortetracycline sup-
presses schizogony in the reticuloendothelial cells and by giving this
drug together with pamaquin the animal can be kept alive until natural
immunity has been established (Neitz, 1953). Treatment with chlortetracycline is expensive, even when the drug is given by mouth in the
form of residues from the manufacturing process which are now being
mixed with animal feeding stuffs to stimulate rapid growth. Unless the
chlortetracycline is given before the infection has become well-established,
it is ineffective and therefore the treatment is of little value to the veterinary surgeon faced with an outbreak of the disease in the field. Nevertheless, it may find a use in the protection of valuable breeding stock by
infecting deliberately and continuing treatment until immunity is
established.

Research into the chemotherapy of theileriasis is hampered by the
lack of suitable piroplasm which can be maintained in small animals
and which has stages in the red cells and in the lymph glands. Infections
of *Babesia rodhaini* in the mouse and *Aegyptianella pullorum* in the chick

are of use, but are susceptible to substances which are without action against *Theileria parva*. At present there is no link between them and the expensive process of testing substances of doubtful efficacy in cattle.

It is clear that rational chemotherapy involves more than treating an infection with a drug which kills the parasite and leaves the host unharmed. The action of many antibiotics on pathogenic bacteria is one of bacteriostasis; the organism is held in check until the defences of the host have had an opportunity for effective counter-attack. The importance of this process in the development of immunity is seen in the treatment of typhoid fever with chloramphenicol which, like the sulphonamides in coccidiosis, if given too early and in too large a dose will control the infection but leave the host without the antibodies he deserves. The action of diethylcarbamazine on the larvae of filarial worms is to remove their antigenic camouflage and make them recognizable by the defences of the host. The drug does not appear to have any action on their structure, metabolism or motility and is inactive *in vitro*. A somewhat similar surface action on a parasitic helminth has been shown to occur when schistosomes are exposed to the action of diaminodiphenoxy-alkane derivatives (Standen, personal communication). It is probable that other chemotherapeutic effects, such as the action of antimony in leishmaniasis, may have their basis in a specific change in the surface structure of the parasite which calls the defence mechanisms into play.

Immunological responses produced by protozoa are feeble compared with those stimulated by some bacteria and viruses; the aim of the present review has been to show that they cannot be ignored and that they probably play a vital part in the action of many chemotherapeutic substances. It is also apparent that full use should be made of the potentialities of effective mixtures of drugs in order to obtain maximal activity and to reduce the chances of producing drug-fast strains of parasite.

Ehrlich aimed to discover a magic bullet which would fly to the invading organism and kill it; the ideal drug would appear to be a magic fish-hook on which the parasite can be played until the defences of the host have made the most of their opportunity to profit from the experience.

REFERENCES

BRUCE-CHWATT, L. J. (1956). Chemotherapy in relation to possibilities of malaria eradication in tropical Africa. *Bull. World Hlth Org.* **15**, 852.

COLBOURNE, M. J. & WRIGHT, F. N. (1955). Malaria in the Gold Coast (Parts I and II). *West African med. J.* **4**, 3, 161.

DAVEY, D. G. (1957). The chemotherapy of animal trypanosomiasis with particular reference to the trypanosomal diseases of domestic animals in Africa. *Vet. Rev. Annot.* **3**, 15.

FIENNES, R. N. T.-W. (1953). The therapeutic and prophylactic properties of antrycide in trypanosomiasis of cattle. A review of work done under Colonial Development and Welfare Scheme R 318, 1949 to 1952. *Brit. vet. J.* **109**, 330.

FINDLAY, G. M. (1951). *Recent Advances in Chemotherapy.* 3rd ed. Vol. II. London: Churchill.

FRIEDHEIM, E. A. H. (1953). MSb and MSbB in the treatment of sleeping sickness due to infection with *Trypanosoma gambiense*. *Ann. trop. Med. Parasitol.* **47**, 350.

GONÇALVES, N. B., CARMO, E. DA S. & TAVARES, B. M. (1956). Novas bases para a quimoterapia da molésta de Chagas. *Rev. Brasil. Med.* **13**, No. 2.

GOODWIN, L. G. & ROLLO, I. M. (1956). *Biochemistry and Physiology of Protozoa.* Edited by S. H. Hutner and A. Lwoff, p. 225. New York: Academic Press.

GUIMARAES, J. L. & LOURIE, E. M. (1951). The inhibition of some pharmacological actions of pentamidine by suramin. *Brit. J. Pharmacol.* **6**, 514.

HAWKING, F. (1955). The pathogenicity of protozoal and other parasites: general considerations. In *Mechanisms of Microbial Pathogenicity. Symp. Soc. gen. Microbiol.* **5**, 176.

HORNBY, H. E. (1952). *Animal Trypanosomiasis in Eastern Africa*, 1949, p. 28. London: H.M. Stationery Office.

JOYNER, L. P. & KENDALL, S. B. (1956). The mode of action of a mixture of pyrimethamine and sulphadimidine on *Eimeria tenella*. *Brit. J. Pharmacol.* **11**, 454.

KENDALL, S. B. & MCCULLOUGH, F. S. (1952). Relationships between sulphamezathine therapy and the acquisition of immunity to *Eimeria tenella*. *J. comp. Path.* **62**, 116.

LAING, S. R. (1957). Refractory anaemia, a problem in diagnosis and epidemiology in a tea garden in Assam. *J. trop. Med. Hyg.* **60**, 131.

LUX, R. E. (1954). The chemotherapy of *Eimeria tenella* (I). Diaminopyrimidines and dihydrotriazines. *Antibiot. Chemother.* **4**, 971.

MCGREGOR, I. A., GILLES, H. M., WALTERS, J. H., DAVIES, A. H. & PEARSON, F. A. (1956). Effects of heavy and repeated malarial infections on Gambian infants and children. Effects of erythrocytic parasitization. *Brit. med. J.* ii, 686.

MALARIA SUB-COMMITTEE OF THE COLONIAL MEDICAL RESEARCH COMMITTEE (1954). Recommendations for the use of antimalarial drugs. *Tropical Dis. Bull.* **51**, 861.

MULLIGAN, H. W. (1955). Recent investigations on trypanosomiasis in British West Africa. *Trans. R. Soc. trop. Med. Hyg.* **49**, 199.

NEITZ, W. O. (1950). The specific action of pamaquin on the haemotropic parasites of *Theileria parva*. *S. African J. Sci.* **46**, 218.

NEITZ, W. O. (1953). Aureomycin in *Theileria parva* infection. *Nature, Lond.* **171**, 34.

ROBERTS, J. M. D. (1956). Pyrimethamine (Daraprim) in the control of epidemic malaria. *J. trop. Med. Hyg.* **59**, 201.

SCHNITZER, R. J. & GRUNBERG, E. (1957). *Drug Resistance of Micro-organisms.* New York: Academic Press.

SOBERON Y PARRA, G. & PEREZ REYES, R. (1956). The activity of primaquine-pyrimethamine (Daraprim) combinations against *Plasmodium relictum* in pigeons. *J. Protozool.* **3**, 43.

SOLTYS, M. A. (1955). Studies on resistance to *Trypanosoma congolense* developed by zebu cattle treated prophylactically with Antrycide Pro-Salt in an enzootic area of East Africa. *Ann. trop. Med. Parasit.* **49**, 1.

TERZIAN, L. A., STAHLER, N. & WEATHERSBY, A. B. (1948). The action of anti-malarial drugs in mosquitoes infected with *Plasmodium falciparum*. *Amer. J. trop. Med.* **29**, 19.

WILLETT, K. C. (1955). Sleeping sickness in East Africa and its treatment. *East African Med. J.* **32**, 273.

WILLIAMSON, J. & DESOWITZ, R. S. (1956). Prophylactic activity of suramin complexes in animal trypanosomiasis. *Nature, Lond.* **177**, 1074.

WILLIAMSON, J. & ROLLO, I. M. (1952). Properties of some recently developed drug-resistant strains of *T. rhodesiense*. *Trans. R. Soc. trop. Med. Hyg.* **46**, 373.

FACTORS AFFECTING THE CHEMOTHERAPY OF AMOEBIASIS

R. A. NEAL

Wellcome Laboratories of Tropical Medicine, London

In the host, *Entamoeba histolytica* lives in the large intestine and is associated with the myriads of bacteria which are naturally present in this organ. Since the first successful cultivation *in vitro* of the parasite, researches of numerous workers have shown that growth and the completion of its life-history is linked closely with bacteria. A clear picture of this association is the first essential for an understanding of drug action, and of the reasons for which a new drug may fail to act satisfactorily in man in spite of promise shown in laboratory experiments.

AMOEBA-BACTERIA RELATION

Growth of amoebae

Amoebae will grow *in vitro* on a wide variety of media ranging from an all-liquid medium composed almost entirely of defined ingredients to Dobell and Laidlaw's original medium of inspissated egg slopes covered with dilute horse-serum. There are two essential factors for all media, the addition of solid rice starch and the presence of suitable bacteria. In fact, any medium which will give suitable growth of bacteria, will support the growth of *Entamoeba histolytica* when rice starch is added. The growth-promoting effect of starch is probably due to its insolubility; it is not readily available for the bacteria to ferment, while amoebae can metabolize it after ingestion.

Entamoeba histolytica is a strict anaerobe (Snyder & Meleney, 1943; Dobell, 1952; Balamuth & Brent, 1954), and one of the functions of the bacteria present in its culture is to eliminate oxygen dissolved in the medium. The bacteria also provide a low redox potential which is necessary for the growth of amoebae (see Balamuth & Thompson, 1955; this paper also contains a valuable survey of amoebicides).

The effect of bacterial flora in cultures of *Entamoeba histolytica* has been studied by many workers who have used different methods to eliminate and replace the original mixed unknown flora with one or more known bacterial species (Chinn, Jacobs, Reardon & Rees, 1942;

Balamuth & Wieboldt, 1951; Dobell, 1952). Although most prolific growth was observed if the amoebae were grown with *Clostridium welchii*, most workers have used either *Escherichia coli*, 'organism t' (a Gram-positive microaerophilic clostridium similar to or even identical with *C. tertium*, Rees, 1955), or *Klebsiella aerogenes* (*Aerobacter aerogenes*). Jacobs (1947) was able to grow *Entamoeba histolytica* for several months in a medium containing a suspension of *Escherichia coli* which had been killed by heating for 2 hr. at 51–65°, and amoebae growing with anti-biotic-inhibited bacteria have been reported by Shaffer (1952) and Karlsson (1952). Nakamura and his colleagues (Nakamura, 1955; Nakamura & Baker, 1956; Nakamura, 1957) are investigating the growth factors provided by bacteria by adding various biologically active substances to a basic medium containing antibiotics. Amoebae are added from stock cultures growing with a mixed flora and it is claimed that the bacteria are eliminated by the antibiotics. In this manner it has been demonstrated that purines, nucleic acids and other substances are growth factors for *Entamoeba histolytica*. However, it is possible that some surviving bacterial cells may still be present, although subcultivation does not reveal cells capable of growth. If this is the case, such bacteria may still be supplying the amoebae with growth substances and the function of the added chemicals is not conclusively elucidated. That the complete requirements of the amoebae are not satisfied, is shown by the failure to prolong cultivation in the absence of viable bacteria for more than 6–7 subcultures over 22–27 days. Cholesterol is the only substance which has been demonstrated as an unquestionable growth factor for *E. histolytica*; its action is reinforced by oleic acid (Griffin & McCarten, 1949).

All these investigations have been made upon amoebae growing *in vitro*. Phillips *et al.* (1955) using guinea-pigs reared aseptically showed that amoebae are also dependent upon bacteria for growth in the intestine. When amoebae growing with *Trypanosoma cruzi* instead of bacteria were introduced into the caeca of bacteria-free guinea-pigs, the amoebae rarely survived beyond 2 days. Some guinea-pigs were infected also with the Shaffer-Frye streptobacillus and this bacterium prolonged the survival of the amoebae, but again the amoebic infection died out after 8 days. The inability to establish an amoebic infection with the streptobacillus is correlated with the low populations of the bacillus in the animal. In several guinea-pigs the streptobacillus could be detected only by cultivation. However, amoebic infections were easily established in animals infected with *Escherichia coli* or *Klebsiella aerogenes*.

From this summary it is clear that drugs with a high antibacterial action may be able to interfere with this relationship. It has, in fact, been demonstrated that the tetracycline derivatives and other anti-bacterial drugs are of some value in the treatment of acute amoebiasis (see Elsdon-Dew, 1956). However, there is evidence that chlortetra-cycline and oxytetracycline have a direct amoebicidal action in addition to their antibacterial properties (see Phillips, 1953a), and it is possible that such drugs have a dual action on *Entamoeba histolytica*. In practice, however, they cannot be relied upon to eliminate the parasite, which frequently reappears in the faeces after administration of the drug has been stopped.

Encystation and excystation

In the life-history of the amoeba the cyst is the dispersal agent (see Neal, 1957a), and although a great deal of information is available on the growth of parasitic amoebae *in vitro*, very little has been published on encystation or excystation. Encystation in *Entamoeba histolytica*, as seen *in vitro*, is dependent upon an acceleration of growth-rate of amoebae, and various culture media have been devised which are based on this principle (Kessel, Allison, Kaime, Quiros & Gloeckner, 1944; Balamuth, 1951); these studies were made with *E. histolytica* cultured with mixed bacterial floras. Experiments on encystation with floras of known species of bacteria were reported by Chinn *et al.* (1942) and Dobell (1952), who concluded that copious encystation occurred only when a spore-bearing anaerobe was present. Chinn *et al.* used *Clostridium welchii*; Dobell's organism was not identified. Balamuth (1951) on the other hand, obtained encystation with a flora consisting only of aerobes, as shown by special methods of examination designed to detect anaerobic bacteria (Balamuth & Wieboldt, 1951). Everritt (1950) studied the physical factors and did not consider the presence of certain bacteria was necessary for encystation. She concluded that the increase in growth-rate resulted in encystation by physical crowding of amoebae or by accumulation of metabolic substances from amoebae.

Entamoeba invadens, a pathogenic species from snakes, differs from *E. histolytica* in that it will encyst in the presence of *Escherichia coli* alone and that encystation coincides with the disappearance of rice starch from the cultures (McConnachie, 1955). Other species of *Entamoeba*, *E. ranarum* and *E. moshkovskii*, which resemble *E. invadens*, in their growth at 24°, are more like *E. histolytica* in their inability to encyst copiously in culture with *Escherichia coli* (Neal, unpublished).

Encystation in these species may prove simpler to analyse than the process in *E. histolytica* itself.

Excystation is a relatively simple process; all that is required is an anaerobic environment. The addition of glucose and cysteine increases the percentage of cysts which hatch (Rees, Reardon & Bartgis, 1950); further growth of amoebae was not observed without the addition of living associates.

Substitution of bacteria

Bacteria have been replaced by the flagellate *Trypanosoma cruzi*. Amoebic growth was satisfactory only when rich suspensions (50 million trypanosomes/ml.) were used and multiplication was not observed if the concentration was as low as 1 million/ml. Other trypanosomid flagellates were studied, and fair growth was obtained with *Strigomonas fasciculata*, but growth was not found with *T. conorhini*, *Leishmania donovani*, *L. tropica* or *L. brasiliensis*. The growth-promoting properties of *T. cruzi* were partly lost by heating to 48° and destroyed completely by heating above this temperature (Phillips, 1953*a*). Later work showed that the slight growth of amoebae with *T. cruzi* inactivated at 48° was due to the presence of surviving flagellates which, although incapable of further growth, did reduce methylene blue and produced acids (Phillips, 1953*b*).

It is clear, therefore, that although growth of *Entamoeba histolytica* has been obtained with antibiotic-inhibited bacteria and heat-killed bacteria and *T. cruzi*, the complete absence of living cells has not been conclusively proved in any of these lines of work. In man, infections of *E. histolytica* frequently spread from the large intestine to the liver via the portal system, where they may form deep abscesses which are apparently sterile. *In vitro* attempts to grow *E. histolytica* with liver have so far failed. However, Shaffer, Sienkiewicz & Washington (1953) observed that *E. histolytica* would grow without bacteria in a medium containing minced chick embryos but growth did not occur when the chick embryo cells and fragments had been removed by centrifuging. Later work has shown that the speed and time of centrifuging are critical since growth of amoebae is dependent upon particulate material derived from the broken chick-embryo cells. The particulate material is removed by strong centrifuging. The technique of Shaffer *et al.* has been developed by two groups of American workers (Reeves, Meleney & Frye, 1957; Baernstein, Rees & Bartgis, 1957) who have been able to maintain *E. histolytica in vitro* in a cell-free medium. The chick-embryo cells were removed by light centrifuging (700 g for 15 min. and 200 g for 2–3 min. respectively).

While growth of *Entamoeba histolytica* in the absence of bacteria is a recent event, *E. invadens* was grown in pure culture, in a medium containing liver tissue, several years ago (Lamy, 1948; Miller, 1951, 1953). There have not been any further reports of an analysis of the growth factors for the reptilian amoeba.

HOST-PARASITE RELATION
Virulence

In vivo, amoebae can live in the lumen of the large intestine or they may invade the mucosa and form ulcers which penetrate to the submucosa; from these ulcers the amoebae frequently wander to the liver and, more rarely, to the lungs and brain. Recent work has shown that strains of *Entamoeba histolytica* vary greatly in their virulence. This conclusion is based on experiments which showed that amoebae from carriers are avirulent while those from acute cases are highly invasive. The virulence of strains which had become attenuated by prolonged cultivation *in vitro* could be revived by serial passage in hamster liver while the virulence of those from carriers could not be raised in this manner. It was further shown that the bacterial component did not contribute to the virulence of the amoebae. This evidence supports the conclusion of previous workers that the amoeba itself is responsible for the intestinal lesion (see Neal, 1957*b*). The mechanism by which amoebae invade the wall of the large intestine is not completely understood and the available evidence has been recently reviewed by Hoare & Neal (1955).

Immunity

In the case of some protozoal diseases, such as malaria, trypanosomiasis and coccidiosis, there is a serological response to infection, the host acquiring characteristic antibodies and a measure of immunity. In amoebiasis the nature of the response, if any, is obscure. In carrier cases where the amoebae are living in the lumen, antibody is not formed, but antibodies are detectable in the sera of hosts with intestinal ulceration or liver abscesses (Craig, 1944). However, the host does not develop active immunity in the usual sense of the term because reinfection is possible, even with the same strain (Beaver, Jung, Sherman, Read & Robinson, 1956*a*) and the case which regularly relapses is frequently seen in clinical practice.

SOME ASPECTS OF CHEMOTHERAPY

The ideal drug for the treatment of amoebiasis should have a threefold distribution in the body: it should reach the amoebae in the lumen of the intestine, it should give a concentration in the blood so as to kill amoebae in the wall of the intestine, and it should reach the amoebae in liver abscesses. In order to reach the lumen amoebae, it would have to withstand bacterial attack. In practice, there is not a single drug which has this threefold distribution. Drugs used to treat the carrier or asymptomatic case without intestinal ulceration are usually insoluble (diodoquin), while patients with ulceration are treated with drugs which produce a high concentration in the blood (the tetracycline derivatives or emetine hydrochloride). Chloroquin and emetine hydrochloride are used for the treatment of amoebic hepatitis and liver abscesses because they accumulate in the liver.

It has been estimated that about 80 % of all human infections remain symptomless, and the main form of infection with *Entamoeba histolytica* is the carrier. There are a number of drugs which will give clinical cure of the acute case, but are not dependable for the elimination of the parasite. The treatment of carriers is similarly uncertain, and it is for this reason that great efforts are being expended on research in amoebicidal drugs.

Prophylaxis has not been extensively studied, owing to the absence of a specific drug of high activity associated with low toxicity. Beaver *et al.* (1956*b*) have shown that diodoquin and milibis may be used prophylactically but the recommended dose is very high, 650 mg. and 250 mg./day respectively.

Estimation of amoebicidal activity in vivo

There are several different laboratory animals susceptible to infection with *Entamoeba histolytica* in which the infection responds to treatment with the clinically effective amoebicides. Infections of *E. histolytica* in monkeys and *E. criceti* in hamsters resemble the carrier in man. In dogs fed on a special fish diet and in guinea-pigs the infection resembles the acute human disease (Thompson, 1955). In rabbits and rats the type of infection can be varied according to the strain of *E. histolytica* employed (Neal, 1957*b*). On practical grounds the animal most used for chemotherapeutic research is the rat infected with a virulent strain.

There is great variation in the response of rat infections to treatment. This factor, coupled with the use of different strains of *Entamoeba histolytica* and various methods of assessing drug activity in different laboratories, makes it difficult to compare results. The degree of virulence of the strain has a profound effect upon its sensitivity to amoebicides. Several of the more recent drugs have been tested in rats infected with virulent and avirulent strains, using emetine hydrochloride and chiniofon for comparison. The results (Table 1) are expressed as the dose required to eliminate amoebae from 50 % of the rats (CD_{50}). The rats were given six daily oral doses of drug.

Table 1. *Amoebicidal properties of new drugs, compared with chiniofon and emetine hydrochloride* in vivo

Results expressed as the dose required to clear 50 % of the rats of amoebae (mg./kg. × 6).

Drug	Invasive amoebae (*M*)	Avirulent amoebae (*EA*)
Emetine HCl	2·6*	0·45*
Chiniofon	128*	63*
Entamide	66	10
Mantomide	156*	Less than 10
Glaucarubin	40	122
Puromycin	50	2·3
Milibis	342	115
Fumagillin	24	Less than 2

* Average of 2 or more experiments.

The variability inherent in amoebicidal tests is seen from the observation that in eight experiments, the CD_{50} of chiniofon varied from 93 to 190 mg./kg. Some of the more recently introduced amoebicidal drugs approach emetine in their activity; however, the most active of them, fumagillin, has shown toxic side-effects in clinical trials. It is not yet possible to assess the relative values or degree of freedom from toxic effect of these substances.

As described above, it is possible to produce experimental infections in rats with avirulent and virulent strains which correspond to the carrier and acute disease in man. From the results in Table 1 it can be seen that with the exception of glaucarubin, all drugs eliminated the avirulent amoebae at a lower dose than the virulent amoebae. In the case of mantomide, puromycin and fumagillin the difference was more than tenfold. In an attempt to discover an explanation for this difference, *in vitro* tests were carried out to see if the avirulent amoebae were more sensitive to the drugs than the virulent amoebae.

This experiment (Table 2) shows that there was no correlation of *in vitro* with *in vivo* results. Therefore, in the rat the drug must reach the amoebae in the lumen (that is, avirulent amoebae), more easily than

those in the tissues. The insolubility of drugs such as milibis and glaucarubin would favour their reaching the amoebae in the lumen, but this
explanation is not applicable to drugs which are absorbed, such as
emetine and chiniofon. Moreover, glaucarubin, which is relatively insoluble, actually proved more effective on the amoebae in the tissues.
There is a further factor which is peculiar to the rat. A poorly absorbed
drug would not form good contact with amoebae because, owing to the
contraction of the ulcerated caecum, the larger part of the contents of
the small intestine are short-circuited into the colon and do not enter
the body of the caecum.

Table 2. *The minimum lethal concentration*
($\mu g./ml.$) of some amoebicides in vitro

Drug	Invasive amoebae		Avirulent amoebae strain *EA*
	Strain *OK*	Strain *M*	
Emetine HCl	5	5	5
Chiniofon	100	100	100
Entamide	10	—	10
Mantomide	10	1	50

The reason for the greater activity of glaucarubin on virulent amoebae
is not clear. In a similar instance with a nitropyridine (Neal & Vincent,
1955), it was postulated that the drug was absorbed into the blood-
stream leaving insufficient to deal with the amoebae in the lumen. This
cannot be the complete answer, as there are always some amoebae
present in the caecal lumen in rats infected with virulent strains.

An answer to this problem would require an analysis of the absorption, distribution and excretion of each drug and its metabolites in the
rat.

Drug resistance and mode of action

During treatment of human amoebiasis, patients are frequently encountered who do not respond to courses of emetine; this failure to
respond is sometimes considered to be due to infection with amoebae
unusually resistant to the drug. Nevertheless, attempts to produce such
emetine-resistant amoebae experimentally *in vitro* and *in vivo* have
failed. Strain *M*, in Table 2, was isolated from a patient who had
suffered numerous relapses of the infection after treatment with emetine,
but *in vitro* it proved just as susceptible as other strains. Attempts to
make *Entamoeba histolytica* resistant to oxytetracycline and chlortetracycline *in vitro* have also proved unsuccessful.

In view of the paucity of knowledge of the biochemistry of *Entamoeba histolytica*, it is not surprising that the mode of action of amoebicides is little known. The highly specific action of emetine has led to studies of the relation of its chemical structure with amoebicidal properties. Unfortunately, all analogues so far prepared have greatly reduced activity (Balamuth & Lasslo, 1952). The nature of the action of emetine is not known, but it was observed by Stewart (1949) and Hansen & Bennett (1952) that dividing amoebae might be found in concentrations which eventually proved lethal. Therefore, the drug does not specifically inhibit nuclear division, and probably acts by interfering with some cytoplasmic reaction. The action of emetine on a series of free-living amoebae showed that the drug was more effective on the more motile species (Kaushiva & Singh, 1955).

Combination of drugs

The treatment of human amoebiasis is often based on a series of amoebicidal drugs given sequentially or sometimes simultaneously but by different routes (Adams, 1956). It is not suggested that these drugs potentiate each other, but their action is more likely to be additive. A further instance of the use of more than one drug is in the treatment of chronic dysentery. In this type of infection the amoebic ulceration is secondarily invaded by bacteria and it is found that treatment with an antibacterial such as penicillin facilitates the eradication of the amoebae by an amoebicide (Hargreaves, 1946).

However, true potentiation with fumagillin and oxytetracycline, and fumagillin and thiocarbasone was demonstrated experimentally by Nakamura, Hrenoff & Anderson (1953). In addition to *in vitro* studies, they found that four of five monkeys were cleared of amoebae by giving fumagillin and oxytetracycline together in a quarter of the smallest effective single dose.

To summarize, *Entamoeba histolytica* is dependent upon bacteria for growth, encystation and excystation, although the details of this relation are not known. Strains vary in virulence, and amoebae may be found in lesions in the intestinal wall or in the lumen of the large intestine. In addition to the problem of finding a drug with selective toxicity against *E. histolytica*, there is the pharmacological problem of ensuring that the drug reaches the amoebae. There appears to be little immunological reaction to infection. An experimentally confirmed instance of drug-resistance is not known.

REFERENCES

ADAMS, A. R. D. (1956). Treatment of intestinal amoebiasis. *Trans. R. Soc. trop. Med. Hyg.* **50**, 109.

BAERNSTEIN, H. D., REES, C. W. & BARTGIS, I. L. (1957). The rate of reproduction of *Entamoeba histolytica* in microcultures from inocula of single trophozoites in cell-free medium prepared from embryos of the chick. *J. Parasit.* **43**, 143.

BALAMUTH, W. (1951). Biological studies on *Entamoeba histolytica*. III. Induced encystation in several mediums including an account of a new procedure. *J. infect. Dis.* **88**, 230.

BALAMUTH, W. & BRENT, M. (1954). Comparative effects of oxygen upon parasitic and small free-living amebae. *J. Parasit.* **40**, suppl. p. 22.

BALAMUTH, W. & LASSLO, A. (1952). Comparative amoebacidal activity of some compounds related to emetine. *Proc. Soc. exp. Biol., N.Y.* **80**, 705.

BALAMUTH, W. & THOMPSON, P. E. (1955). Comparative studies on amebae and amebicides. In *Biochemistry and Physiology of Protozoa*. Vol. II. Edited by S. H. Hutner & A. Lwoff. New York: Academic Press.

BALAMUTH, W. & WIEBOLDT, M. L. (1951). Comparative growth cycles of *Endamoeba histolytica* with different combinations of bacteria. *Amer. J. trop. Med.* **31**, 192.

BEAVER, P. C., JUNG, R. C., SHERMAN, H. J., READ, T. R. & ROBINSON, T. A. (1956*a*). Experimental *Entamoeba histolytica* infections in man. *Amer. J. trop. Med. Hyg.* **5**, 1000.

BEAVER, P. C., JUNG, R. C., SHERMAN, H. J., READ, T. R. & ROBINSON, T. A. (1956*b*). Experimental chemoprophylaxis of amebiasis. *Amer. J. trop. Med. Hyg.* **5**, 1015.

CHINN, B. D., JACOBS, L., REARDON, L. V. & REES, C. W. (1942). The influence of the bacterial flora on the cultivation of *Endamoeba histolytica*. *Amer. J. trop. Med.* **22**, 137.

CRAIG, C. F. (1944). *The Etiology, Diagnosis and Treatment of Amebiasis*. Baltimore: The Williams and Wilkins Co.

DOBELL, C. (1952). Researches on the intestinal protozoa of monkeys and man. XII. Bacterial factors influencing the life history of *Entamoeba histolytica* in cultures. *Parasitology*, **42**, 16.

ELSDON-DEW, R. (1956). Further aspects of amoebiasis in Africans. *Central Afr. J. Med.* **2**, 291.

EVERRITT, M. G. (1950). The relationship of population growth to *in vitro* encystation of *Endamoeba histolytica*. *J. Parasit.* **36**, 586.

GRIFFIN, A. M. & McCARTEN, W. G. (1949). Sterols and fatty acids in the nutrition of entozoic amoebae in cultures. *Proc. Soc. exp. Biol., N.Y.* **72**, 645.

HANSEN, E. L. & BENNETT, B. M. (1952). Effects of toxic agents on *Endamoeba histolytica*. *Exp. Parasit.* **1**, 143.

HARGREAVES, W. H. (1946). The treatment of amoebiasis with special reference to chronic amoebic dysentery. *Quart. J. Med.* **15**, 1.

HOARE, C. A. & NEAL, R. A. (1955). Host-parasite relations and pathogenesis in infections with *Entamoeba histolytica*. In *Mechanisms of Microbial Pathogenicity*. *Symp. Soc. gen. Microbiol.* **5**, 230.

JACOBS, L. (1947). The elimination of viable bacteria from cultures of *Endamoeba histolytica* and the subsequent maintenance of such cultures. *Amer. J. Hyg.* **46**, 172.

KARLSSON, J. L. (1952). Studies of the physical properties of a growth factor for *Endamoeba histolytica*. *Amer. J. trop. Med. Hyg.* **1**, 548.

KAUSHIVA, B. S. & SINGH, B. N. (1955). Studies on the *in vitro* effect of emetine and conessine on various intestinal and free-living amoebae. *J. sci. indust. Res.* **14C**, 86.

KESSEL, J., ALLISON, D., KAIME, M., QUIROS, M. & GLOECKNER, A. (1944). Cysti-cidal effects of chlorine and ozone on cysts of *Endamoeba histolytica* together with a comparative study of several encystment media. *Amer. J. trop. Med.* **24**, 177.

LAMY, L. (1948). Le problème de la culture pure des amibes parasites. *C.R. Soc. Biol., Paris,* **142**, 633.

McCONNACHIE, E. W. (1955). Studies on *Entamoeba invadens* Rodhain, 1934, *in vitro*, and its relationship to some other species of *Entamoeba. Parasitology,* **45**, 452.

MILLER, M. J. (1951). A method for *in vitro* culture of *Entamoeba invadens* free from bacteria. *Canad. J. comp. Med.* **15**, 268.

MILLER, M. J. (1953). Bacteria-free *Entamoeba invadens. Nature, Lond.* **172**, 1192.

NAKAMURA, M. (1955). Growth factors for *Endamoeba histolytica. Proc. Soc. exp. Biol., N.Y.* **89**, 680.

NAKAMURA, M. (1957). Methylthioadenosine, a growth factor for *Endamoeba histolytica. Exp. Cell Res.* **12**, 200.

NAKAMURA, M. & BAKER, E. E. (1956). Nutritional requirements of *Endamoeba histolytica. Amer. J. Hyg.* **64**, 12.

NAKAMURA, M., HRENOFF, A. K. & ANDERSON, H. H. (1953). Drug effects on the metabolism of *Endamoeba histolytica; in vitro* and *in vivo* tests of synergism. *Amer. J. trop. Med. Hyg.* **2**, 206.

NEAL, R. A. (1957*a*). Dispersal of pathogenic amoebae. In *Biological Aspects of the Transmission of Disease.* Edited by C. Horton-Smith. London: Oliver & Boyd for Institute of Biology.

NEAL, R. A. (1957*b*). Virulence in *Entamoeba histolytica. Trans. R. Soc. trop. Med. Hyg.* **51**, 313.

NEAL, R. A. & VINCENT, P. (1955). The amoebicidal activity of 2-diethanolamino-5-nitropyridine. *Brit. J. Pharmacol.* **10**, 434.

PHILLIPS, B. P. (1953*a*). Studies on the cultivation of *Endamoeba histolytica* with *Trypanosoma cruzi. Ann. N.Y. Acad. Sci.* **56**, 1028.

PHILLIPS, B. P. (1953*b*). The effects of various treatment procedures on the meta-bolism of *Trypanosoma cruzi* and on its ability to support growth of *End-amoeba histolytica. Amer. J. trop. Med. Hyg.* **2**, 47.

PHILLIPS, B. P., WOLFE, P. A., REES, C. W., GORDON, H. A., WRIGHT, W. H. & REYNIERS, J. A. (1955). Studies on the ameba-bacteria relationship in amebiasis. Comparative results of the intracecal inoculation of germ-free, monocontami-nated, and conventional guinea-pigs with *Entamoeba histolytica. Amer. J. trop. Med. Hyg.* **4**, 675.

REES, C. W. (1955). *Problems in Amoebiasis.* Springfield, Illinois: Thomas.

REES, C. W., REARDON, L. V. & BARTGIS, I. L. (1950). The excystation of *Entamoeba histolytica* without bacteria in microcultures. *Parasitology,* **40**, 338.

REEVES, R. E., MELENEY, H. E. & FRYE, W. W. (1957). Bacteria-free cultures of *Enta-moeba histolytica* with chick-embryo tissue juice. *Z. Tropenmed. Parasit.* **8**, 213.

SHAFFER, J. G. (1952). Studies on the growth requirements of *Endamoeba histoly-tica.* V. Studies on the nature of some of the factors in the Shaffer–Frye medium that affect the propagation of *E. histolytica. Amer. J. Hyg.* **56**, 119.

SHAFFER, J. G., SIENKIEWICZ, H. S. & WASHINGTON, J. E. (1953). The propagation of *Endamoeba histolytica* in tissue-bearing culture without accompanying bacteria or other micro-organisms. *Amer. J. Hyg.* **57**, 366.

SNYDER, T. L. & MELENEY, H. E. (1943). Anaerobiosis and cholesterol as growth requirements of *Endamoeba histolytica. J. Parasit.* **29**, 278.

STEWART, G. T. (1949). Nature of the action of emetine upon *Entamoeba histolytica. Nature, Lond.* **163**, 842.

THOMPSON, P. E. (1955). The evaluation of antiamebic drugs in experimental animals. *Antibiotic Med.* **1**, 603.